Control of
ELECTRIC
MOTORS

Control of
ELECTRIC
MOTORS
THIRD EDITION

PAISLEY B. HARWOOD

Vice-President in Charge of Engineering
Cutler-Hammer, Inc., Milwaukee
Fellow, American Institute of Electrical Engineers

New York · JOHN WILEY & SONS, *Inc.*
London · CHAPMAN & HALL, *Ltd.*

PREFACE

When the first edition of this book was published, in 1936, it seemed necessary to call attention in the preface to the importance of motor control to men in many different fields of activity. There was at that time very little written on the subject and almost no recognition of it in college engineering courses. The picture is very different today. In addition to the great increase in the electrification of industry, a number of books and hundreds of papers have been written, and now almost every college electrical engineering course includes some work on control.

Since the publication of the second edition, in 1944, new devices and circuits have been developed, and new standards have been created. The data and diagrams in this edition have been brought into conformity with present standards, and many new standards have been added to the text.

When the first edition was published, electronic motor control was in its infancy, and the basic principles of the subject were included in the text. Today electronic motor control is almost an industry in itself, and it would be impossible to do the subject justice in this book. There are many excellent textbooks available, and so it has seemed best to omit the material on electronics. In its place, a chapter on regulating devices and circuits has been added.

The requests for a series of problems have been rather insistent, and so they have been added.

Methods of calculating accelerating and decelerating times and distances, both with constant torque and with variable torque, have been included.

I have again to express my thanks to those companies and organizations that have so willingly supplied information, photographs, and permission to reprint material. I am also indebted to those who offered the comments and suggestions that have been so helpful, and in particular to Mr. Jesse E. Jones, manager of drafting of Cutler-Hammer, Inc., for his work on the chapter on regulating systems.

P. B. Harwood

Milwaukee, Wisconsin.
October 1952

NOTE

Many of the control schemes and devices described and illustrated in this book are covered by letters patent or by an application for letters patent. No attempt has been made to indicate whether or not such patents exist. Service men can repair a patented device or patented apparatus purchased from a duly authorized seller. Persons desiring to build any of the devices described in this book or to use any of the control schemes described are advised to check the patent situation before doing so. Neither the publishers nor the author will assume any responsibility for damages arising out of patent litigation or suits involving any apparatus described in this book.

CONTENTS

ix

1

INTRODUCTION

The success of any installation of electrically driven machinery is dependent upon the proper selection and correlation of the machine, the motor, and the controller. Each is important, and the improper application of a motor or a controller will lower the efficiency of the installation and may cause it to be a failure.

In order to make successful installations, it is necessary to understand the factors which enter into the selection of the machine, motor, and controller, and therefore to have a good working knowledge of the characteristics of the three devices. The requirements of the machine with respect to speed, torque, and special functions must be known. An understanding of motor characteristics is necessary to proper selection of a motor which will accomplish the desired results, and a knowledge of control apparatus is required to insure the application of a controller which will cause the motor to perform the functions required of it.

Machine builders often supply their machines complete with motor and control. It is advantageous for them to do so, as they are thoroughly familiar with the requirements for good operation and are vitally interested in the satisfactory operation of the complete installation. If the machine is supplied without motor and control, or with the motor but without the control, then the ultimate user is faced with the problem of selecting suitable control apparatus. He is also vitally interested in the success of the entire installation, which will be endangered if improper control is applied. In that case, the machine is likely to be blamed for failure to produce the results which the manufacturer claimed for it, or the blame may be placed on the motor. The design and application of motor controllers are, therefore, of interest to many men engaged in widely different kinds of work. They are of interest to machine designers and builders, to motor designers and builders, to the men selling these devices, and to anyone using or contemplating the use of an electrically driven machine.

The five factors which enter into the study of a motor and control application fall logically into a definite order. They are:

The machine.
The power supply.
The motor.
The operator.
The controller.

The Machine. The machine is a known factor. It has been designed to accomplish certain results, and it has certain speed and torque requirements. These are known to the designer and builder, and information concerning them is therefore available. Specific information should be obtained covering the following functions:

Check List of Machine Characteristics

(For use as an aid in the selection of control apparatus)

STARTING

Will the machine be started by an operator?
If so, what type of starting device is preferred:

Pushbutton?
Safety switch?
Drum controller?
Other means?

If not, what type of automatic starting device will be used:

Float switch?
Pressure switch?
Time clock?
Thermostat?
Interlock in another machine?
Other means?

How often will the machine be started?
Is the starting torque light or heavy?
Has the machine a high inertia?
How much time will be required for starting?
Is a particularly smooth start necessary?
Will the machine always start under load, or always unloaded, or will conditions vary?

STOPPING

Will the machine be stopped by an operator?
Will it be stopped by a limit switch, or some other automatic device?

Is a quick stop essential?

Is an accurate stop essential?

Is a particularly quick stop in an emergency required?

Is a magnetic brake required for stopping, or for holding the machine stationary?

Reversing

Will the motor be reversed in regular operation?

If so, how often will this occur?

If the machine is essentially non-reversing, will emergency reversing be required?

Will the motor be plugged?

Must the machine perform the same functions in the reverse direction as it does in the forward direction?

Running

Will the machine run continuously or intermittently?

Will the load be overhauling at any part of the cycle?

Are any special functions required during the cycle?

Speed Control

Has the machine essentially a single constant speed?

Has the machine two or more constant speeds?

Is adjustable speed required? If so, over what range?

Will the speed be adjusted while running, or will it be preset?

Are different speeds required in different parts of the cycle?

Must the running speed be relatively constant under different load conditions, or may it vary with the load?

Is slowdown required during any part of the cycle?

Safety Features

Are any of the following protective features required:

> Overload protection?
> Open field protection?
> Open phase protection?
> Reversed phase protection?
> Overtravel protection?
> Overspeed protection?
> Reversed current protection?

At first sight, this seems to be a very formidable list, but it will be evident that only a few of the items will apply to any one machine. Furthermore, the machine builder who must supply the information will be entirely familiar with his machine and will be able to supply the data without a great deal of effort. Even though the requirements are apparently simple, it is a good plan to check against a list of this nature, simply to be sure that nothing is overlooked.

Power Supply. The question of power supply is sometimes definitely settled by the motor requirements and is always closely tied in with the motor selection. Direct current is particularly valuable where a wide range of speed control is required. Another advantage of its use is the ease of obtaining dynamic braking. One of the chief advantages of alternating current is that it is available almost everywhere. Furthermore, the voltage of the supply may easily be changed by means of transformers. Alternating-current machines have relatively constant speeds, and it is difficult to obtain satisfactory speed variations.

A crane hoist is an ideal application for direct current. Heavy loads must be hoisted at low speeds, but it is desirable that light loads be hoisted at considerably higher speeds. Similarly, heavy loads must be lowered slowly, with safety, and light loads may be lowered at a higher rate of speed. A direct-current series motor has exactly the right speed-torque characteristics to accomplish these results and is easily arranged for dynamic lowering at any desired speed.

Most woodworking machines use alternating-current motors since relatively high speed and constant speed are desired. Dynamic braking is not often required.

Where there is only one kind of power supply it will usually be possible to select a suitable motor and controller. If the requirements are such that the available power cannot be utilized, it will be necessary to arrange to get the required type of power by using a motor-generator set or some other means of transformation.

The quantity of power available and the rules governing its use should also be investigated. It may be found necessary to limit the current inrushes during starting, in order to avoid voltage disturbances on the line, even when such a limitation is not required for satisfactory starting of the machine.

The Motor. The power supply may be determined by the necessity of using a particular motor, or the motor may have to be selected to suit the power available. Each type of alternating- or direct-current motor has definite speed and torque characteristics. A motor which is exactly suited to one application may be entirely unsatisfactory for another. Since a motor having the proper characteristics must be selected, a knowledge of the characteristics of the available types is essential. Also the methods which may be employed to take advantage of the motor characteristics, to start and stop it properly, and to control its speed must be understood.

The Operator's Function. There is generally a choice in the selection of the method of operation of a machine. Sometimes it is necessary that the operator be called upon to exercise a considerable amount of judgment and to take a great deal of responsibility. He may be required to initiate every motion of the machine himself by pushing buttons or by moving levers. In the other extreme, it may be desirable to make the entire operation automatic, taking the responsibility entirely out of the hands of the operator. Even the starting and stopping may be automatically controlled. Between these two extremes are many arrangements giving an operator a greater or lesser degree of responsibility.

As an example, consider the installation of a large crusher which is driven by a motor and which is lubricated under pressure. The oil is pumped by a separate small motor. Failure of the lubricating system may ruin the crusher. The simplest arrangement will be to have a starting controller for the crusher and a separate starter for the oil pump. Obviously, however, this does not provide any safety feature, as we are dependent upon the operator to start the oil pump before he starts the crusher, and to stop the crusher any time the oil pump stops. A better arrangement would be to interlock the two controllers, so that the oil pump must be running before the crusher can be started, and also so that, if the oil-pump motor stops at any time, the crusher will automatically be shut down. Still better would be an arrangement using only one starting button which, when pressed, would first start the oil pump, then, after the pressure was up, would start the crusher. This arrangement would include interlocking to shut down the crusher if the oil pressure fell below a safe value. A number of other schemes giving fair degrees of safety are possible. For instance, instead of shutting down the crusher when the oil pressure is low, it would be possible to ring a bell, warning the operator, whose responsibility it would be either to restore the oil pressure or to shut down the crusher.

The final solution of this problem, or of any one like it, would be a matter of judgment. Some of the factors to be considered would be the necessity of safety, the amount of damage which might be caused by an operator's mistake or neglect, the mental capacity and skill of the operator, and the relative cost of the various control schemes.

The Controller. When the characteristics of the machine are known, and when the motor has been selected and the operator's part has been determined, it is possible to select the proper control. If the requirements are simple, this may be a standard catalog device. For more complicated machines, the controller will have to be specially designed. When the great variety of machines in use in all the industries is considered, it will be evident that many special controls will be required. Their number is further multiplied by the many different types of motors and by the various sizes required. Still further complication is introduced by the many voltages and frequencies which are standard, and the use of single-, two-, or three-phase power.

The control engineer has at his disposal a number of devices which have previously been designed, and he may be able to combine certain of these to accomplish the result he desires. If no available device will meet the requirements, he will have to modify some existing design or create an entirely new one. The devices with which he works are:

> Transformers and capacitors.
> Manually operated switches and drums.
> Pilot devices.
> Contactors and relays.
> Resistors or their equivalent.
> Electronic apparatus.
> Tachometers and rotating regulators.

A study of the requirements will enable the engineer to decide how the control is to function and to determine approximately the apparatus required. An elementary or line diagram will then be made and the exact scheme worked out. This diagram will determine the number and type of contactors and relays required, and the power requirements of the installation will determine their current rating. The next step is to combine the parts into a unit by arranging to mount them on a common base, which is usually a slate or composition panel. The panel, in turn, will be mounted on a framework, or in an enclosing cabinet, which may also be arranged to mount any resistor material that is required. Pilot devices are usually complete in themselves and separately mounted.

Controllers are built in accordance with the rules of the National Electrical Code and the standards of the American Institute of Electrical Engineers. The majority of them also meet the standards of the National Electrical Manufacturers' Association.

Some controllers are required to meet the standards of the National Fire Protection Association, those of the Association of Iron and Steel Engineers, or those of departments of the federal government or of the Bureau of Mines.

It is the purpose of this book to describe some of the control devices that are in common use, and to show how they are assembled and connected to make a complete controller. The characteristics of various kinds of motors are described, and ways of using these characteristics in the control of the motor are discussed in detail. The design of magnetic structures has not been included, as that information is available in many textbooks.

References

Books on Motor Control

G. H. Hall, *Motor and Control Applications,* McGraw-Hill Book Company, New York, 1937.

H. C. Roters, *Electromagnetic Devices,* John Wiley & Sons, New York, 1941.

D. R. Shoults, C. J. Rife, and T. C. Johnson, *Electric Motors in Industry,* John Wiley & Sons, New York, 1942.

H. D. James and L. E. Markle, *Controllers for Electric Motors,* McGraw-Hill Book Company, New York, 1952.

G. W. Heumann, *Magnetic Control of Industrial Motors,* John Wiley & Sons, New York, 1947.

"Bibliography on Industrial Control," *AIEE Publication S-39,* September, 1950.

2

WIRING DIAGRAMS

Purpose of the Diagram. The wiring diagram serves a number of different purposes, all of which must be kept in mind in order to insure that the diagram is properly made. Its primary purpose is to enable the wireman to locate the bus bars and control wires in their proper places. It also serves as an instruction and a guide in testing the controller. Another important purpose of the diagram is to enable the purchaser of the equipment to install the wiring between the motor, control panel, and auxiliary devices. The diagram is also of assistance in locating and correcting any trouble which may develop or in making any changes which may be found necessary after installation. From an engineering standpoint, the diagram serves as a record of the equipment supplied, and also as a basis for designing a new controller which may differ slightly from the original equipment.

Definitions. There are several different forms of wiring diagrams, any or all of which may be made for a particular installation.

Illustrative Diagram. An illustrative diagram is a diagram whose principal purpose is to show the operating principle of a device or group of devices without necessarily showing actual connections or circuits. Illustrative diagrams may use pictures or symbols to illustrate or represent devices or their elements.

Illustrative diagrams may be made of electric, hydraulic, pneumatic, and combination systems. They are applicable chiefly to instruction books, descriptive folders, or other mediums whose purpose is to explain or instruct.

One-line Diagram. A one-line diagram is a diagram which indicates, by means of single lines and simplified symbols, the route and component devices or parts of an electric circuit or system of circuits. Physical relationships are usually disregarded.

One-line diagrams are useful in showing the overall relations between component devices, machinery, and circuits, and between circuits.

Schematic Diagram or Elementary Diagram. A schematic or elementary diagram is a diagram which shows all circuits and device elements of an equipment and its associated apparatus, or any clearly defined functional portion thereof. Such a diagram emphasizes the device elements of a circuit and their functions as distinguished from the physical arrangement of the conductors, devices, or device elements of a circuit system.

To emphasize the device elements and show their functional relationships and sequence, physical relationships of devices and device elements are usually disregarded. Circuits are usually drawn in the most direct possible line between and perpendicular to parallel lines representing opposite polarities of voltage sources, and circuits which function inherently in a definite sequence are arranged to indicate that sequence.

Schematic or elementary diagrams are useful where electrical relationships of circuits and device elements are the principal consideration.

Connection Diagram. A connection diagram is a diagram which shows the connections of an installation or its component devices, controllers, and equipment. It may cover internal or external connections, or both, and will contain such detail as is needed to make or trace connections that are involved. It usually shows the general physical arrangement of devices and device elements, and also accessory items, such as terminal blocks, and resistors.

(A connection diagram excludes mechanical drawings, commonly referred to as wiring templates, wiring assemblies, cable assemblies, etc.)

Controller Diagram. A controller diagram is a diagram showing the electric connections between the parts comprising the controller, and indicating the external connection.

Construction Diagram. A construction diagram is a diagram indicating the physical arrangement of parts, such as wiring, busses, and resistor units (example: a diagram showing the arrangement of grids and terminals in a grid-type resistor).

Interconnection Diagram. An interconnection diagram is a special form of diagram which shows only the external connections between a controller and associated machinery, equipment, and extraneous components.

Control Sequence Table. A control sequence table is a tabulation of the connections which are made for each successive position of the controller.

Order of Procedure. The diagrams necessary for a control equipment are made up in the following order: (1) the elementary diagram, (2) the control sequence table, (3) the controller diagram, (4) the construction diagram. This order is logical because, when an engineer starts to design a controller, he must first work out the elementary design in order to arrive at the proper functioning of the equipment. The control sequence table is then made to indicate which contactors are closed on each point of the control. After these two diagrams have been made, the next step is to determine the apparatus which is to be used on the control panel, and to make a layout drawing of the panel. One of the points which determines the arrangement of apparatus on a panel is the wiring, as it is desirable to arrive at the simplest and shortest arrangement of wires. The elementary diagram will serve as a guide for the layout of the work. After the panel layout has been made and the arrangement of the devices determined, work can be started on the controller diagram. This diagram will show the apparatus in its proper arrangement, and it is the one which the wireman will use.

The construction diagram cannot be completed until the working drawings of the panel are completed, and in order to make the construction diagram it will be necessary to know the location of each stud to which a wire or bus bar is connected. This drawing then shows the actual lengths and shape of bars or wires which are used. Evidently a construction diagram is required only when a number of duplicate controllers are being made. A diagram of this kind permits the wireman to prepare all the wires and bus bars in advance, making all duplicate ones at the same time and so securing the benefits of quantity manufacture.

Extremely simple controllers will not require an elementary diagram or a sequence table.

An external wiring diagram will ordinarily be made up only when it is impossible or undesirable to show all the connections involved on a single diagram. If such a diagram is made, adequate cross-references should be supplied between it and the controller wiring diagram.

Designation of Devices. Devices such as contactors, relays, and limit switches are designated by letters as given in the NEMA standard table which follows. So far as possible, letters which fit the function have been selected, as BR for brake. Where there is more than one device of the same function, numbers are affixed to identify them, as $1BR, 2BR$, etc. Letters with suffixed numbers designate a connection terminal. For example, $1BR$ is a brake relay, but BR1 is the marking for the terminal stud to which the brake is connected. $L1$ and $L2$ designate line terminals, but $1L$ and $2L$ are contactors used in the lowering direction of a hoist or an elevator controller.

Armature accelerator	*A*	Final limit, up	*LSU*
Armature shunt	*AS*	Final limit, down	*LSD*
Balanced voltage	*BV*	Forward	*F*
Brake	*BR*	Full field	*FF*
Brake contactor or relay	*B*	High speed	*FS*
Circuit breaker	*CB*	Hoist	*H*
Compensator, running	*RUN*	Jog	*J*
Compensator, starting	*S*	Kickoff	*KO*
Control	*CR*	Limit switch	*LS*
Control power transformer	*CPT*	Lowering	*L*
Decelerating contactor	*DE*	Low speed	*SS*
Down	*D*	Low torque	*LT*
Dynamic braking	*DB*	Main or line	*M*
Field accelerator	*FA*	Master switch	*MS*
Field decelerator	*FD*	Maximum torque	*MT*
Field discharge	*FD*	Open phase relay	*OPR*
Field failure (loss of field)	*FL*	Overload	*OL*
Field forcing (decreasing)	*FD*	Plug	*P*
Field forcing (increasing)	*FA*	Reverse	*R*
Field protective (fiel l		Series relay	*SR*
weakened at standstill)	*FP*	Slowdown	*SD*
Field weakening	*FW*	Thermostat	*TS*
Final limit, forward	*LSF*	Time	*TR*
Final limit, reverse	*LSR*	Up	*U*
Final limit, hoist	*LSU*	Undervoltage	*UV*
Final limit, lower	*LSD*	Voltage relay	*V*

Abbreviations. It is sometimes necessary to use abbreviations on diagrams. In order that the meaning shall be clear and that confusion between the diagrams of different manufacturers may be eliminated, NEMA has compiled the list of standard abbreviations given below:

Alternating-current		Degree centigrade	C (not °C)
(adjective)	a-c	Degree Fahrenheit	F (not °F)
Ampere(s)	amp	Diameter	diam
Ampere-hour(s)	amp-hr	Direct-current	
Average	avg	(adjective)	d-c
Brake horsepower	bhp	Efficiency	eff
Brinell hardness number	Bhn	Electric	elec
British thermal unit(s)	Btu or B	Electromotive force	emf
Center to center	c to c	Engineer	engr
Centimeter	cm	Engineering	engg
Circular	cir	Feet per minute	fpm
Circular mils	cir mils	Feet per second	fps
Conductivity	cond	Foot (feet)	ft
Constant	const	Foot-pound(s)	ft-lb
Counterelectromotive		Frequency	spell out
force	cemf	Gallon(s)	gal
Cubic	cu	Horsepower	hp
Cubic foot (feet)	cu ft	Hundred	C
Cubic inch(es)	cu in.	Inch(es)	in.

Inch-pound(s)	in.-lb	Pound-foot (feet)	lb-ft
Kilogram(s)	kg	Pound-inch(es)	lb-in.
Kilovolt(s)	kv	Pounds per square	
Kilovolt-ampere(s)	kva	inch	spi
Kilowatt(s)	kw	Power factor	spell out or pf
Kilowatt-hour(s)	kwhr	Reactive kilovolt-	
Logarithm (common)	log	amperes	kvar
Logarithm (natural)	$\log_e$ or ln	Reactive volt-amperes	var
Magnetomotive force	mmf	Revolutions per minute	rpm
Maximum	max	Revolutions per second	rps
Megohm(s)	spell out	Root mean square	rms
Mho(s)	spell out	Second(s)	sec
Mile(s) per hour	mph	Specific gravity	sp gr
Milliampere(s)	ma	Specific heat	sp ht
Millimeter(s)	mm	Square	sq
Millivolt(s)	mv	Square foot (feet)	sq ft
Minimum	min	Square inch(es)	sq in.
Minute(s)	min	Square root of mean	
National Electrical Code	NEC	square	rms
Ohm(s)	spell out	Standard	std
Ounce(s)	oz	Temperature	temp
Ounce-foot (feet)	oz-ft	Thousand	M
Ounce-inch(es)	oz-in.	Volt(s)	V
Potential	spell out	Volt-ampere(s)	va
Potential difference	spell out	Watt(s)	w
Pound(s)	lb	Watt-hour(s)	whr

Note that periods are omitted except after in. (inch).

Marking of Terminals. A list of standard terminal markings is given below. These markings are used only for terminals to which connection must be made from outside circuits or from auxiliary devices which must be disconnected for shipment. They are not intended to be used for internal machine connections. The letters for terminal markings should not be used for markings other than those listed in the table. All terminals should be marked with some designation, and connections between devices should be marked at both ends. Control circuit terminals or studs should be numbered in sequence from 1 up, preferably from those beginning at the master switch. The number 9 should be avoided as the marking tag may easily be inverted and confused with the number 6. Studs and terminals which are connected together should have the same number.

Wires leading from stud to stud on a controller, but not to any external connection, may be numbered on the diagram for convenience, but such numbers need not be marked on the control.

	DIRECT CURRENT	ALTERNATING CURRENT
Brake	$B1$–$B2$–$B3$, etc.	$B1$–$B2$–$B3$, etc.
Brush on commutator (armature)	$A1$–$A2$	$H1$–$H2$–$H3$, etc.
Brush on slip ring (rotor)		$M1$–$M2$–$M3$, etc.
Field (commutating)	$C1$–$C2$	
Field (series)	$S1$–$S2$	
Field (shunt)	$F1$–$F2$	$F1$–$F2$
Line	$L1$–$L2$	$L1$–$L2$–$L3$, etc.
Resistor (armature)	$R1$–$R2$–$R3$, etc.	$R1$–$R2$–$R3$, etc.
Resistor (shunt field)	$V1$–$V2$–$V3$, etc.	
Stator		$T1$–$T2$–$T3$, etc.
Transformer (high-voltage)		$H1$–$H2$–$H3$, etc.
Transformer (low-voltage)		$X1$–$X2$–$X3$, etc.
Transformer (testing winding)		$Y1$–$Y2$–$Y3$, etc.

Symbols. The symbols on wiring diagrams to represent contactors, relays, and other devices were at one time practically outline diagrams or pictures of the device. However, this method of showing the device has been very much simplified in order to reduce the time and expense of making the diagrams. It is not essential to show a symbol which looks like the device if the symbol is so made that the wiring to the various parts of the device is apparent and the operation of the device easily determined from the symbol. Some of the symbols commonly used by control manufacturers are shown on the following pages, but space permits showing only a few. For a complete list see American Standard Z32.

The usual practice is to indicate the function of each part of a device by a standard symbol; that is, there is one symbol representing a power contact, another representing a coil, a third symbol for an interlock, etc. These symbols are then arranged in a definite location, according to the way the complete device is built. That is, the coil may be on the left of the contacts, or it may be on the right of the contacts, but in either case the same symbols for both coils and contacts are used.

Elementary Wiring Diagram. In making the elementary wiring diagram, the first essential is simplicity. The two power lines should be drawn vertically on the sheet, and the devices should be connected between them in as near to a straight-line run as possible. The whole purpose of this diagram is to enable the scheme to be easily determined and easily understood. In order to aid in simplicity, it is permissible to separate the parts of a device and show them in different portions of the diagram.

Bell	
Battery	
Capacitor, fixed	
Capacitor, adjustable	
Air circuit breaker (one pole)	
Power circuit breaker (one pole)	
Three-pole power circuit breaker (single throw) (with terminals)	or
Three-pole power circuit breaker (double throw) (with terminals)	or
Rotary auxiliary switch (with terminals)	Handle end Closed position indicated by diagonal line
Non-magnetic-core inductors, reactors, and coils	or
Magnetic-core inductors, reactors, coils, etc.	or

Operating coil	∿ or ◯
Blowout coil	N With leads | N̥ With terminals
Mechanical connection or shield	 — — — — —
Mechanical connection with fulcrum	 — — —⋋— — —
Mechanical interlock	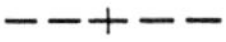 — —+— — or by note. For example: Contactors *F* and *R* are mechanically interlocked.
Direct-connected units	 ◯— — — — —◯
Conductors	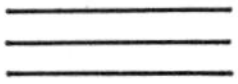 ≡
Spliced conductors, or change of type or size	 ≡ with dots
Crossing or conductors not connected 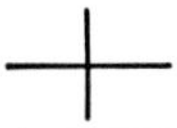 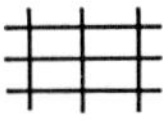	+ | ▦
Crossing of connected conductors  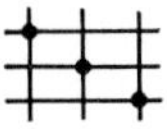	┿ | ▦
Ground connection  	⏚ | ⏚
Conduit or grouping of leads	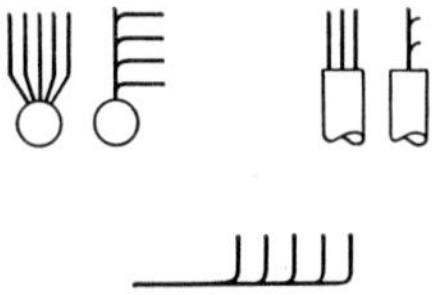 (conduit symbols)
Conductor with polarity mark	 ┼ or ╋ or  ✳ or �

Normally closed contact *(NC)*	
Normally open contact *(NO)*	
NO contact with timed closing *(TC)* feature	*TC*
NC contact with timed opening *(TO)* feature	*TO*
Three-pole electrically operated contactor with blowout coils and 2 *NO* & 1 *NC* auxiliary contacts	
Single-pole electrically operated contactors without blowout coil, with operating coil and series holding coil 1 *NC* auxiliary contact	
Fuse	
Instruments showing terminals: ammeter	
3 φ or 2 φ, 3-wire squirrel-cage induction motor or generator	
3 φ wound motor induction motor, synchronous induction motor, or induction generator	
3 φ synchronous motor or generator or capacitor	
D-c series motor or 2-wire generator with commutating and/ or compensating field winding	
D-c shunt motor or 2-wire generator with commutating and/ or compensating field winding	

Dry or electrolytic rectifier: (for schematic or elementary diagram)	Half wave	a-c d-c d-c a-c Full wave
Resistor, fixed	With leads	With terminals
Resistor, continuously adjustable		
Rheostat	or	
Knife switches	or	
Pushbutton open and closed (spring return)		
Pushbutton open and closed (non-spring return)	L-+-	

All connected apparatus shown on the controller diagram should also be shown on the elementary diagram, including meters, instrument transformers, and limit switches.

All terminal markings should appear in the elementary diagram and must agree with those on the controller diagram.

If the elementary diagram is made on a sheet separate from the controller diagram, a cross-reference should be included on both.

Incoming lines should go first to the upper clips of the knife switch and from the blades of the knife switch to the fuses. This insures that the fuse is dead when the knife switch is open. Knife switches should open in the direction of gravity.

Terminals $A1$ and $F1$ should be connected to the $L1$ side of the line. Terminals $A2$ and $F2$ should be connected to the $L2$ side of the line.

In a two-phase, four-wire system, $L1$ and $L3$ are one phase, $L2$ and $L4$ are the other phase. Alternating-current diagrams should be made to show the four lines and should contain a note that for three-phase supply $T3$ and $T4$ are connected together. Control circuits must therefore be connected between $L1$ and $L2$, and series overload coils must be in lines $L1$–$L4$.

The series coils and the contacts of a device should be of the same polarity. It is also advisable to arrange the circuits so that two sets of interlock fingers on the same contactor are of the same polarity. When showing double-coil relays it is better not to attempt to indicate the electrical relation of the windings, but instead to add a note explaining the polarity of the coils.

When two or more coils are connected in parallel, they are likely to cause sluggish operation of the contactor owing to discharge between the coils. This is especially true with large contactors or with those of different sizes. It is advisable to separate the coil circuits. When two or more large coils are connected in series, they do not build up together, and the contactors are likely to close in sequence instead of closing together.

Resistance connected in parallel with the coil slows up the dropping out of the contactor. The lower the ohmic value of the resistor, the more slowly the contactor will open. Resistance in series with a coil does not delay the opening of the contactor but increases the speed of closing.

A capacitor connected in parallel with the coil may cause the contactor to operate either faster or slower. Capacitors are sometimes used in this manner in order to cut down arcing on pilot contacts which are handling a coil circuit. Care is necessary in applying them to avoid trouble in the event of a capacitor failure.

Master controllers and pushbuttons should be connected in the line opposite to the grounded line. When two masters operate a single control panel, care is necessary to avoid improper operation which may occur if both masters are moved at the same time, or if the second one is moved after the first one has been operated.

When two or more panels are operating in a tandem arrangement, it is usually better to have only one control knife switch and one set of fuses. It will be evident that, if more than one are used, they must be connected either in series or in parallel. If they are in series, no particular purpose is accomplished by having more than one; if they are in parallel, it is necessary to open all of them in order to disconnect the circuit.

When contactors having carbon-to-copper tips are used, the current must flow from the carbon to the copper in order to obtain reasonable life of the contact tips. In this case it is necessary to indicate polarity on the diagram.

Wherever it is possible to open the shunt field without a discharge path, a field discharge resistance should be shown. Some non-reverse controllers have a discharge path through the armature and the controller resistor; a separate discharge resistor is then not necessary.

When limit switches are used, it is advisable to connect the coils of the main contactors behind the limit switch contacts if possible, and not to depend upon relays alone to open the main contactor coils.

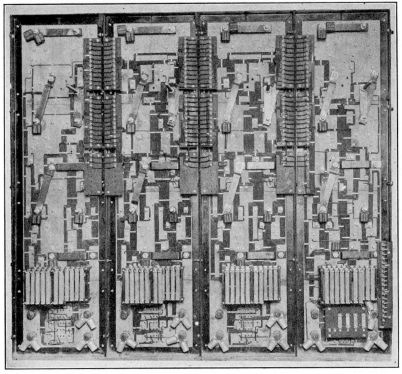

FIG. 1. Wiring of a Large Controller.

Controller Wiring Diagrams. A controller wiring diagram is a picture of the wiring on the panel and that to the external devices. Consequently, the various devices mounted on the panel are shown in their relative locations, and all terminals, interlocks, etc., which are furnished are shown whether they are connected or not. The contacts of pushbuttons, relays, contactors, etc., are shown in the normal position with power off.

If the elementary diagram is made on a sheet separate from the controller diagram, cross-references should be included on both.

Connections are preferably shown looking at the rear of the panel, when the wire is to be on the rear, as it is from this side the wireman looks, and it is also from this side that any changes are to be made.

Standard symbols and standard markings for contactors, relays, terminals, and auxiliary devices should be used wherever possible.

The lines indicating the wires should be at least $\frac{1}{8}$ inch apart and should be either horizontal or vertical. Crosses and right-angle turns should be kept at a minimum. Double crosses should be avoided. Heavy lines indicate the main motor circuits, such as the motor armature, series field, series brake, and dynamic braking connections. Light lines indicate control circuits and shunt field and shunt brake connections. The difference between light control wiring and heavy control wiring must be readily distinguished. The light lines should be heavy enough to print well, and the heavy lines light enough not to appear cumbersome.

Incoming leads should be shown outside of the panel limits until directly opposite to the terminal to which they connect. When there are more than three wires between the panel and other devices, the wires should be shown in cable to simplify the wiring and make the diagram easier to read.

The armature, fields, and brake associated with one motor should be shown close together. If more than one motor appears on the diagram, the resistor and accessories applying to each motor should be grouped as well as possible.

The control terminals should be so arranged that wires running to the same external device (master, limit switch, etc.) are connected to terminals that are grouped together. Connections from meters to their shunts must be made directly, and must not pass through terminals on their panels.

Resistors mounted directly on the panel should be shown in their relative positions. A resistor in a frame behind the panel may be shown in any convenient position on the diagram within the panel limits, or, if this complicates the diagram, it may be shown separate from the panel. If it is shown separate, a note should be included, saying: "Resistor connected to similarly marked points on control panel." Resistors which are not mounted on the panel or on a frame at the rear of the panel should be shown outside the panel limits on the diagram.

A contactor sequence table should be included on diagrams for multi-speed magnetic contactor controllers.

Identical Panels. When two or more identical panels are shown on one diagram it is preferable to indicate complete internal connections for one only. The other panels may be represented by an enclosure including the terminals for outgoing connections, and a note stating that connections for panel 2 are the same as for panel 1. When two or more panels are identical except for a few connections, it is permissible to show complete connections for one only, and the changed connections only for the others. A note should then be included stating that connections for panel 2 are the same as for panel 1 except as shown.

Grounding. Any metal device, or metal part of a device, which is mounted on a control panel and might reasonably be expected to be dead, must be grounded to the panel mounting frame. Grounding wires should be shown on the diagram. This includes instrument cases, pushbutton cases, lamp sockets, and manual operating levers or metal enclosures, but not contactor levers.

Controller Construction Diagram. This diagram, in general, should be a picture of the rear of the panel and should show all parts to scale, although no dimensions need to be given. The drawing should include not only the wires and bus bars, but also the various nuts, washers, and lock washers necessary to the assembly, and also the method of assembling the wires to the studs.

Resistor Diagrams. Diagrams for self-contained resistors are made only for manufacturing purposes and are really assembly drawings for the material. However, if the resistor is separately mounted it is necessary to make a diagram to enable the purchaser to install and connect the resistor properly. A diagram of this type should show the resistor frames in outline as well as the location and marking of the terminals, the number of leads or units in each step, and the interconnection of the various frames. If the frame has a type number stamped on its name plate for identification, this number should be indicated on the diagram as a guide to the purchaser. Diagrams should also include the ohmic value of each step of resistance, and directions for mounting and installing. The terminal markings must, of course, agree with those on the main wiring diagram.

It is customary, in direct-current work, that a step marked $R1$ shall be the first one short-circuited in acceleration. In three-phase alternating-current work, the steps marked $R1$, $R11$, and $R21$ are the first ones short-circuited.

Notes. It is sometimes necessary to furnish explanatory notes on a main diagram. It is good practice to group these notes in one location on the sheet and number them. Reference to the notes may then be made by numbers located at the proper points on the diagram. Some of the points that it is sometimes necessary to cover by such notes are listed below:

On three-phase diagrams it is desirable to include a note saying: "If connection is made to a three-phase system, one line of which is grounded, make $L2$ the grounded line."

Where current transformers are furnished a note should state: "The secondaries of current transformers should be grounded; if they are mounted on the back of the panel, securely ground them to the frame before shipment."

Diagrams should show a note to cover the grounding of supports or enclosing case. This applies also to drum frames: "Panel supports should be grounded." "Enclosing cases should be grounded."

If the purchaser is to make changes in the standard wiring of the controller, each such wire should be marked: "Purchaser to make (or remove) connections."

Material shown, the use of which is optional, should be marked: "If used."

Material shown but furnished by the purchaser should be marked: "Not furnished by manufacturer."

If mechanical interlocks between contactors are used and the diagram does not otherwise indicate them, a note should state which contactors are so interlocked.

On diagrams showing a field discharge resistor not furnished by the manufacturer, a note should state: "Field discharge resistance recommended (not furnished by manufacturer)."

If accessories such as limit switches are used with devices to which they are mechanically connected, the fact should be noted unless perfectly obvious: "Limit switch geared to winding drum."

Typical Examples. A manufacturer of control apparatus finds it necessary to make a very great number of diagrams. For instance, a typical controller selected at random from a manufacturer's catalog showed the following possible variations. The controller was a reversing direct-current magnetic equipment, and six different sizes were listed to cover various horsepower ratings. Options were given for the omission of the main knife switch and also for that of the overload relays. Further options were given for the addition of a low-voltage protective relay and an open-field protective relay. The controller, though intended for a series motor, could be used with a compound motor by the addition of a field discharge resistance and a clip on the knife switch. An enclosure could be supplied, if required, which would probably necessitate a different arrangement of the parts on the panel. The controller was arranged to operate from either a two-speed or a multispeed master. If all these various options are multiplied out, their combinations give a total of 768 possible diagrams for this one type of controller.

It must further be considered that any change in the arrangement of the parts on the panel, or any additions to or subtractions from these parts, or any change in the details of a part which would cause a change in the symbol would render all these diagrams obsolete and necessitate a complete new set. When it is considered that a manufacturer lists many different standard types of control and is also called upon constantly to supply many entirely new and special designs, it will be evident that the number of diagrams required is very great.

The following examples are mentioned merely to show some different forms from the standpoint of the mechanical make-up of the diagram rather than from that of the circuit design.

Figure 72 shows a compound manual-type starter and speed regulator for a direct-current motor. The starter has an armature resistor for starting purposes and a field resistor for regulating purposes. The method of showing the buttons for the armature resistor and the field resistor, the levers, and the low-voltage release magnet may be clearly seen.

Figure 77 shows a direct-current reversing drum-type controller. The cylinder is developed in the same manner as that of a drum-type master controller. The resistor shown is separately mounted. This diagram illustrates the use of dotted lines to show optional features, and notes in connection with these features.

These two figures are representative of main or controller wiring diagrams.

Figure 202 is a line diagram of an alternating-current magnetic controller which is master-operated.

Figure 131 illustrates a line diagram of a direct-current controller which is master-operated, and which is arranged to make a complete cycle and stop each time the master controller is moved to the on position. The stopping is under control of limit switches, which are shown in their proper place in the circuit. These limit switches are of the rotating-cam type, and the small auxiliary sketch shows the portion of the cycle during which each contact is closed.

Wireless Diagrams. It is possible to make a controller wiring diagram without actually drawing lines to indicate the wires. The device symbols, designations, and terminal markings are the same as for the conventional diagram, and the devices are shown in their proper relative location. Points on each device which are to be connected together are given like numbers, and the wiring desired is then shown in tabular form. For example, if a wire is to connect between contacts on contactors *F*, *R*, and *DB* and this wire is given the number 6, then there will be a point numbered 6 on each of the three device symbols, and a line of the table will be:

6   F R DB

The wireman sees from the table that wire 6 runs to the three devices indicated, and by looking at the symbol for each device he sees exactly where wire 6 is to be connected.

This method is said to save time in wiring. It undoubtedly saves drafting time, and makes changes in the diagram much easier to accomplish.

References

G. M. Heine and C. H. Dunlap, "How to Read Electrical Blueprints," American Technical Society, Chicago, 1943.

H. B. Dwight, G. W. Andrew, and H. W. Tileston, Jr., "Temperature Rise of Bus Bars," *General Electric Review*, May, 1940.

Terminal Markings for Electrical Apparatus, *American Standard C6.1*.

Graphical Symbols for Electric Power and Control, *American Standard Z32.3*.

Abbreviations for Use on Drawings, *American Standard Z32.13*.

Problems

Make schematic diagrams for the following controllers:

1. A non-reversing pushbutton-operated controller for a shunt motor, consisting of

> DPST knife switch.
> 2 single-coil overload relays.
> 2 main line contactors.
> 3 accelerating contactors without timing.
> Resistors.
> Start-stop pushbuttons.

2. A controller duplicating that of problem 1, except with the addition of dynamic braking and a field discharge resistor.

3. A controller duplicating that of problem 1, except with the addition of a field rheostat, a field-loss relay, and some means of short-circuiting the rheostat during acceleration.

4. A controller duplicating that of problem 1, except with the addition of a jogging pushbutton.

5. A reversing pushbutton-operated controller for a series motor, consisting of

> DPST knife switch.
> 2 single-coil overload relays.
> 1 main line contactor.
> 4 SP reversing contactors.

3 accelerating contactors without timing.
Resistors.
Forward-reverse-stop pushbuttons.

6. A controller duplicating that of problem 5, except operated by a four-speed, drum-type master controller instead of by pushbuttons, and having a no-voltage relay.

7. A controller duplicating that of problem 1, but with the addition of three series relays for current-limit acceleration.

8. A controller for starting and reversing two series motors in parallel, consisting of

DPST knife switch.
3 single-coil overload relays.
1 main line contactor.
8 SP reversing contactors.
2 SP plugging contactors.
3 SP accelerating contactors without timing.
No-voltage relay.
Resistors.
Four-speed, drum-type master controller.

9. A controller duplicating that of problem 5, except equipped with a shunt brake, and with 2 SP limit switches, one for stopping in each direction of travel.

10. A controller duplicating that of problem 1, except with the addition of a normally closed armature-shunt contactor and resistor, and with individual dashpot timing relays for controlling the accelerating contactors.

11. A reversing magnetic controller, master-operated, for a 50-horsepower 230-volt series motor driving a crane bridge. Use inductive timing without inductor.

12. A reversing controller for a squirrel-cage motor, consisting of

TPST disconnect device.
3 single-coil overload relays.
2 three-pole contactors.
Shunt brake.
Forward-reverse-stop pushbuttons.

13. A reversing autotransformer starter for a squirrel-cage motor, consisting of

1 three-pole circuit breaker.
3 single-coil overload relays.
2 three-pole contactors for reversing.
1 five-pole contactor for starting.
1 three-pole contactor for running.
2 autotransformers.
1 dashpot timing relay operated by starting contactor.
Forward-reverse-stop pushbuttons.

14. A non-reversing, primary-resistance increment starter for squirrel-cage motor, consisting of:

1 three-pole line contactor.
3 single-coil overload relays.

3 three-pole resistor commutating contactors.
3 dashpot timing relays operated by contactors.
Resistor in three phases.
Start-stop pushbutton.

15. A selective controller for the motor of Fig. 188.

16. A variable-frequency control for three squirrel-cage motors. This consists of a direct-current motor with a non-reverse three-step time-limit controller, and an alternator driven by the motor. Each squirrel-cage motor is equipped with an across-the-line magnetic starter with overload and disconnecting circuit breaker. A field rheostat controls the speed of the direct-current motor.

17. A controller for a wound-rotor motor, similar to the controller of Fig. 200, except reversing, and operated by a four-step drum-type master controller. Note that undervoltage relay must be added.

18. A controller for a synchronous motor, similar to the controller of Fig. 219, except with single-step primary-resistance starting.

19. A controller of the part-winding type like Fig. 181, with the addition of a step of resistance in each leg of the first section of the motor winding, and a timed contactor to short-circuit the resistor before the second section of the winding is energized.

20. A controller for a wound-rotor motor like the controller of Fig. 200, except with three-phase series relay acceleration, and with a four-point master controller instead of a pushbutton.

21. Complete the diagram of Fig. 201 by drawing the master and control circuits.

22. Make a sequence table for the controller of Fig. 201, showing the contactors which are closed on each point of the master controller.

3

CONSTRUCTION OF CONTROL APPARATUS

Material for Panels. The material used for control panels is generally slate, asbestos composition, or steel. The best variety of slate is known as Monson slate; it is free of iron and other impurities and may safely be used for up to approximately 1600 volts. Other varieties of slate are satisfactory for many purposes provided that they are reasonably free of impurities. In general, their use is limited to approximately 1000 volts. The slate, after being drilled, is either sprayed with an insulating finish or oiled.

The asbestos composition is used for many purposes and especially for voltages above 1600. It has a slightly greater tendency to take up moisture. The asbestos composition excels slate chiefly in its resistance to impact and volume resistance. The impact strength of the composition is two to four times that of slate. On the other hand, slate has about twice the resistance to rupture. The cost of working the materials is about the same.

Fabric-base phenolic material is sometimes used for control panels because of its strength. It has a tendency to char under arcing; also, it is too expensive for general use.

Steel panels, being strong and relatively inexpensive, are being used in increasing quantity. The apparatus mounted on steel must be of dead-back construction having terminals on the front. Steel panels are wired on the front.

Arrangement of Panels. A number of factors enter into the arrangement of apparatus on a panel. The common method of making such layouts is to use paper templates cut to the exact size and shape of the various pieces of equipment which are to be mounted. These templates may then be laid out on a table and shifted around until the best arrangement is found. One of the first considerations is to make the size of the panel as small as possible, both from a cost standpoint and also because space is important in most installations. Appearance is another consideration. The parts should be arranged symmetrically and should be lined up as nearly as possible.

Both the internal wiring of the panel and the external wiring, which the user must install, should be considered in making a layout. It is important to have the wires and bus bars on the panel as short and as straight as possible, and also to have a minimum number of heavy connections. The terminals to which the user will connect his cables should be placed in an accessible position; it is generally advisable to group them either at the top or at the bottom of the panel.

It is preferable to have the heavier pieces of apparatus mounted near the bottom of the panel, so that it will not be top-heavy. It is also advisable to mount oil dashpots, or other devices using oil, near the bottom so that if there is leakage the oil will not run down onto other pieces of apparatus. Dashpots and other devices which require adjustment should be located so that the adjustment is accessible.

Knife switches should be arranged to open in the direction of gravity and should be mounted at a convenient height. For ease of reading, meters and instruments should be mounted at approximately eye level. Current and potential transformers, if mounted on a panel, are usually mounted on the rear, metal straps or supports being used for the purpose.

Thermal overload relays are preferably mounted at the bottom of the panel, especially if the panel is enclosed. Heat generated by other devices will rise to the top of the enclosure and so will not be likely to affect the operation of the thermal devices.

If panels are enclosed, adequate ventilation must be provided, and, for dust-tight equipment, it may be necessary to make the enclosure relatively large in order to prevent overheating of the apparatus in it.

Line contactors, or other contactors in which considerable arcing occurs, are preferably mounted at the top of the panel, so that the arcing will not affect other apparatus on the panel. It is necessary to provide adequate clearance in the direction of the arc. Minimum clearances are given in Table 1.

Open-type Frames. Small panels are usually mounted on a frame of sheet metal having a wire grillwork at the top and bottom for ventilating purposes. The resistor material is then mounted either on the rear of the panel or to the sides of the frame. Larger panels may be mounted on angle-iron or pipe framework. If the resistor is to be separately mounted, the panel framework may consist merely of upright angles, or it may have, in addition, cross-angles to increase the strength. If the resistor is mounted as part of the controller, a floor frame of angle iron with sheet-metal sides and back is used. The resistor is then mounted at the sides of the framework.

For crane or coal bridge installations, or any installation in which the floor panel may be under severe vibration or strains, it is customary to use a heavy frame of angle iron and to divide the slate panel into a number of small sections to lessen the danger of breakage. This construction is relatively expensive and does not present so good an appearance as the switchboard construction, but it does very greatly increase the strength of the equipment.

For an example of open-frame construction see Fig. 218.

Definitions. The following definitions, applying to the construction and the enclosure of controllers, are quoted from NEMA Industrial Control Standards.

Gas-proof apparatus is apparatus so constructed or protected that the specified gas will not interfere with its successful operation.

Gas-tight apparatus is apparatus so constructed that the specified gas will not enter the enclosing case under specified conditions of pressure.

Fume-resistant apparatus is apparatus so constructed that it will not be readily injured by the specified fumes.

Dust-proof apparatus is apparatus so constructed or protected that the accumulation of dust will not interfere with its successful operation.

Dust-tight apparatus is apparatus so constructed that the dust will not enter the enclosing case.

Moisture-resistant apparatus is apparatus so constructed or treated that it will not be readily injured by moisture. Such apparatus shall be capable of operating in a very humid atmosphere, such as that found in mines or evaporating rooms.

Drip-proof apparatus is apparatus so constructed or protected that its successful operation is not interfered with when it is subjected to falling moisture or dirt.

Drip-tight apparatus is apparatus so protected as to exclude falling moisture or dirt. Drip-tight apparatus may be semi-enclosed apparatus if it is provided with suitable protection integral with the apparatus, or so enclosed as to exclude effectively falling solid or liquid material.

Splash-proof apparatus is apparatus so constructed and protected that external splashing will not interfere with its successful operation.

Water-tight apparatus is apparatus so constructed that a stream of water from a hose (not less than 1 inch in diameter) under a head of about 35 feet and from a distance of about 10 feet can be played on the apparatus for several minutes without leakage.

Submersible apparatus is apparatus so constructed that it will operate successfully when submerged in water under specified conditions of pressure and time.

Weather-proof apparatus is apparatus so constructed or protected that exposure to the weather will not interfere with its successful operation.

Sleet-proof apparatus is apparatus so constructed or protected that the accumulation of sleet will not interfere with its successful operation.

Acid-resistant apparatus is apparatus so constructed that it will not be readily injured by acid fumes.

Types of Enclosures. NEMA defines standard types of non-ventilated enclosures as outlined below, and the same type numbers, followed by the word "ventilated," apply to ventilated enclosures.

Type I. General Purpose. (Fig. 172.) A case designed to meet the Underwriters' Laboratories general specifications for enclosures that may be in effect from time to time, and primarily to protect against accidental contact.

Fig. 2. NEMA Type-IA Semi-dust-tight Enclosure, Using Felt Gaskets.

Type I case is suitable for general-purpose application, indoors, and where atmospheric conditions are normal. It serves as protection against dust and light indirect splashing, but is not dust-tight.

Type IA. Semi-dust-tight. (Fig. 2.) A case similar to Type I, with the addition of a gasket around the cover.

Type IA case is suitable for general application indoors and provides additional protection against dust, although it is not dust-tight. It has come to be known in the trade as "semi-dust-tight."

Type IB. Flush Type. (Fig. 3.) A case similar to Type I, designed for mounting in a wall and provided with a cover which also serves as a flush plate.

Type II. Drip-tight. (Fig. 4.) A case similar to Type I, with the addition of drip shields or their equivalent.

Fig. 3. NEMA Type-IB Flush-mounted Enclosure.

Fig. 4. NEMA Type-II Drip-tight Enclosure.

Type II case is suitable for application where condensation may be severe, as in cooling rooms and laundries. It meets the requirements of the definitions for drip-proof apparatus and drip-tight apparatus.

Type III. Weather-resistant. (Fig. 5.) A case which provides proper protection against weather hazards, as rain and sleet.

Type III case is suitable for outdoor application, as on docks, canal locks, and construction work, and also for application in subways and

FIG. 5. NEMA Types-III, IV, V Weather-resistant, Dust-tight, or Water-tight Enclosure.

tunnels. It meets the requirements of the definitions for splash-proof apparatus, weather-proof apparatus, sleet-proof apparatus, and moisture-resistant apparatus.

Type IV. Water-tight. (Fig. 5.) Water-tight means provided with an enclosing case which will exclude water applied in the form of a hose stream for a specified time, as stated in the following note:

Note. Enclosures shall be tested by subjection to a stream of water. A hose with a 1-inch nozzle shall be used and shall deliver at least 65 gallons per minute. The water shall be directed on the enclosure from a distance of not less than 10 feet and for a period of 5 minutes. During this period it may be directed in any one or more directions as desired. There shall be no leakage of water into the enclosure under these conditions.

Type V. Dust-tight. (Fig. 5.) A case provided with gaskets or the equivalent to exclude dust. It meets the requirements of the definition for dust-tight apparatus and of the National Electrical Code for Class III and Class IV locations that may be in effect from time to time.

Type V case is suitable for application in steel mills, cement mills, and other locations where it is desirable to exclude dust.

Type VI. Submersible. (Fig. 6.) A case designed to operate successfully when submerged in water under specified conditions of pressure and time.

Type VI case is suitable for application where it may be subject to submersion in water, as in quarries, mines, and manholes. The design will depend on the specified conditions of pressure and time.

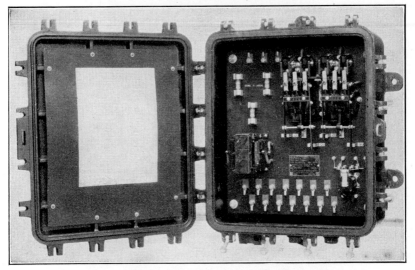

Fig. 6.   NEMA Type-VI Submersible Enclosure.

Type VII. Hazardous Locations. Class I. Air Break (See Note III). (Fig. 7.) A case designed to meet the application requirements of the National Electrical Code for Class I, Group D, hazardous locations that may be in effect from time to time, and designed in accordance with the Underwriters' Laboratories specifications that may be in effect from time to time.

Type VIII. Hazardous Locations. Class I. Oil-immersed (See Note III). (Fig. 8.) A case designed for the application requirements of the National Electrical Code for Class I, Group D, hazardous locations that may be in effect from time to time, and designed in accordance with the Underwriters' Laboratories specifications that may be in effect from time to time, the apparatus being immersed in oil.

Type IX. Hazardous Locations. Class II. (Fig. 9.) A case designed for the application requirements of the National Electrical Code for Class II, Groups F and G, hazardous locations that may be in effect from time to time, and designed in accordance with the Underwriters' Laboratories specifications that may be in effect from time to time.

FIG. 7. NEMA Type-VII Hazardous Locations, Class I, Air-break Enclosure.

FIG. 8. NEMA Type-VIII Hazardous Locations, Class I, Oil-immersed Controller. Oil Tank Removed.

Type IXA. Hazardous Locations. Class II, Group E. These enclosures are designed to meet the application requirements of the National Electrical Code for Class II, Group E, hazardous locations, which are in effect from time to time and are designed in accordance with the latest specifications of Underwriters' Laboratories.

Type X. Bureau of Mines. (Fig. 10.) A case designed to meet the requirements of the U. S. Bureau of Mines that may be in effect from time to time.

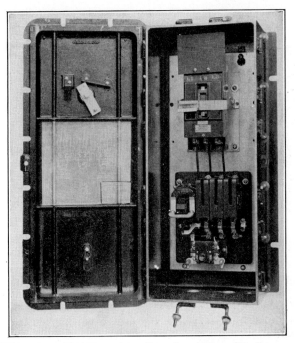

Fig. 9.   NEMA Type-IX Hazardous Locations, Class II, Groups F and G, Enclosure.

Type X case is for application in coal mines.

Type XI. Acid- and Fume-resistant, Oil-immersed. These enclosures are suitable for application where the equipment is subject to corrosive acid or fumes, as in chemical plants, plating rooms, and sewage plants. The equipment in the case is immersed in oil.

Type XII. Automotive. A Type XII enclosure has a cover construction meeting the requirements of a Type IA enclosure, the cover being hinged to swing horizontally and held in place with screws, bolts, or other suitable fasteners, which require the use of a tool such as a screw driver or wrench to release. The fastener parts shall be held in place when the door is opened so that they will not become lost. There shall be no holes through the enclosure for mounting or for mounting controls within the enclosure and no conduit knockouts or conduit openings.   Mounting feet or other suitable mounting means shall be provided.

A Type XII enclosure is suitable for application to machine tools and other industrial processing machines in locations where oil or coolant might enter the enclosure through holes used for mounting the enclosure or for mounting the equipment within the enclosure or through unused conduit knockouts.

Note I.   When an enclosure is required to meet the definitions of gas-proof or gas-tight, the selection of a suitable type will depend

FIG. 10.   NEMA Type-X Bureau of Mines Enclosure.

on whether protection is desired against corrosion or against explosion and fire.

Note II.   When an enclosure is required to meet the definitions of acid-resistant or fume-resistant, the design will depend on the conditions of exposure.

Note III.   In order to standardize the practice in referring to equipment sometimes known as explosion-proof (Types VII and VIII) it is recommended that apparatus designed for use in Class I, Group D, locations be described in one of the following manners, whichever is applicable.

1. Control listed by Underwriters' Laboratories for use in Class I, Group D, locations.

2. Control designed to conform with the manufacturer's interpretation of the Underwriters' Laboratories Standards, but not listed or tested by the Underwriters' Laboratories.

3. Control of size and nature for which there are no existing Underwriters' Laboratories standards or testing facilities.

Note IV.   When a non-ventilated enclosure is specified for equipment consisting in part of devices which require ventilation (electron tubes, resistors, etc.), it is understood that such devices may be mounted in a ventilated portion of the enclosure, provided that they are capable of operating satisfactorily and without hazard when so mounted.

Design of Enclosures. 1. There must be sufficient space within the enclosure to permit uninsulated parts of wire terminals to be separated so as to prevent their coming in contact with each other. Enclosures must be such as to permit proper wire connections to be made with adequate spacing of the terminals and ends of conductors from adjacent points of the enclosures.

2. Exposed non-arcing current-carrying parts within the enclosures shall have an air space between them and the uninsulated walls of the enclosure, including conduit fittings, of at least $\frac{1}{2}$ inch for 600 volts or less. Enclosures of sizes, material, or form not securing adequate rigidity must have greater spacing. A suitable lining of insulating material not less than $\frac{1}{32}$ inch in thickness may be considered acceptable where the spacing referred to above is less than $\frac{1}{2}$ inch.

Exception: For fractional-horsepower controllers, and other small devices, of 300 volts or less, where the enclosure is rigid, an air space of $\frac{1}{4}$ inch is permitted between non-arcing current-carrying parts and the uninsulated part of the enclosure.

3. All enclosures and parts of enclosures such as doors, covers, and tanks must be provided with means for firmly securing them in place. Among the available means are locks, interlocks, screws, and seals.

4. Where the walls of the enclosure are not protected by barriers or by a lining of non-combustible insulating material, the arc-rupturing parts of the controller should have air spaces, as per Table 1, between

TABLE 1

CLEARANCES BETWEEN ARC-RUPTURING PARTS AND ENCLOSURE

Horse-power Rating	Distance from Contacts in Direction of Blowout in Inches D-c and A-c Circuits		Vertical Distance above Contacts, without Blowout in Inches				Horizontal Distance from Contacts and Distance below Contacts in Inches D-c and A-c Circuits	
			D-c Circuits		A-c Circuits			
	300 Volts	600 Volts	300 Volts	600 Volts	300 Volts	600 Volts	300 Volts	600 Volts
5	$1\frac{3}{4}$	3	4	Barriers	$1\frac{3}{4}$	3	$\frac{3}{4}$	$1\frac{1}{2}$
10	2	4	5	Barriers	2	4	$\frac{3}{4}$	$1\frac{1}{2}$
50	3	5	6	Barriers	3	5	1	2
100	4	Barriers	Barriers	Barriers	4	Barriers	2	3
Above 100	Barriers	Barriers	Barriers	Barriers	Barriers	Barriers	Barriers	Barriers

Note 1. All distances shall be measured from the contact tips or arc horns.

them and the walls of the enclosure, unless a test on any specific device demonstrates that a smaller space is safe for that particular device.

Material. 1. In the following paragraphs it is assumed that steel (or gray iron for castings) will be the metal employed. Copper, bronze, and brass are sometimes used, in which case the requirements given for steel shall be complied with.

2. *Thickness of Castings.* Cast metal for enclosures, whether of iron or other metal, shall be at least $\frac{1}{8}$ inch thick at every point and of greater thickness at reinforcing ribs and at door edges, except that die-cast metal may not be less than $\frac{3}{32}$ inch thick for an area greater than 24 square inches or having any dimension greater than 6 inches, and may be not less than $\frac{1}{16}$ inch in thickness for an area of 24 square inches or less or having no dimension greater than 6 inches. Cast metal shall be at least $\frac{1}{4}$ inch in thickness.

3. *Sheet-metal Thickness.* The minimum thickness required for sheet-metal enclosures varies with the size. For solid enclosures without slot or other opening, and for solid enclosures except for a slot for the operating handles or openings for ventilation or both, the sheet metal shall be of gage not less than given in Table 2, except that metal shall not be less than No. 20 USS gage in thickness at points where rigid conduit is to be connected.

TABLE 2

MINIMUM THICKNESS OF SHEET-METAL ENCLOSURES

Maximum Volume of Enclosure, cubic feet	Maximum Area of Any Surface, square inches	Maximum Dimension, inches	Without Supporting Frame; Minimum U. S. Sheet-Steel Gage	With Supporting Frame or Equivalent Reinforcement; Minimum U. S. Sheet-Steel Gage
$\frac{3}{4}$	....	12	20(0.0359)	24(0.0239)
1	....	18	18(0.0478)	20(0.0359)
..	360	24	16(0.0598)	18(0.0478)
..	1200	48	14(0.0747)	16(0.0598)
..	1500	60	12(0.1046)	16(0.0598)
..	Over 1500	..	10(0.1345)	16(0.0598)

4. All enclosures composed of wire mesh, perforated screens, or grill-work shall be provided with supporting frames.

5. Ventilating openings in an enclosure, including perforated holes, louvers, and openings protected by means of wire screening, expanded metal, or perforated covers, shall be of such size or shape that no opening will permit passage of a rod having a diameter greater than $\frac{1}{2}$ inch; except that, when the distance between live parts and the enclosure is greater than 4 inches, openings may be larger than those previously mentioned, provided that no opening will permit passage of a rod having a diameter greater than $\frac{3}{4}$ inch. The wires of a screen shall not be less than No. 16 AWG when the screen openings are $\frac{1}{2}$ square inch or less in area, and shall be not less than No. 12 AWG for larger screen openings.

Except as noted in the following paragraph, sheet metal employed for expanded metal mesh, and perforated sheet metal, shall not be less than No. 18 USS gage in thickness when the mesh openings or perforations are ½ square inch or less in area, and shall not be less than No. 13 USS gage in thickness for larger openings.

In a small device where the indentation of a guard or enclosure will not affect the clearance between uninsulated, movable, current-carrying parts and grounded metal, No. 24 USS gage expanded metal may be employed, provided that (a) the exposed mesh on any one side or surface of the device so protected has an area of not more than 72 square inches and has no dimension greater than 12 inches, or that (b) the width of an opening so protected is not greater than 3.5 inches.

A floor-mounted controller for use on circuits not in excess of 600 volts may be built without a covering for the bottom, provided that the surrounding enclosure is within 6 inches of the floor, and exposed live parts are not less than 6 inches above the lower edge.

Spacings. (a) The distance between non-arcing, uninsulated live parts of opposite polarity and between non-arcing, uninsulated live parts and parts other than the enclosure which may be grounded when the device is installed shall be not less than given in Table 3.

TABLE 3

ELECTRICAL CLEARANCES

Rating in volts	Through		Across Clean Dry Surfaces	
	Air	Oil	Air	Oil
51– 150	⅛	⅛	¼	¼
151– 300	¼	¼	⅜	⅜
301– 600	⅜	⅜	½	½
2001–2500	1	¾	2	1
2501–5000	2	1½	3½	2
5001–7500	3½	2	5	3

Distance in inches (column span over Through and Across Clean Dry Surfaces)

Note. The clearance distance should be increased for dirty or moist conditions.

(b) The spacings in snap switches, lamp holders, and similar wiring devices supplied as part of industrial control equipment need not comply with the requirements of these standards, provided that such devices are not employed in the motor circuits.

There are a number of conditions under which other spacings may be used, and anyone interested in these requirements is referred to NEMA Standards for Industrial Control.

Special Service Conditions. A standard line of control equipment is designed to meet the requirements of the average installation, where the ambient temperature does not exceed 40 C, where the altitude does not exceed 6000 feet, and where only an ordinary amount of moisture and no acid nor conducting or abrasive dust is present. If the conditions do not conform with these specifications, special construction or special protection should be provided as outlined below.

Unusual conditions of installation usually incorporate a number of factors which must be carefully considered before a definite recommendation is made. It is therefore advisable to give complete details of the conditions to be met when the equipment is ordered, in preference to designating any particular condition as listed below. With such information each point affecting the design can be considered, and the equipment best suited to the conditions can be supplied.

A. Exposure to Damaging Fumes. Use cast-iron or welded-steel enclosing cases with red-lead paint and acid-resisting paint. Joints between case and cover should be gasketed, the material of the gasket depending somewhat on the nature of the fumes, but rubber and felt are the most common. In certain instances, oil-immersed equipment may be necessary, but it cannot be used on direct current. For hydrogen sulphide gas (sewage plants) use blue lead instead of red lead. Cadmium plating should be avoided.

B. Operation in Damp Places. Large iron and steel parts should be red-lead-painted before regular painting. Bearings should be of bronze or brass. Enclosing cases should be of corrosion-resisting material (such as brass or aluminum) or should be red-lead-painted before final painting. Joints between case and cover should be gasketed with rubber in extreme instances. Small iron and steel parts should be well plated with zinc or cadmium.

C. Exposure to Excessive Dust. Enclosing cases should be of cast iron or welded steel with dust-tight joints, gaskets of felt or similar material being used.

D. Exposure to Gritty or Abrasive Dust. Same as Item B above.

F. Exposure to Excessive Oil Vapor. This is similar to Item A above. Special enclosing cases should be used, and in some instances oil-immersed equipment will be required. If gasketed joints are not considered sufficiently gas-tight for the particular installation, a very expensive case with wide flanges, carefully machined and fitted, will be required.

G. Exposure to Salt Air. Same as Item B above.

H. Subject to Vibration, Shocks, and Tilting. Special equipment and construction will be required. Although modifications of standard parts may be used, precautions will be necessary in order to prevent breakage of certain parts and loosening of others. This applies to resistors as well as to other parts of controllers. The nature of the equipment required will depend upon the degree of the special conditions to be met.

I. Exposure to Explosive Dust or Gases. This is similar to Item A above. Special enclosing cases should be used, and in some instances oil-immersed equipment will be required. If gasket joints are not considered sufficiently gas-tight or dust-tight for the particular installation, a very expensive case with wide flanges, very carefully machined and fitted, will be required.

J. Exposure to Weather or Dripping Water. Same as Item B above.

K. Ambient Temperatures in Excess of 40 C but not Exceeding 80 C.

High air temperature must be taken into consideration in the rating of all current-carrying parts. Unless special parts are used, this will result in the derating of contacts, blowout coils, etc. Shunt coils must also be protected or rated.

L. High-altitude Installations. General-purpose and special-service controllers designed in accordance with the usual standards are satisfactory for use at altitudes of 6000 feet or less.

For altitudes greater than 6000 feet, control equipment should be selected as follows:

Continuous-duty resistors should be derated to 75 per cent of their normal wattage rating.

Intermittent and starting duty resistors should be applied on a duty cycle selected on the basis of the next higher "time-on" classification.

A magnetic contactor should be used to open the main line circuit when drum controllers are applied.

Autotransformers and control circuit transformers should be derated to 75 per cent of their normal kilovolt-ampere rating.

Built-in Apparatus. In designing control for certain applications, particularly in the machine-tool industry, there is often an advantage in a construction which allows the control apparatus to be built in as a part of the machine.

The first step toward building in the electric equipment was the design of the shell-type motor. This motor is sometimes called a shaftless motor, because the driving shaft is omitted and the armature is mounted directly on the machine spindle. The frame of the motor does not have any housing or any mounting feet but is clamped into a specially prepared cavity in the machine.

In planning for built-in control equipment it is advisable to determine the control before the machine is designed, so that the space provided may be suitable for the necessary control apparatus. The method of wiring must also be considered, and the housing arranged so that it will not be difficult to make a good wiring job and one that will present a neat appearance. Since the control panel is likely to be totally enclosed in a very small space, it is also necessary to consider the matter of temperature rise. The coils of magnetic contactors liberate a certain amount of heat which must be conducted away. This is particularly true of alternating-current contactors. If thermal overload relays are included as part of the control, the heat generated by the contactor must not be sufficient to affect the tripping point of the overload relay. If starting resistance is used, a greater amount

FIG. 11.   Compact Reversing Contactor for Built-in Control.

FIG. 12.   Woodworking Machine with Built-in Control.

of ventilation will be required. Vibration must also be considered, as any great amount of it may affect the operation of the control.

For examples of built-in control see Figs. 11, 12, and 14.

Control Centers. When a number of motor controllers are to be located near one another, it becomes a considerable advantage to house

Fig. 13. Control Desk. Front and Sides Removed to Show Construction.

them in a common structure. If they are mounted individually on a wall or building column, they will take up a good deal of room and may not present a satisfactory appearance. If the individual controllers are grouped on a large steel panel, or on an angle-iron framework, there is a difficult job of conduit wiring to do, and again the space required is excessive. The cost of designing and building a special housing for all the controllers of a given installation is generally too great to make it practical.

The control center was developed in 1940 as an answer to the problem, and it is being built in various forms by a number of control manufacturers. Figures 14 and 15 show the general construction. The structure is made up of three main items, the panels, the door frames, and the sections.

Fig. 14.   Panel and Door Frame for Control Center.

The individual panels which mount the control devices are available in standardized sizes, to suit the more popular controllers, such as magnetic across-the-line starters, reversing line starters, disconnect devices, and circuit breakers.

The door frame is the supporting structure for the panel. Its construction is shown in Fig. 14. The panel is mounted to straps on the door frame. These frames are available in standardized sizes. The construction meets NEMA Type-IA enclosure specification.

FIG. 15. Control Center.

The section is a self-standing cubicle or enclosure on which the door frames are assembled and which also houses the wiring, bus bars, and terminal boards. A group of sections becomes a control center. Horizontal and vertical bus bars, and terminal boards, are usually built in at the factory, so that installation becomes very simple.

Analysis of the cost of a completely installed control center, as against the installed cost of the same number of individual controllers,

Fig. 16.   Cutler-Hammer Factory-assembled Mill Control Showing Resistor Mounting.

shows that the two are just about the same. The control center is compact and neat in appearance, and it offers good accessibility for

FIG. 17. Cutler-Hammer Factory-assembled Mill Control Showing Wiring, Bus-bar, and Terminal Construction.

maintenance. Its greatest advantage is its flexibility, as controllers can readily be changed around or others added as the requirements of the installation change.

References

F. A. Wright, "Modern Construction of A-c Motor Control," *Iron and Steel Engineer,* November, 1942.

Standard for Industrial Control Equipment, Underwriters' Laboratories.

Standard for Industrial Control Equipment for Use in Hazardous Locations, Underwriters' Laboratories.

C. W. Falls, "Motors and Controllers for Hazardous Areas," *Factory Management and Maintenance,* June, 1944.

"Motor Controls for Adverse Conditions," *Electrical Manufacturing,* April, 1939.

4

PILOT DEVICES AND ACCESSORIES

Pushbuttons. Undoubtedly the most frequently used pilot device is a pushbutton station. Such a station may include one or more buttons of the momentary contact type only, or the buttons may be of the snap switch type, or both types may be included. For very light duty, pushbuttons similar to those for house lighting circuits might be suitable. These buttons have relatively light operating mechanisms, copper current-carrying contacts, and punched sheet-metal enclosing boxes. However, a button of this construction would be entirely unsatisfactory for most control applications. A much stronger and heavier construction is required to withstand frequent operation and rough handling. As control-circuit voltages are generally higher than lighting-circuit voltages, better insulation and greater clearance to ground must be provided. Also, control pushbuttons are subject to relatively high momentary voltages caused by the inductive effect of the contactor coils which are handled by the buttons.

Pushbuttons for motor control are made in two general classes. Standard-duty buttons are suitable for most general-duty applications where the current to be handled is not excessive, and where the service is not extremely severe. They are available in one-, two-, and three-button styles. Table 4 gives typical ampere ratings when handling inductive circuits.

TABLE 4

STANDARD-DUTY PUSHBUTTON RATINGS

	Alternating Current				Direct Current		
	110 V	220 V	440 V	550 V	115 V	230 V	550 V
Make	25	12	6	5	1	1	1
Break	2	1	0.5	0.4	1	0.5	0.1
Carry	10	10	10.9	10	10	10	10

Heavy-duty pushbuttons are, as the name indicates, of heavier construction, and are able to handle higher currents and withstand severe service. They are available in almost any desired combination of

49

buttons, up to six or more in one station. Table 5 gives typical ampere ratings when handling inductive circuits.

TABLE 5

HEAVY-DUTY PUSHBUTTON RATINGS

	Alternating Current				Direct Current		
	110 V	220 V	440 V	550 V	115 V	230 V	550 V
Make	40	25	12	10	2	2	2
Break	4	2	1	0.8	1.5	0.75	0.2
Carry	10	10	10	10	10	10	10

The case of a control button may be a phenolic molding or a fabricated metal box of either aluminum or iron, with knockout holes for conduit wiring. The current-carrying parts are of silver, either in the form of disks which bridge two stationary contacts or in the form of a bar or rod which bridges two fingers, similar to those used as electric interlocks on magnetic contactors. In the disk type the disk is provided with a follow-up spring to insure good wiping contact. In the bar type the follow-up spring is provided in the contact fingers. In both types the stationary contacts and the moving contacts should be easily renewable.

Momentary contact buttons are made either normally open or normally closed, or they may be provided with two sets of stationary contacts, so that one set is opened and the other set closed when the button is pressed. A button, with its control disk and stationary contacts, is usually a unit in itself, removable as a unit, and interchangeable with similar units which differ in function. That is, it is desirable to be able to remove a normally open unit or element and substitute a normally closed unit, or to perform any desired interchange of elements, and a well-designed line of pushbuttons will provide this feature.

The operating buttons are generally of phenolic or molded insulation, and they should be large and easy to operate. They are colored for easy identification, the start button commonly being black and the stop button red. The start button is generally enclosed by a guard ring to prevent accidental operation. For certain functions locking rings are provided. It is possible, by means of these locking rings, to press the button part way down, so that the normally closed contacts are broken, and then lock it in that position by turning the ring. For other requirements it is possible to press the button part way down, breaking the circuit of the normally closed contacts, but it is not possible to press the button on down, to close the normally open contacts, until the locking ring is turned.

Name plates are provided on the front of the station to indicate clearly the function of each button. Indicating lamps with bull's-eyes are sometimes mounted in the station to show whether the motor is running or to indicate that a desired function has been performed.

FIG. 18. Pushbutton Stations for Motor Control.

FIG. 19. Pushbutton Station with Oil-immersed Contacts for Hazardous Locations.

For service in wet locations, as on shipboard, water-tight pushbuttons are required. These have a heavy case, fitted with gaskets to make it completely water-tight. A flexible rubber or leather diaphragm is mounted on the inside of the cover, and the buttons are operated through this diaphragm. Another possible construction is a shaft extending out of the case, through a water-tight stuffing box. Cams for operating the buttons are mounted on the shaft, inside the case, and a lever or button is fastened to the shaft on the outside.

Explosion-resisting buttons are required in hazardous locations, as where gasoline or other explosive fumes are present. To meet this requirement heavy cast cases are made, having wide flanges where the case and cover join together, and using no gaskets. The contacts are immersed in oil, which quenches any arc that may occur and prevents it from coming into contact with the explosive gas.

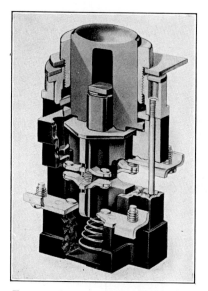

FIG. 20. Cut-away View of One-hole-mounting Pushbutton.

It is often desirable to mount pushbutton elements or contact units directly into a machine housing, and for this purpose one-hole mounting elements are available. These are also useful in building up assemblies of a large number of buttons; the elements are mounted on a sheet-metal panel, which is supported on a metal frame. The elements are made in all sorts of contact arrangements, including indicating light elements and selector switch elements. Figure 20 shows the construction of one of these devices.

Master Controllers. A master controller is a device, generally manually operated, for energizing and de-energizing the coils of the contactors and relays of a magnetic controller. By this definition, a pushbutton station is a master, and the term is sometimes used that way, but in general it is understood to mean a device of the drum or face-plate type. Both types are in general use.

The face-plate type of master (Fig. 21) consists of a slate or composition board on which contact buttons or segments are mounted, and a lever which mounts contact brushes or shoes. As the lever is moved from point to point the brushes make contact with one or another of the stationary segments and energize coils which are connected to those segments. The line feed is connected to one continuous segment ring, so that connection to the moving lever through pigtail leads is avoided. A structure of this type has the advantage of requiring very little thickness, permitting a number of such masters to be mounted in a small space. Also the contacts are easily accessible for wiring and for maintenance. However, the brush does not leave the segment in such a direction that the arc is always drawn upward, and it is not feasible to obtain a very long gap between brush and contact; hence the arc-breaking capacity of a face-plate master is relatively low. Care must be taken in the design of the bearing for the lever, because the bearing shaft can be supported at only one end.

Fig. 21. Face-plate-type Master Controller.

However, it is perfectly possible to design satisfactory bearings which will give long life and easy operation, and which will assure that the lever runs true.

Drum-type masters are made in a number of forms and sizes. Most manufacturers offer one type for single- and two-speed controls, and a larger type for multispeed controls, which require a greater number of control fingers. Six circuits will ordinarily be sufficient for a two-speed controller, and twelve to twenty for a multispeed controller.

Figure 22 shows a master of the segment and finger type. The frame and operating lever are cast steel. The contact segments are of copper, mounted on a cast-iron spider. The spider is mounted on a square steel shaft, from which it is insulated by means of mica tubing. The stationary contact fingers are also mounted on a square shaft and insulated from it. They are provided with follow-up springs to provide a pressure contact. Connections are brought to terminals mounted on the contact finger supports. The cylinder is positioned by means of a star wheel on the frame and a pawl incorporated in the lever.

Insulating shields are provided between the fingers. The whole device is easily accessible for repair or maintenance.

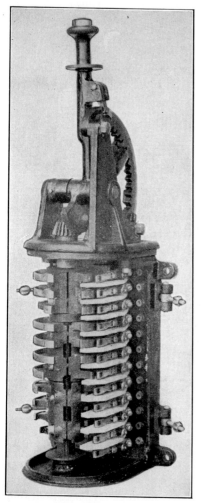

FIG. 22. Multispeed Master. Cover Removed.

There are many other types and forms of master controllers, but those described are typical. Some applications require very small masters; others, masters with levers which must be held in the on position and which will return to the off position when released. A spring is often used for this purpose, but where absolute certainty of return is required the master is inverted and the handle heavily weighted. Some masters must be arranged for foot operation. Some require an auxiliary switch which may be closed or opened by means of a latch on the operating lever. A master with cam-operated contacts is shown in Fig. 23. This construction is becoming increasingly popular, since it saves space, is easy to maintain, and has each circuit insulated and independent of the other circuits.

Diagrammatic Representation of Master Controllers. In making drawings or diagrams of a master cylinder, or in fact of the cylinder of any type of drum, it is necessary to follow certain conventions in order to avoid confusion. Most manufacturers follow the method outlined below, which is logical and easy to understand and apply.

Figure 24a represents a drum or master controller, the lower view showing the mounted drum as it appears from the front and the upper view the top as it appears when looking down on the shaft end. If the cover is removed, the fingers are seen, and the half of the cylinder which is in front and is marked A. This is called the top half of the cylinder. The bottom of the cylinder, marked B, is not visible from the front.

Figure 24b shows the development of the cylinder of the drum. The top half of the cylinder A is shown between the fingers C and D just

FIG. 23. Radial-drive 16-circuit Cam-type Master Controller.

as it appears in Fig. 24a. The bottom half of the cylinder B is projected to the right and appears as shown. The shaft is shown just as it would actually appear. This arrangement applies the following rules for the representation of cylinders on drawings or diagrams:

1. With the drum mounted as in a, the top of the cylinder is A, and is shown between the fingers C and D.

2. The bottom of the cylinder B may be projected to the right or left, but the right is preferred.

3. If only one row of fingers is used, the fingers should appear between the halves of the cylinder. For instance, if row D only is used, the bottom of the cylinder should be projected to the right. If row C only is used, the bottom of the cylinder should be projected to the left.

4. The shaft should appear on the center line as shown, if the keyway is on the center line. If the keyway is not on the center line, the location of the shaft should be changed to correspond. Figure 24c presents an example, the keyway being 45 degrees off center. This applies to working drawings only; diagrams may disregard the location of the keyway and always show the shaft on the center line as in b.

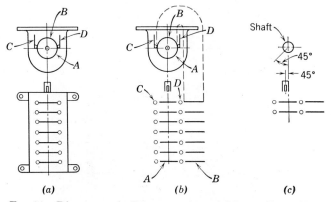

(a)   (b)   (c)

Fig. 24. Diagrammatic Representation of Master Controllers.

Transfer Switches. When it is desired to operate from either of two masters, or from either of two pilot devices of any type, a transfer switch may be provided. By this means, either device may be connected into circuit. The transfer switch is simply a double-throw pilot switch of the required number of poles. If only a few circuits must be transferred, and if an open switch is satisfactory, a small double-throw knife switch may be used. Generally an enclosed device is preferred, and the small drum-type switches, used for starting multi-speed motors, are widely used as transfer switches. They may be separately mounted, or mounted on the controller panel (see Fig. 25).

Automatic Starting Devices. It is often desirable that a motor shall start and stop automatically, without the attention of an operator.

Automatic starting devices accomplish this result, the type of device depending upon the nature of the requirements. Float-operated pilot switches are used to maintain the level of water, or other liquid, in a tank or basin. Pressure-operated switches maintain a desired pressure on a closed system, as, for instance, automatic sprinklers, or compressed-air tanks in a filling station. There are also switches responsive to temperature and to humidity. They may control motors driving fans or stokers, or furnace draft doors. Time-clock switches serve to start and stop motors at desired intervals. Speed governors can be equipped with electric contacts to open or close at a required speed. Limit switches of many types are employed to open or close circuits after a desired function has been performed. As an example, a piece of material moving on a conveyor may be arranged to strike

Fig. 25. Small Drum-type Transfer Switch.

a limit switch at a certain point in its travel, and so start a machine which will push the material off the conveyor belt.

Float-operated Switches. Figure 26 shows a four-pole float-operated switch. The switch mechanism consists of a set of control fingers mounted on an insulated shaft, and a corresponding set of stationary contacts. Operation of the lever on the outside of the switch will turn the finger shaft and engage or disengage the contacts. A star wheel is provided to make the switch snap open or closed, that is, to make it quick making and breaking. This feature should be provided on any float switch, as the change of liquid level may be slow, and without quick make and break the contacts may sometimes hang in an intermediate position where the circuit is just at the point of being opened or closed. A very slight change in liquid level will then cause the contacts to open a small amount, and arcing will occur, which will soon damage the contacts. Also the contacts will be subject to rapid opening and closing when at this point, and the motor will be started and stopped too often.

The float to operate the switch is hung from one chain and a counterweight from the other. The counterweight must be amply heavy to operate the switch when the weight of the float is supported by the liquid. The float must be heavy enough to operate the switch and

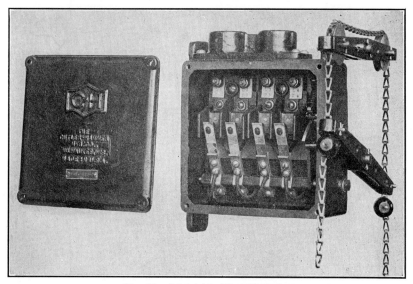

Fig. 26. Multipole Float Switch.

also to overcome the counterweight. It must, therefore, weigh twice as much as the counterweight. The float must be buoyant enough to float with approximately half of its volume submerged. It is evident that floats of large diameter will be more sensitive to changes in level than those of small diameter, since a smaller change in level will be required to displace a given volume of water. The float is usually made of copper and weighted with cast iron.

In order to get a variable setting between the opening and closing points of the switch, the chain is allowed to run freely through holes in the float switch lever, and its travel is limited by two stops. As the float rises, the chain moves freely until one of the stops strikes the switch lever. The switch is then operated. When the liquid level falls, the first stop moves away from the lever. The switch is not reset until the second stop, on the counterweight chain, strikes the lever.

Float switches are often used to connect small motors directly to the supply lines without magnetic contactors. For this purpose they may be two-, three-, or four-pole. Pilot float switches are single- or double-pole.

For such applications as controlling the level of water in a sewage settling basin, where the inflow may vary widely, a number of pumps are necessary, and some of them may be required to run at several different speeds. The number of pumps in service at any one time will be determined by the level of the water, so that, as the level rises, one after another will be brought into service, and, as the level falls, the pumps will be cut off one at a time. Such an application requires a multipoint float switch, which will generally have to be designed to suit the particular application in question. If a pump is started at each 1-inch change in level, it will be necessary to arrange the float switch to close a new contact in each 1-inch travel of the chain. Any other specification for starting levels will mean a different arrangement of the float switch. Each contact should be quick make and quick break. It is therefore difficult to design such a switch when more than about six contacts are required, as it becomes very large and complicated. For applications requiring more than about six contacts it is possible to use a special control scheme in which the quick make and break feature is accomplished magnetically by relays on the control panel, and the float switch may be a single rheostat lever moving over a set of control buttons.

FIG. 27.   Diaphragm-type Pressure Regulator.

Pressure Regulators. Pressure regulators are used on closed systems to maintain a desired pressure. The regulator has a rubber or metal diaphragm against which the pressure of the fluid is exerted. A heavy spring opposes the liquid pressure, and the device is set for the desired pressure by varying the spring tension. A lever is operated from the diaphragm and so arranged that it multiplies the amount of movement of the diaphragm sufficiently to operate an electric contact. The contact is opened and closed through a toggle mechanism, in order to obtain a quick make and break. This arrangement prevents chattering of the contact with each stroke of the pump or compressor. Figure 27 illustrates one type of regulator and shows the parts described.

Pressure regulators are often equipped with an unloading device which relieves the back pressure against the compressor during the starting period and so lessens the torque required of the motor. The unloader is a valve, which is held closed by the air pressure while the regulator switch is closed, and is opened when the switch opens. It is connected to the compressor discharge line by means of a small pipe. A check valve in the line between the unloader and the tank must be used in connection with the unloader valve, to prevent discharging the tank when the unloader valve is open.

Some designs of diaphragm pressure regulators are equipped with an unloader valve. Some are double-pole devices which are suitable for pilot circuits but are also able to handle small motors directly. NEMA standard horsepower ratings when handling motor circuits are given in Table 6.

TABLE 6

Maximum Pressure, psi	Single-phase Alternating Current			Two- or Three-phase Alternating Current			Direct Current		
	115 V	230 V	440–550 V	110 V	220 V	440–550 V	32 V	115 V	230 V
80	1	1	..	1	1	..	¼	¼	¼
80	1½	2	3	2	3	3	¼	½	½
200	1½	2	3	2	3	3	¼	½	½
250	2	3	5	3	5	5	½	1	1
250	2	3	5	3	5	5	½	1	1

When installing a pressure regulator, care should be taken to connect it in a part of the system which is not subject to fluctuations in pressure; this will increase the accuracy and permit close setting. It is preferable to connect the regulator to the storage tank and not to the discharge pipe from the pump. If the device must be connected to the discharge pipe, an air chamber should be interposed between the pipe and the regulator, and the feed to the air chamber should be throttled by means of a needle valve or stopcock. This arrangement will smooth out the pulsations from the discharge pipe.

Where visible indication of the pressure is required, a regulator of the gage type is used. This type of regulator is similar in construction to the ordinary indicating pressure gage except that, in addition to moving an indicating needle, the pressure tube is used to move an arm which will make an electric contact at desired high and low pressures. The device usually includes a relay, because the current capacity of the gage contacts is small, and the movement is not quick make and break. As the pressure tube expands and contracts, the contact arm moves back and forth, making contact with the stationary contacts at either end of its travel. When the arm makes contact with the stationary contact at the low setting, the relay is energized and closes. This energizes the coil of the motor-starting switch, and the motor is started. The relay remains closed until the swinging arm makes contact at the high setting, when the relay coil is short-circuited and the relay drops open, stopping the motor. The high and low settings are adjustable by moving the stationary contacts. With the arrangement described, the equivalent of quick make and break is secured, and the light contacts in the gage never have to break the circuit.

The pressure tubes in these regulators are made of brass or of steel, depending upon the nature of the fluid with which they are to be used. A brass tube should be used for water, air, steam, sulphur dioxide, acetylene, carbon dioxide, carbon monoxide, helium, hydrogen, and illuminating gas; a steel tube for ammonia, alcohol, benzol, chlorine, creosote, cyanide, gasoline, nitrogen, oxygen, ethylene, and ethylene oxide.

Thermostats. Thermostats are made in a number of forms, the common moving element being either a bimetallic strip which changes its shape when heated or a coiled tube which changes its length. The strip or tube is arranged to move an electric contact. Various types of contacts are employed to insure a quick make and break. Mercury switches are used by some manufacturers. These switches are glass tubes containing a small amount of mercury. Contact wires are brought into the tube through the glass and sealed in position. When the tube is tilted in one direction, the mercury flows to one end of the tube and in doing so immerses the contact wires and closes the circuit between them. The circuit is broken by tilting the switch in the opposite direction, allowing the mercury to run away from the contacts. Some thermostats have light silver contacts and include a small permanent magnet. When the contacts approach within a certain distance of each other, the magnet draws them quickly the rest of the way into contact. In breaking contact, the pull of the bimetallic strip must build up sufficiently to overcome the holding force of the magnet before the contacts move at all. Then, when they do move out of contact, they move quickly for a short distance.

Some thermostats use simply a single-pole make-and-break contact, so that the contact is closed to make the circuit and opened to break it. Since the thermostat contacts are of necessity quite light, it is essential that there should be no arcing on them. A positive method of preventing arcing on the contacts is to arrange them so that they do not break the circuit. This may be done by means of the relay scheme described in connection with gage pressure regulators, which of course requires that the thermostat have three point contacts.

Speed Governors. Centrifugal speed governors are employed to protect machinery against overspeed or underspeed and also to control some functions in the operation of a magnetic controller which must be performed at a given speed of the motor or machine. For instance, a governor can be used with a controller for a two-speed alternating-current motor. When slow speed is desired, the high-speed winding of the motor is disconnected from the line and the slow-speed connected into circuit. If the slow-speed winding were connected immediately upon disconnecting the high speed, a severe jar would occur and the motor would take a high inrush of current. To avoid this, the connection of the slow-speed winding can be controlled by a governor set to close its contacts at the slow speed of the motor. Then, when the high-speed winding is opened, the motor is allowed to drift down in speed until its slow running speed is reached, and at that exact speed the governor will operate to connect in the slow-speed winding. There will then be no inrush of current and no jar to the machine.

Plugging Switches. If it is desired to obtain a certain control function when a motor is running and to discontinue that function when the motor stops, a plugging switch can be used. The switch can also be used to obtain a function when a motor is running in one direction and to discontinue the function if the motor is reversed.

The switch illustrated in Fig. 28 has a double control arm held in a center position by a spring. In this position, both contacts are opened. A belt connected to the arm passes over a pulley driven from the motor. If the motor starts to run in a clockwise direction, the belt pulls the contact arm over until the right-hand contacts are closed. The arm is prevented from moving further, and the belt slips on the pulley, holding the contacts closed by means of friction. When the motor is stopped, the centering spring has sufficient strength to move the arm back to the center position. Counterclockwise rotation of the motor will close the left-hand contacts.

With a reversing controller, particularly in an alternating-current installation, it is often desirable to stop the motor quickly by connecting it to the line in the reverse direction until it stops. The forward and reverse magnetic contactors are mechanically and electrically interlocked, so that only one can close at a time. When the forward contactor is closed, the motor starts to turn, and the friction switch closes its contacts to energize the reverse contactor. This contactor, however, cannot close because of the interlocking; but as soon as the stop button is pressed the forward contactor opens, and then the reverse contactor is free to close. In this way the motor is connected to the line in a reverse direction until it stops, when the friction switch moves to the center position and opens the circuit to the reverse contactor.

Another type of relay, which accomplishes the same results, is constructed on a different principle. The relay has an oil pump which pumps in one direction only, and in that direction builds up pressure

FIG. 28.   Mechanism of a Belt-type Friction Switch.

in a Bourdon tube similar to those in pressure gages. When the tube is under pressure, it operates to close electric contacts. A relay of this type may have a number of independent electric contacts arranged to close at different pressures, and may be used to perform desired functions at predetermined motor speeds.

Still another type of plugging switch has an Alnico rotor, permanently magnetized in four poles, and mounted on a shaft for connection to the motor. The frame of the switch is steel. Between the rotor and the frame is an aluminum cup which is free to turn through a limited arc and to which a contact arm is mounted. The driven Alnico rotor produces a rotating magnetic field that induces eddy currents in the walls of the cup, causing it to turn and bring the contacts into engagement. An adjustable spring determines the force required to turn the cup and so determines the rotor speed at which the switch contacts will close. The switch is provided with a safety latch to prevent closing of the contacts when the switch is turned by hand.

Limit Switches. A limit switch is a device mechanically operated from a motor or machine in its operation, and arranged to perform some electrical function. The term limit switch indicates its primary function, namely, to provide a limit to the travel of a machine and to stop it at that point. This is usually done by opening the circuit to magnetic contactor coils, and so allowing them to open and disconnect the motor from the line. If the installation includes a magnetic brake, the circuits will be arranged so that the brake is set in the limit of travel. Dynamic braking may be applied by the limit switch.

In addition to the function of stopping, limit switches may serve many other purposes. They are often used to provide slowdown at a point ahead of the stopping point, so that the stop may be more accurate. They may also act to vary the speed of a machine in different parts of its cycle. They frequently provide an interlocking means between two or more machines. In this capacity they may be made to start one machine when another is at a certain point in its travel, or to prevent operation of one machine unless another machine has reached a desired point.

The electric contacts of a limit switch may be made either normally closed or normally open. To insure safety, normally closed contacts are generally used for stopping and also for any other function which must be performed without fail. The reason for this is obvious, as, with such an arrangement, any electric failure like a broken wire or a burned-out coil or a failure of the power supply will stop the equipment. With a normally open limit switch contact, any of these failures would prevent a stop. The normally closed limit switch may fail because of a ground around it. To guard against this, stopping limit switches are often made double-pole, one pole being connected in each side of the control circuit. Installations where failure to stop is very hazardous, as, for instance, elevators, make use of two sets of stopping limit switches, one set ahead of the other. In normal operation the first switch will always stop the motor, but in case of failure the car will run through the first limit and be stopped by the second, or overtravel, limit switch. Normally open contacts are generally satisfactory for obtaining slowdown, as failure of this function is not so vital. Also, it is usually necessary to close magnetic contactors to obtain slowdown, so that a normally open limit contact does not add any hazard, as a circuit failure would prevent closure of the contactor in any event. Where slowdown is vital to safety, the controller should be arranged to use normally closed slowdown limit switches.

Track-type Limit Switches. Figure 29 illustrates a limit switch of a type common for elevator installations and many other applications. It consists of a double-pole electric contact which, in the normally closed form, is opened when the roller wheel is depressed. The roller wheel is sometimes made of fiber or provided with a rubber tire to make the operation quiet. It is made of solid iron for other applications, as in steel mills where it may be operated by a hot bar of steel. Switches of this type are made either normally open or normally closed or with one pole open and the other closed.

For elevator applications the switch is mounted in the hatchway and is operated by a cam on the elevator car. It will be noted that the switch is spring-returned, and so the cam must be sufficiently long to hold the roller depressed for the required time. In a steel mill, switches of this type may be used with such machines as furnace pushers. These machines have a ram which moves forward and pushes a billet of steel into a furnace. When the forward limit of travel is reached, the ram strikes the limit switch, which operates to reverse the motor and brings the ram back to the starting point. When this point is reached, the ram strikes another limit switch, which stops the motor.

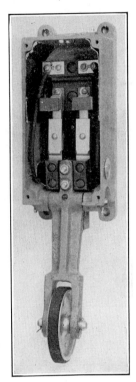

FIG. 29. Hatchway Limit Switch.

The switch illustrated in Fig. 29 is suitable for use only where the cam which strikes it is closely guided, as the movement for operating the switch is small and not much overtravel is permissible. An elevator meets this condition, but a car running on a horizontal track, at fairly high speed, would probably sway enough to prevent satisfactory operation of the switch. Roller switches similar to the one illustrated, but with much greater arm movement, can be built for such an application.

Another type of track switch differs from the roller type in that it will remain in the position to which it is moved until the returning

cam moves it back to the original position. In other words, the device
is not spring-returned, but has instead a star wheel and pawl, which
cause it to snap quickly from one position to the other when the lever
is moved. Switches based on this principle are made in a number of
different sizes, depending on the number of electric contacts desired.

Traveling-cam Switches. When a machine travels forward and
reverse in a fixed cycle, and within fixed limits, it is possible to use a
limit switch having a rotating shaft geared directly to the machine.

Fig. 30. Traveling-cam Limit Switch. Cover Removed.

Elevators and skip hoists are typical examples. These are driven
from cables on a winding drum, and a limit switch can be geared to
the drum. Geared limit switches cannot be used on such applications
as crane trolleys or bridges, as any slip of the wheels would cause the
switch to trip at the wrong point of travel. Figure 30 illustrates one
form of geared switch, known as a traveling-cam switch. The operating shaft is threaded and has a nut, or crosshead, mounted on it.
This crosshead moves along the shaft as the shaft turns, and acts as
a cam to operate electric contacts. Each electric contact is a double-
pole quick-acting switch, which may be either normally open or
normally closed or may have one pole open and the other pole closed.
Each switch with its operating mechanism is mounted on rods parallel
to the main shaft. The tripping point of the switch is adjusted by
moving it along on the mounting rods, until the crosshead operates
it at the desired point. The device shown has a total of four sets of

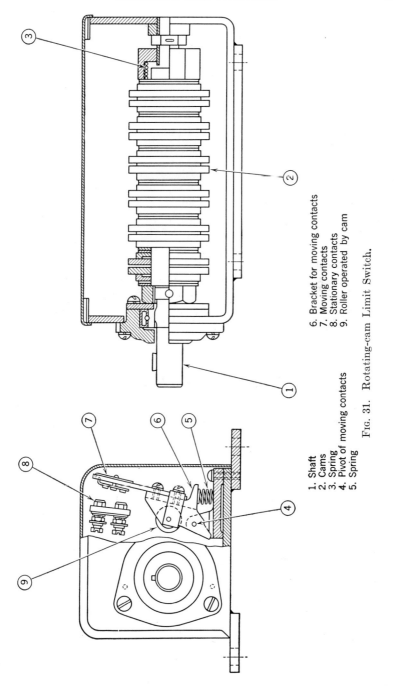

1. Shaft
2. Cams
3. Spring
4. Pivot of moving contacts
5. Spring

6. Bracket for moving contacts
7. Moving contacts
8. Stationary contacts
9. Roller operated by cam

FIG. 31. Rotating-cam Limit Switch.

electric contacts, two on each side of the shaft. Similar devices are made with eight elements for more complicated control requirements.

It is evident that the accuracy of a switch of this type is dependent upon the length of the shaft. For a skip-hoist installation the switch is geared directly to the winding drum of the machine. The total travel of the crosshead must, therefore, occur in the same number of turns as is required for the full travel of the hoist. If the shaft is short, a small movement of the crosshead will represent a considerable movement of the hoist, and an accurate setting will be difficult to obtain. A longer shaft will allow the crosshead to move a greater distance for the same movement of the hoist, and so more accurate settings can be secured. For very long hoists, and where great accuracy is required, a compound limit switch has been used. This switch has a mechanism that greatly multiplies the movement of the crosshead when the hoist is approaching the limit of travel. Its use is too infrequent to warrant a complete description.

Rotating-cam Switches. The rotating-cam limit switch, illustrated in Fig. 31, is a form of geared limit switch particularly applicable to eccentric drives making one revolution, or a part of one revolution, for a complete cycle. Such drives are extensively used in steel mills. The shaft of the limit switch is geared to the driving shaft of the machine.

The switch consists of a number of electric contacts operated by cams on the switch shaft. The length and location of the cam face determine the portion of the cycle during which the contact is open or closed. Adjustment is made by rotating the cam around the shaft and by changing the length of its face. An easy means of making adjustments around the shaft is necessary, as this determines the tripping point of the electric contacts. It is better practice to use two cams and two contacts to get a function in each direction rather than to use one cam and depend upon its length being accurate. In designing switches of this type, the principal points to keep in mind are ease of adjustment and the use of fairly large cams for accuracy of setting and of hardened cams and rollers to prevent excessive wear.

References

"Small-travel Limit Switches for Precision Controls," *Electrical Manufacturing*, February, 1941.

W. Staffel, "Mechanically Operated Auxiliary Switches for Contactor Circuits on Machine Tools," *Engineers Digest*, Vol. 2, 1945, p. 175.

Problems

1. It is desired to ring an alarm bell and light a signal light when the pressure in a tank reaches a critical value. The ringing of the bell may be stopped by pressing a pushbutton, but the light is to remain on until the pressure goes down. Draw a circuit for this arrangement, using a single-pole pressure regulator, two relays, and a pushbutton.

2. The lights in a building are turned on and off by a time clock, which has an electric contact. The control circuit may be transferred to momentary-contact pushbuttons, which will then control the lights. If power fails while the control is from the pushbuttons, control is to be automatically returned to the time clock. Draw a circuit for this arrangement, using such relays as may be necessary.

3. The float of a float switch is a hollow cylinder of copper having a diameter of 12 inches. It is rigidly fastened to a vertical rod, which in turn is rigidly fastened to the arm of the float switch. If the float and rod weigh 5 pounds together, and it takes 3 pounds to operate the switch, how far will the water rise before the switch operates, if it is assumed that the water level at the start is at the bottom of the float?

4. If the water level starts down as soon as the switch operates, how far will it recede before the switch resets?

5. A rotating-cam limit switch having six circuits is equipped with a double sheave wheel on the shaft. A rod is hung from a cable on one sheave wheel and a counterweight from a cable on the other sheave wheel. A float is arranged to slide up and down on the rod as the water level in a tank changes, and two adjustable stops are provided on the float rod. The device is to be used to start and stop three motors, as follows:

At water level	10 feet	Start motor 1
	11 feet	Start motor 2
	12 feet	Start motor 3
	4 feet	Stop motor 3
	3 feet	Stop motor 2
	2 feet	Stop motor 1

Make a sketch showing the arrangement of the device, and the location of the stops on the rod.

6. Draw the electric circuit for problem 5, using circles to represent the motors.

7. Draw a circuit to show how a solenoid may be energized and de-energized from any one of three locations, using momentary-contact pushbuttons, and having a single-pole snap switch at each location which, when it is open, will prevent operation of the solenoid from any of the three locations.

8. A solenoid is operated from a three-point thermostat, using one double-pole normally open relay, and one single-pole normally closed relay. Draw a circuit which will close the solenoid when one contact of the thermostat closes, maintain the circuit as the thermostat moves away from its contact, and open the circuit when the other contact of the thermostat closes.

9. Draw a circuit using a master controller, a relay, a solenoid, and a hatchway limit switch, and arranged so that, if the limit switch opens when the solenoid is energized, the master controller must be returned to the off position before the solenoid can again be energized.

10. A switch in the track of a model railroad is operated by a device consisting of two solenoids and a single plunger. When one solenoid is energized, the plunger moves to the right, moving the track switch for main-line operation. When the other solenoid is energized, the plunger moves to the left, moving the track switch for branch-line operation. In each direction of travel the plunger closes an auxiliary contact, like a normally open limit switch. Two momentary-contact pushbuttons are used, and two signal lights to show the track switch position. It is also necessary to connect a circuit across the switch points in each position of the track switch, to insure that there is a circuit through the track to run the train.

Draw a circuit diagram for the arrangement, using such relays as may be necessary.

5

DIRECT-CURRENT CONTACTORS AND RELAYS

The standards of the National Electrical Manufacturers' Association define magnetic contactors and relays as follows:

Magnetic Contactor: A magnetically actuated device for repeatedly establishing or interrupting an electric power circuit.

Relay: A device which is operated by a variation in the characteristics of one electric circuit to affect the operation of other devices in the same or another electric circuit.

The electromagnetically operated contactor is one of the most useful mechanisms that has ever been devised for closing and opening electric circuits. Since the problem of controlling an electric motor resolves itself largely into one of opening and closing electric circuits, and since the magnetically operated contactor is extremely versatile and flexible in its forms and applications, it follows that a manufacturer of a diversified line of control apparatus will have available standard contactors and relays in a wide variety of types and sizes.

Advantages of Using Contactors. A number of advantages are to be gained by the use of magnetic contactors instead of manually operated control equipment. One of the most important is the saving of time and effort. Where large currents or high voltages have to be handled it is difficult to build suitable manual apparatus; furthermore, such apparatus is large and hard to operate. On the other hand, it is a relatively simple matter to build a magnetic contactor which will handle large currents or high voltages, and the manual apparatus may then have only to control the coil of the contactor. Also, where there are a large number of functions to perform, or where the operation must be repeated many times an hour, a distinct saving in effort will result if contactors are used. Controllers may be so arranged that the operator has simply to push a button and the contactors will automatically initiate the proper sequence of events. The operator is then saved the trouble of having continually to keep his mind upon doing the right thing at the right time, so far as the motor is concerned, and can put his entire attention on his work.

Magnetic contactors considerably increase the safety of an installation. High voltage may be handled by the contactor and kept entirely away from the operator. The operator also will not be in the proximity of high-power arcs, which are always a source of danger from shocks, burns, or perhaps injury to the eyes.

A third advantage of contactors is the saving of space, which is often valuable in the vicinity of a motor-driven machine. With contactors the control equipment may be mounted at a remote point, and the space required near the machine will be only that necessary for the pushbutton. This is a particular advantage where the control equipment is large or where the operation of a number of equipments is under the control of one man.

With contactors it is possible to control a motor from a number of different points. A good example is the control equipment for a newspaper printing press, which must be started and stopped from many different points around the press. It would be difficult to do this by means of manual control, because all the control stations would have to be mechanically interlocked against each other to insure proper operation and fool-proof control, and such an interlocking would involve a large amount of mechanical equipment. The problem is relatively simple with contactors, since it is possible to control one contactor from as many different pushbuttons as are desired, with only the necessity of running a few light control wires between the stations.

The control of such equipment as pumps and compressors, which are automatically started and stopped from pilot float switches or pilot pressure regulators, is greatly simplified by the use of contactors. It is evident that pilot devices of this nature, and also many other types, such as thermostats and sensitive gages, are limited in power and size, and it would be difficult to design them to handle heavy motor current directly.

Automatic acceleration is readily accomplished by means of contactors, and thus acceleration is taken entirely away from the operator's control. The motor is started in successive steps automatically, and in the proper time for safe acceleration. The acceleration may either be directly set for a definite time, or it may be under the control of the current which is drawn by the motor, and which is a measure of the rate of acceleration. Any danger of damage to the motor or machinery due to improper starting is thereby avoided.

Automatic control by contactors results in a saving in wiring expense if the point of operation is at any distance from the motor and controller. With manual control it is necessary to run a heavy power circuit wire to the point of operation. With contactors it is necessary to run only the small control wires.

To meet the requirements of the above-outlined functions, a number of different types of magnetic contactors and relays have been developed. Some of the more common forms for direct-current work will now be described.

Shunt Contactors. Shunt contactors are so called because they are operated by a shunt coil, which is supplied with energy from a constant-potential circuit. They are usually made single-pole or double-pole for direct-current work. The contactor is said to be normally open when it is arranged to open its contacts if the coil is de-energized and to close them if the coil is energized. A normally closed contactor opens its contacts when the coil is energized. Contactors may also be arranged to have one set of contacts normally open and one set normally closed, or in fact with almost any desired arrangement of normally open and normally closed contacts.

A typical shunt contactor of the normally open type is shown in Fig. 32. The magnet frame is a steel casting, and the coil is mounted on a core of steel. When the coil is de-energized the contactor is opened by gravity. Energizing the coil attracts the movable armature to the stationary core, and the contactor closes. The copper current-carrying tips close first, compressing the spring under them and building up a heavy contact pressure as the armature moves in to seal against the core. The current-carrying capacity of the contactor depends on the area of contact surface and also on the pressure of the contacts. The stationary contact is mounted on a brass or copper post through which the current flows to the rear of the panel where a wire or bus bar is

FIG. 32. Shunt-type Direct-current Contactor, with Laminated-brush Contact. Arc Shields Raised.

connected. The movable contact has a heavy flexible cable, or pig-tail, which is connected to an independent stud through the slate, so that the current does not flow through the steel frame of the contactor. The stationary contact is provided with a metal arcing horn which serves to direct the arc upward away from the contacts. The movable contact has a metal guard to prevent an arc from striking the contact spring. The shaft and moving parts are of hardened steel to prevent wear.

Magnetic Blowout. At the top of the contactor a heavy bar wound coil may be seen. This coil, wound on a core of steel, is mounted between two pole pieces, also of steel. The inside of the pole pieces is lined with a refractory insulating material. This structure, called a magnetic blowout, is used to extinguish the arc rapidly. In the illustration the blowout has been raised to make the contacts visible, but in actual operation the blowout is lowered down over the contacts, which are thus enclosed in an insulated box. The arcing tip on the stationary contacts guides the arc into the box. The blowout coil is connected in series with the contactor itself, so that motor current is flowing through the coil as long as the contactor is closed, or as long as there is an arc between the contacts. The current sets up a magnetic field through the core and pole pieces of the blowout structure and across the arcing tips of the contactor. When an arc is formed, the arc sets up a magnetic field around itself. The two magnetic fields repel each other, and the arc is forced upward and away from the contacts. It thus becomes longer and longer until it breaks and is extinguished. The extinguishing action is extremely rapid, and it not only speeds up the operation of the contactor but also greatly reduces the wear and burning of the contacts. Proper blowout design, therefore, is an important factor in contact life.

Contacts. Contacts are ordinarily made of copper and may be either left plain or plated with cadmium or silver. The oxides of copper are poor conductors, and an oxidized contact tip is liable to overheating. Of course, plating at the surface where arcing occurs does not last very long, and it is necessary to arrange the contacts so that they will be self-cleaning. The plating is of value on the bottom and back of the contact tip, where it joins the post on which it is mounted. The plating here assures a good electric contact at the joint. Self-cleaning of the contacts is accomplished by arranging them so that they strike first at the tip, and then, as the contactor closes, they come together with a rolling motion, finally resting together close to the bottom of the tip. Small pin arcs which may occur when the contacts close, and which pit and oxidize the tips, are thus confined to the top of the contacts, while the current is actually carried at the bottom where the arcing has not occurred.

If a contactor is to be closed for a long period of time with infrequent operation, the contacts will not get a chance to clean properly and may eventually give trouble as a result of heating. In such ap-

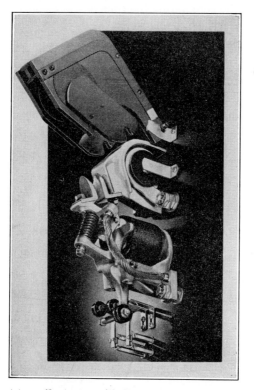

Fig. 33.   Shunt-type Contactor with Butt Contacts.   Arc Shields Raised.

plications silver contact tips are used, or copper tips with a silver plate welded into the face of the tip.

Contactors for rapid intermittent service, and often for continuous service also, have contacts of the butt type as illustrated in Figs. 33 and 34.   For continuous service, leaf-brush contacts are sometimes used.   A contactor of this type is shown in Fig. 32.   It will be noted that in addition to the leaf-brush contacts there are auxiliary butt-type contacts.   These are to handle the arcing, as a single arc would probably ruin the leaf brush by welding the leaves together.   The arcing tips close before the main contacts, and open after the main contacts, so that any arcing always occurs on the auxiliary tips.

When a contactor closes it does so with a considerable force, and there is always a certain amount of rebound of the contacts. Small arcs are formed during this rebound, and, if the contactor closed again at exactly the same point, there would be a likelihood of its welding closed. However, since the armature of the contactor has moved in farther toward the core during the time of the rebound, when the contacts come together again they touch at a different point and so do

FIG. 34. General Electric Shunt-type Contactor. One Arc Shield Removed.

not weld. High spring pressures are used on the contacts to insure that they open. In spite of all precautions, copper contacts occasionally weld. A common cause is low line voltage. If the voltage is just high enough to cause the contactor to close part way, the contacts may come together, but without sufficient pressure on them to seal completely. When this happens the contacts touch only lightly, and an arc is formed, which, owing to the light contact pressure, is likely to weld the contacts together. The same result is sometimes obtained by inching or jogging a controller, as the coil circuit may be interrupted at a time when the contacts are just about to touch. At the instant of touching they may be practically stationary, with very little force either to close or to open them. Welding is almost certain to occur under these conditions.

Another cause of welding contacts is improper relationship among the pull of the closing coil, the initial pressure when the contacts first touch, and the pull required to seal the armature magnet. This is most likely to occur with large contactors, the coils of which have a relatively high inductance and so are slow in building up to full power. If the contactor is relatively easy to start, the armature may move far enough to close the contacts by the time that the pull of the closing coil is only partly built up. Then when the contacts touch there may not be enough pull to make the armature continue its travel, and it will hesitate until the coil pull builds up enough to pull it on in. During this hesitating period the contact pressure is relatively light and the contacts may weld. Care must be taken in the design of the contactor and the coil to insure that, once started, the armature will pull right on through to the fully sealed position.

When it is essential that a contactor always open when it is de-energized, and not under any circumstances weld shut, carbon contacts are used. Such contacts are common for elevator work, where human life might be endangered if a contactor failed to open. They also find application where quiet operation is essential, as they are less noisy in operation than copper contacts. The disadvantage of carbon contacts is that the current-carrying capacity per square inch of the contact surface is low, and the contacts are, therefore, relatively large. Also, the rate of wear of carbon contacts is greater than that of copper contacts.

Electric Interlocks. It is often necessary to make the operation of one contactor dependent upon the operation or non-operation of another contactor, or to interlock one against the other. For this purpose auxiliary contacts are mounted on the contactor and arranged to open or close a circuit when the contactor is operated. The auxiliary contacts may consist of copper fingers mounted by means of brackets on the panel. An insulated bar on the contactor is arranged to short-circuit the fingers. A set of auxiliary fingers is said to be normally open if the auxiliary circuit is open when the contactor coil is de-energized, and normally closed if the circuit is closed when the contactor is de-energized.

By using different lengths of fingers and brackets, different results may be accomplished. Normally closed fingers may be arranged to open the instant that the contactor starts to close, or they may be made longer so that they will not open until the contactor has practically sealed. Similarly, normally open fingers may be arranged to close immediately upon energization of the contactor, or not to close until the contactor is practically sealed. Interlocks of this type are shown in Fig. 32.

A cam-operated, insulated interlock is shown in Fig. 33. It has a bridging contact bar which completes the circuit between two stationary contact posts. The contacts proper are of silver.

Mechanical Interlocks. It is often desirable to insure that two or more contactors close together, as for instance two single-pole contactors which are serving in the place of a double-pole contactor. To accomplish this positively, the contactors are mechanically tied together by means of an insulating strip between their armatures. The strip is rigidly fastened to one contactor, and a little play is allowed at the other in order to compensate for inequalities in wear of the two contactors.

When it is necessary to tie together a series of more than two contactors, the amount of play allowed must be carefully considered, so that the total play between the first contactor and the last contactor will not be enough to prevent proper interlocking.

It is also often necessary to insure that a certain contactor does not close when another is closed. For this purpose a mechanical interlock is used. The mechanical interlock may consist of a piece of metal hinged at the center, and arranged so that with both contactors open the center piece is in a neutral position. When one contactor closes it strikes one end of the interlock, moving it in toward the panel, and, of course, causing the other end of the interlock to move out into such a position that it will interfere with the closing of the second contactor. Such a device is called a walking-beam type of interlock. There are many other forms of mechanical interlocks, all of them arranged to operate so that, when one contactor closes, it will move the interlock parts into such a position that they interfere mechanically with the closing of the second contactor.

Coils. The coil of a contactor must provide enough ampere turns to operate the contactor properly, not only on normal line voltage but also under low- and high-voltage conditions. NEMA Standards say that direct-current contactors shall withstand 110 per cent of their rated voltage continuously without injury to the operating coils, and shall close successfully at 80 per cent of their rated voltage. In testing, consideration must also be given to the fact that the resistance of a coil will increase as the coil heats, so that the test voltage must be lower than 80 per cent of rated voltage if the coil is tested cold. If the coil is expected to increase in resistance by 20 per cent when hot, the cold test voltage will be 0.80/1.20, or 0.67 times the normal rated voltage.

Shunt-wound contactor coils have a high self-induction, which is sometimes troublesome, especially on higher voltages, but which may sometimes be put to valuable service. The coils are wound with many turns of fine wire, and they are used on a nearly closed iron magnetic circuit. Consequently, when the circuit to the coil is suddenly broken, high voltages, sometimes reaching 15 times normal values, are induced. These induced voltages tend to puncture the insulation of the coil. It is possible to reduce them by connecting a discharge resistance across the coil terminals or encircling the iron core of the magnet with a copper sleeve. In general, however, these methods are unsatisfactory, because they slow up the speed of operation of the contactor. The most satisfactory solution for this trouble is to provide adequate insulation, with a large factor of safety wherever such voltages are likely to occur.

Advantage may be taken of the phenomenon of self-induction to delay the opening of a contactor for a short time after the current is cut off from the coil. With almost any contactor half a second may be secured by connecting a discharge resistance across the coil, or by having a copper sleeve on the magnet core. If a longer time is desired, it may be obtained by special design. Comparatively little delay in the time of closing can be secured by such electromagnetic damping.

In contactor design residual magnetism must be guarded against or it may cause the contactor to remain closed after the coil is de-energized. The usual method of guarding against residual magnetism is to provide a thin non-magnetic spacer in the back of the contactor core, and to use a soft grade of steel or malleable iron for the magnet circuit, or for at least part of it. Care must be taken particularly when the pressure on the contacts is light, as there is then less tendency for the contactor to open when the coil is de-energized.

Most contactor coils are wound on a form and are then taped up and thoroughly impregnated with some compound which will hold the windings in place and prevent moisture from entering the coil. Other coils are wound on a phenolic spool or bobbin. It is generally possible to get a winding of greater wattage capacity into a given space by the use of a bobbin type of coil, which, however, is more expensive than the form-wound type.

For a number of reasons it is desirable to use coils which are not wound to stand full line voltage continuously. Such coils are less costly and have the further advantage that they take a larger size of wire than a coil which is wound for continuous duty at full voltage. A heavier wire, of course, has less tendency to break under vibration or rough handling. Furthermore, such intermittent-duty coils, having relatively low inductance, operate contactors more quickly. It is common practice to use coils wound for intermittent service, and then to arrange to insert a protecting resistance in series with the coil after the contactor has closed. This may be done by means of an interlock finger on the contactor itself or by interlock fingers on succeeding contactors of the controller.

Lockout Contactors. Magnetic lockout contactors were primarily designed for use as an accelerating means for direct-current motors. For such service the contactor is normally open and is required to remain open when an inrush of current occurs and until the current has fallen to a predetermined value. Figure 35 shows a lockout contactor of the double-coil type. Its operating characteristics are shown in Fig. 36. There are two separate magnetic circuits, each excited by a coil which is in series with the main motor circuit. The upper coil is the closing coil, the magnetic circuit of which is largely iron, and is so designed that the magnetic leakage is high and the circuit is easily saturated. The lower coil is the lockout coil, which tends to prevent the contactor from closing. Its magnetic circuit has a large air gap included, and it is so designed that the iron in the circuit does not approach saturation.

FIG. 35.   Lockout Contactor.

The pull exerted by the lockout coil, therefore, varies much more widely with changes in current than the pull of the closing coil, and because of the difference in magnetic characteristics the circuit can be so proportioned that there will be a definite value of current above which the lockout coil will be the stronger and below which the closing coil will predominate. Referring to the characteristic curve of Fig. 36, this critical point is B. At the point A, the pull of the closing coil is enough greater than that of the lockout coil to overcome the weight of the contactor lever and friction and to close the contactor.

In using the contactor as an accelerator, the current inrush would be above the point *B*. The contactor would, therefore, lock out on the initial current inrush and would remain so until the current had dropped to point *A*. Point *A* would probably be selected as slightly

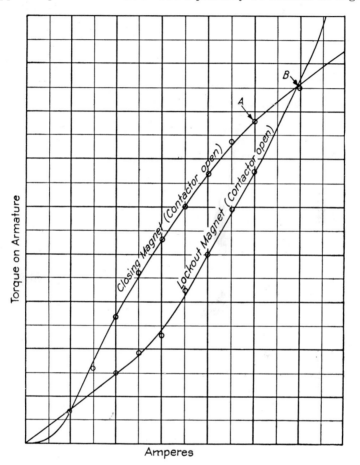

Fig. 36. Characteristics of Lockout Contactors.

above full-load motor current. At that point the contactor would close and cut out the starting resistance or a portion of it.

When the contactor closes, the circuit is so arranged that the lockout coil is short-circuited with the resistance step and consequently has no longer any tendency to open the contactor. This insures that the contactor will remain definitely closed after it has once operated. Of course, since the closing coil is in series with the motor circuit, the contactor would open if the load dropped off far enough. In order to guard against this, a small shunt-wound holding coil is usually provided. This is mounted on the same core as the closing coil and has just sufficient ampere-turns to hold the contactor closed. The ampere-turns are not sufficient to close the contactor, although they add to the strength of the series closing coil. The series coil must, therefore, be reduced correspondingly in strength when the shunt coil is to be used.

Sometimes the series coil is entirely replaced by a shunt-wound coil which is energized directly across the line. This arrangement gives a definite closing pull regardless of load, and it also permits opening the contactor at will, by means of a pushbutton or master controller, to obtain slow speed by re-inserting the resistance. The only disadvantage of this arrangement is that the effect of the closing coil depends upon voltage, and, therefore, the setting at which the contactor will close is somewhat dependent upon variations in line voltage.

There are other types of magnetic lockout contactors, some of them having only one coil and depending upon a difference in saturation of two iron circuits for their operation. A contactor of that type has a large air gap and a damping winding in the closing-coil circuit, so that the flux builds up faster in the lockout circuit when an inrush occurs. The reluctance of the lockout circuit is higher, and, as the current drops, the lockout circuit loses its magnetism faster, than the closing circuit, until a point is reached at which the closing circuit has sufficient excess pull to close the contactor.

At one time lockout accelerating contactors were very popular because of their simplicity. In recent years, their use has dropped off a great deal owing to the development of better and simpler accelerating means of other types.

Inductive Accelerating Contactors. Figure 37 shows an inductive-type accelerating contactor similar in appearance to a double-coil lockout contactor. However, it differs in the arrangement of the lockout magnet. The lockout magnet of the inductive contactor is provided with a heavy iron magnetic circuit. The relative strength of the closing and holdout coils is so adjusted that the contactor will remain open with full line voltage on the closing coil and approximately 1 per cent of full line voltage on the holdout coil.

In operation, the closing coil and the holdout coil are energized at the same time, and then the holdout coil is short-circuited. The holdout magnetic circuit is so designed that a certain length of time is required for the flux to die down to a value which will permit the contactor to close. The time is adjusted by varying an air gap in the holdout magnetic circuit. The use of this type of contactor is de-scribed in Chapter 6.

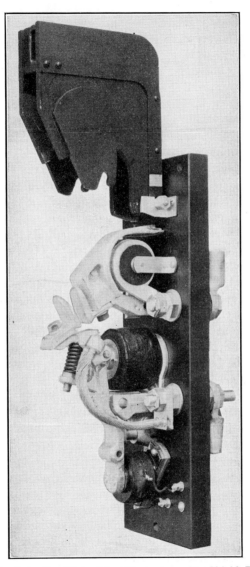

FIG. 37. Inductive Time-delay Contactor. Arc Shield Raised.

Shunt Relays. Shunt relays are similar to shunt contactors, except that they are required to handle only small amounts of current, since they commutate the coils of other relays and contactors and do not handle motor current. Shunt relays are of many different sizes and forms. Some are very small and have light contacts, being so arranged that they will require a minimum current in the operating coil. The contacts of pressure regulators, thermostats, and other automatic pilot devices are often very light and incapable of handling much current. Consequently, low-wattage relays are required in connection with those devices. Other shunt relays are made larger and heavier for hard service and may be provided with a blowout magnet on any or all of the contacts if necessary. They may also be provided with mechanical interlocks. Shunt relays are available in many different combinations of normally open and normally closed contacts, to suit the requirements of the control designer.

Overload Relays. The purpose of an overload relay is to protect a motor against excessively heavy loads. The relay usually has a series coil, which is connected in the motor circuit and carries motor current. The coil is arranged to lift an iron plunger when a certain value of current has been reached. The plunger is pulled up into the center of the coil and, when it is lifted, acts to trip a set of contacts which, in turn, disconnect the coil of a motor contactor and open the circuit to the motor. Adjustment for tripping on different values of current is made by varying the initial position of the plunger in respect to the coil. If the plunger is farther up in the coil to start with, it will, of course, move at a lower value of current.

It is often desirable to set an overload relay to trip at a value of current which is below the inrush current obtained when the motor is started. To accomplish this result, the overload is provided with a small oil dashpot, which causes a time delay in tripping. The time delay can be so adjusted that the overload will not trip when the motor is started, but if an overload continues for a short time the relay will trip and disconnect the motor.

For some types of control circuits only a single-coil overload relay is required, and the circuit is so arranged that, once it has been opened, the operator has to push a button to start the motor again. The overload relay will, of course, reset as soon as it has disconnected the motor, since there will no longer be any current in the relay coil. Other arrangements require that the overload relay remain tripped after it has operated. This is sometimes accomplished by making the contact of a latching type, so that it is necessary to reclose it by hand. More frequently it is accomplished by supplying the overload relay with a small shunt coil, in addition to the series coil, which shunt coil has just sufficient strength to keep the plunger lifted after it has once operated. In order to reset, it is then necessary to break the circuit to the shunt coil, which will allow the plunger to drop back to its initial position.

Figure 38 shows the Westinghouse Electric Corporation type-TI overload relay, which has both time delay and instantaneous tripping features.

The relay is made up of magnetic and mechanical parts mounted on a molded base to form a unit common to all ratings, on which are assembled coils and heaters that vary with the rating.

The relay operates according to a combination of magnetic and thermal principles. A clapper-type magnet is magnetized by a series coil and carries a horizontal armature, the free end of which may take an upper or lower position depending on the magnetic and thermal conditions. The armature is normally biased to its lower position where it is held by the magnetic attraction of a strip of nickel-iron alloy called Invar. Under tripping conditions, the lockout effect of the Invar strip is neutralized or overpowered and the armature is drawn to its upper position by the magnetic attraction of an upper pole formed by the bent end of the rear frame. In moving upward, the armature lifts a push rod which opens a normally closed contact at the top of the relay. A spring is arranged to engage a notch in the push rod in its upper position and thus hold the contact open for "hand-reset" operation until the latch is disengaged by depressing the reset pushbutton. If "automatic-reset" operation is wanted, the spring latch is permanently held out of engagement by depressing the reset pushbutton and giving it one-quarter turn clockwise.

The time delay features of the relay depend on the special physical property of Invar by which it loses its magnetic permeability at a temperature of about 240 C. This property is utilized by connecting the Invar lockout strip or "heater" in series or parallel to the coil and passing the load current or a fraction of it through the heater. On moderate sustained overloads the internally generated heat is sufficient to raise the temperature of the heater to its demagnetization point, and the lockout effect of the heater is neutralized, allowing the relay to trip. For overloads which exceed the instantaneous trip setting of the relay, a vertical auxiliary armature, attracted toward the coil, strikes the horizontal armature and raises it from the Invar $\frac{1}{32}$ to $\frac{1}{16}$ inch, which is sufficient to break the lockout, allowing it to trip.

The relay has two adjustments: (1) to vary the rating, and (2) to vary the instantaneous tripping current.

The adjustment for rating is made by turning an adjusting plate attached to the horizontal armature, so that the lockout pin registers with a hot spot (low current rating) at the right or with a cool spot

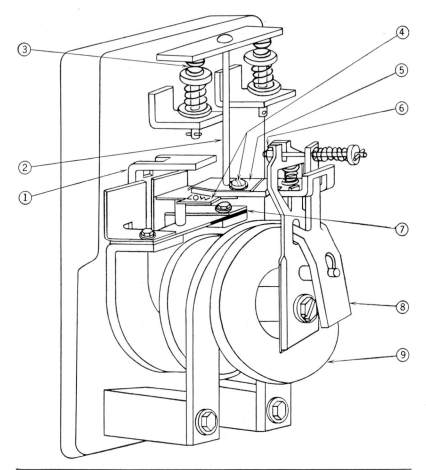

Item	Description or Name of Part
1	Bent end of rear frame
2	Push rod
3	Normally closed contact
4	Rating adjustment—loosen screw, and turn adjusting plate so that "low" or "high" marking is exposed, as desired
5	Horizontal armature thermal trip
6	Instantaneous trip adjustment—increase spring tension for higher tripping current
7	Invar heater
8	Vertical armature instantaneous trip
9	Coil

Fig. 38. Westinghouse Type-TI-2 Overload Relay.

(high current rating) at the left of its motion. The change of current rating which may be expected between "low" and "high" adjustments is about 12 per cent for large current heaters and 20 per cent for small ones. This adjustment is changed by loosening a screw.

A nut adjustment is provided for varying the spring tension on the auxiliary armature to vary the percentage overload at which instantaneous trip occurs. The travel of the nut is limited, to provide adjustment between about 200 and 600 per cent of rating. The adjustment is set at the factory to give instantaneous trip at 300 to 400 per cent.

Series Relays. Figure 39 shows a relay of the series accelerating type, the use of which is described in Chapter 6. The coil is connected

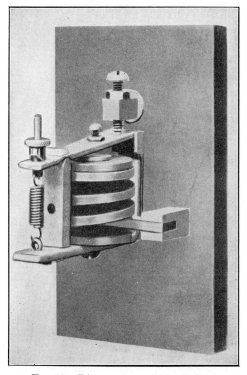

Fig. 39. Direct-current Series Relay.

in the motor circuit, and the contacts are arranged to handle the coils of a magnetic contactor. The armature of a relay of this type is light and the magnetic gap is very small, so that the relay is fast in operation. It may be set to operate on any desired current by adjusting the tension spring which holds the armature open.

Latched-in Relays. Sometimes it is necessary to have a relay so arranged that, once it has closed, it will remain closed even though voltage fails. To accomplish this result, relays of the latched-in type are used. Such relays usually have two coils, one for closing the relay and the other for opening it. When the relay closes, a latch operates to lock it in the closed position. The tripping coil is arranged to raise the latch and permit the relay to open.

Timing Relays. Figure 40 shows a direct-current timing relay arranged to close a number of circuits in sequence within a definite time

FIG. 40. Direct-current Timing Relay.

after the coil has been energized. The coil of the relay pulls upward on a plunger, which is prevented from instantaneous operation by means of a dashpot to which the plunger is connected. The dashpot may be of either the oil or the air type. It consists of an iron pot in which a piston operates. The piston has a valve which permits the oil or air to flow through only very slowly in one direction but very rapidly in the other direction. Consequently, the plunger of the relay moves upward slowly and downward instantaneously. The timing is adjusted by varying the opening of the valve.

As the plunger goes upward, it moves a finger board on which a number of pilot fingers are mounted. The mountings are staggered, so that the fingers close in rotation from left to right. In other words, the first finger may have to move only $\frac{1}{8}$ inch to close, whereas the last finger may have to move $\frac{1}{2}$ inch to close, and the others somewhere between these values. The fingers may be connected to the coils of contactors, which will then close in a definite sequence.

By the use of a bypass, which will permit the plunger to move upward a short distance before the dashpot has any effect, it is possible to close the first finger immediately and then obtain timing for the closure of the other fingers.

Relays of this type are also available with all contacts normally closed, so that they open in sequence in a definite time. Such relays are used for inserting successive steps of resistance in series with the shunt field of a motor, to increase its speed.

Field Relays. Figure 41 presents a relay of a very useful type. As shown, it is a series relay with a normally open contact. It has a relatively light armature, an adjusting spring which may serve to vary the closing and opening points, and an adjustable air gap. The armature is prevented from sealing against the iron core by means of a brass screw. This screw may be adjusted to vary the gap. If the air gap is wide, the opening point of the relay will be close to the closing point. If the air gap is small, the relay will remain closed on a current much less than that which was required to close it. By varying the air gap, the range between the opening and closing values may be adjusted. The value of both opening and closing points may be adjusted by varying the tension spring.

With series coils, as shown in the illustration, the relay may be used for automatic acceleration and deceleration of motors by means of field weakening. This is described in Chapter 8.

A relay of this same type may serve as a jamming relay. For such a purpose it would have a series coil connected in the motor circuit and would be so arranged that when the current reached a definite value the relay would open. Normally closed contacts would, of course, be required. When the relay opened, it would act upon the coil of a magnetic contactor, which in turn would insert a step of resistance in series with the motor to slow it down somewhat. This arrangement is often used on such installations as electric shovels, where, in digging, an obstruction may be met which will tend to overload the motor and perhaps stall it. It is not desired to have an overload relay cut off power under these conditions, but instead

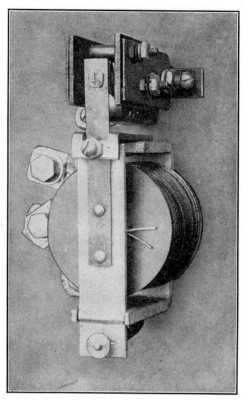

FIG. 41. Vibrating Field Relay.

a jamming relay is used to insert a certain amount of resistance, and slow the motor down, at the same time preventing the current from reaching an excessive value.

The same type of relay could be used for a voltage relay, since its ease of adjustment would permit its being set to open and close on definite voltages.

There are many other forms of control relays, and manufacturers are almost constantly having to design new types to meet special applications. However, the majority of them are modifications in one form or another of the types which have been described above.

Maintenance of Contactors. Contactors should be kept reasonably clean. If dust or scale accumulates on the controller, it should be blown off with compressed air.

The contacts should not be lubricated, as oil or Vaseline will be decomposed by the heat and will increase the destructive effect of the arc.

The contacts should be kept smooth by filing occasionally with a fine file, care being taken to remove no more metal than is necessary to secure a smooth surface. Contact tips should be replaced when they are worn approximately half through. Definite instructions on this point are generally sent out by the manufacturer with each contactor. As the tips wear, the spring pressure behind them is reduced; if they are allowed to go too long, the contactor will not be able to handle the load properly and may be seriously damaged by overheating or by welding of the contacts.

Hinge pins and bearings should be lubricated with a light machine oil.

Interlock fingers should be replaced when they are worn nearly through. The bar which short-circuits them is usually arranged so that it can be rotated to present a new surface as one part becomes worn.

Arc shields should be replaced before the arc has burned through them. If a shield is burned clear through, the arc will strike the metal pole piece of the blowout and the contactor will be damaged.

The surfaces of the core and the armature which seal together when the contactor is closed should be kept clean and free from rust, oil, or grease. Rubbing these surfaces occasionally with emery cloth will accomplish the desired results.

Standard Ratings. The NEMA standard 8-hour open ratings of direct-current contactors are 25, 50, 100, 150, 300, 600, 900, 1350, and

TABLE 7

CONTINUOUS-DUTY RATINGS OF DIRECT-CURRENT CONTACTORS

NEMA Size Number	8-hour Open Rating, amperes	115 volts		230 volts		550 volts	
		Horse-power	Number of Accelerating Contactors	Horse-power	Number of Accelerating Contactors	Horse-power	Number of Accelerating Contactors
1	25	3	1	5	1	..	..
2	50	5	2	10	2	20	2
3	100	10	2	25	2	50	2
4	150	20	2	40	2	75	3
5	300	40	3	75	3	150	4
6	600	75	3	150	4	300	5
7	900	110	4	225	5	450	6
8	1350	175	4	350	5	700	6
9	2500	300	5	600	6	1200	7

2500 amperes. Their intermittent rating in amperes is 133⅓ per cent of the 8-hour rating.

For general-purpose magnetic controllers and machine tool controllers, the rating of the line, reversing, and final accelerating contactors is given in Table 7. Intermediate accelerating contactors are selected so that the open 8-hour ampere rating will not be less than one-fourth of the peak current obtained during acceleration.

For intermittent service in steel mills, the ratings are given in Table 8. The smaller contactors are not used for this service. For crane service the ratings are the same, but an additional accelerating contactor is used.

TABLE

INTERMITTENT RATINGS OF CONTACTORS

8-hour Contactor Rating	Contactor Mill Rating	Horsepower Mill Rating	Minimum Number of Accelerating Contactors
100	133	35	2
150	200	55	2
300	400	110	2
600	800	225	2 or 3
900	1200	330	3
1350	1800	500	4
2500	3350	1000	5

References

G. L. Moses, "Magnet Coils," *Product Engineering*, December, 1938; February, March, July, 1939; January, February, 1940.

C. P. Nachod, "Nomogram for Coil Calculations," *Electronics*, January, 1937.

C. Stansbury, "Impulse Operation of Magnetic Contactors," *Electrical Engineering*, May, 1937, p. 583.

L. E. Markle, "Which Contactor Where?", *Mill and Factory*, February, 1941, p. 99.

F. Didszuns, "Magnetic Latching of Relays," *Product Engineering*, April, 1948, p. 110.

Problems

1. A direct-current coil of circular cross-section has the following characteristics:

Diameter of inside turn	1.12 inches
Diameter of outside turn	2.86 inches
Terminal volts	240
Wire used	No. 35 cotton-covered
Wire resistance	329 ohms per 1000 feet, at 25 C
Number of turns in coil	N

Calculate the ampere turns which the coil will produce at the specified voltage, at 25 C.

2. The length of the winding space of the coil of problem 1 is 2.4 inches, and 9243 turns of the wire specified can be wound in 1 square inch. Calculate the resistance of the coil at 25 C.

3. Calculate the watts in the coil at 25 C.

4. Calculate the resistance of the coil, and the watts, at 100 C.

5. It has been found that this coil will dissipate heat at a rate which will prevent its exceeding a safe temperature of 100 C if its continuous wattage is determined on the basis of 0.7 watt per square inch of surface, figuring on the cylindrical surface plus the area of one end. What is the continuous wattage rating of the coil?

6. A coil of this type is wound with no. 28 cotton-covered wire, which has a resistance of 64.9 ohms per 1000 feet, and a winding factor of 3462 turns per square inch. Calculate the resistance of the coil.

7. Calculate the continuous voltage rating of the coil of problem 6.

8. A contactor having the coil of problem 6 is used on a 250-volt circuit. The coil is protected by a series resistor which is cut into circuit by interlock contacts on the contactor. What is the minimum value of the protecting resistor, allowing for a possible 10 per cent overvoltage?

9. A certain shunt contactor will pick up and close on 2020 ampere turns, and drop out at 530 ampere turns. If this contactor is equipped with the coil of problem 1, and it is desired that it operate at 80 per cent of rated voltage at 100 C, what is the minimum rated voltage on which it may be used?

10. At what voltage will the contactor open?

11. If the contactor is equipped with the coil and resistor of problem 8, what will be the minimum rated voltage on which it may be used?

12. At what voltage will the contactor open?

13. An overload relay has a single series coil. The calibration range of the relay is 950–3750 ampere turns. The desired maximum current density in the coil is 1500 amperes per square inch at the motor rating. Calculate the number of full turns, and the cross-sectional area of a coil for use with a 100-horsepower 230-volt 375-ampere motor when the relay is to be calibrated at 125–150–175 per cent of the motor rating.

14. Sketch a series coil blowout magnet and its coil, and show the contactor contact tips. Indicate the direction of current in the turns of the coil around the magnet and between the contact tips, and show which direction an arc will be blown from the tips. Show the direction of the magnetic flux lines.

6

AUTOMATIC ACCELERATING METHODS
FOR DIRECT-CURRENT MOTORS

Although it is satisfactory to connect some small motors directly to the line when starting, the majority of installations require a more gradual application of power. Resistance is connected in series with the armature to limit the initial current, and this resistance is then short-circuited in one or more steps.

Various devices are employed to short-circuit resistance steps automatically as the motor accelerates. A satisfactory device must meet a number of requirements.

1. It must properly protect the motor against high peak currents and against high stresses and strains. Some years ago this was the principal requirement, but today motors are built to withstand hard service and a great deal of abuse, so that this function is not so important as it formerly was.

2. The accelerating device must protect the machinery by applying the starting torque gradually and in limited amounts.

3. The current taken from the line must be limited in order to prevent line disturbances. Most power companies have definite rules regarding the increments of current that may be drawn from the line when starting a motor.

4. Smooth acceleration is a requirement of many installations, as, for instance, elevators, and the trolley or bridge motions of a crane.

5. The rate of acceleration is important to many drives. Rapid acceleration saves time and power. Frequently the operation of a machine is very rapid, and the motor is required to get up to speed in a short time.

6. The accelerating device should be reliable and should operate for long periods of time without maintenance. It should be simple, easy to understand and adjust, and easy to maintain and repair.

Obviously, these requirements vary in importance, depending upon the application. A centrifugal casting machine requires an extremely smooth acceleration. Speed is essential in accelerating the motor that drives the manipulator fingers of a rolling mill. The current taken from the line may be of no importance if the power system has a relatively large capacity. In selecting the method of acceleration, therefore, the application must be considered and the vital require-

94

ments determined. An accelerating method which will best meet these requirements can then be adopted.

Theory of Acceleration. Figure 42, showing what happens during the acceleration of a shunt motor, will serve to illustrate the theory for any motor. At no load the motor runs at a speed near 100 per cent. A slight drop in speed is caused by the voltage drop in the armature and leads. At any given load the speed will fall at a corresponding point on the curve ae. If the motor were connected directly to the line to start, the initial inrush current would be limited

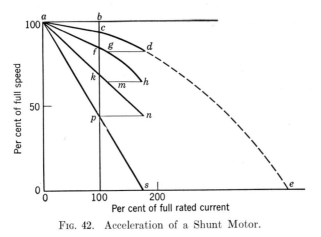

FIG. 42. Acceleration of a Shunt Motor.

only by the resistance of the armature and leads and would reach point e. To limit the inrush to a reasonable value external resistance is connected in series with the armature. The resistance is designed to allow an inrush which will be enough higher than full load to insure starting. In the diagram the initial inrush is shown at s. When the motor starts, it begins to develop a countervoltage opposing the line voltage and in proportion to the motor speed. Consequently, as the motor speed increases, the current in the armature decreases along the line sa. If the motor had no load, it would accelerate to full speed with the resistance in circuit; but, if the motor is loaded, it will accelerate only until the armature current is just enough to provide the necessary running torque. With a fully loaded motor the maximum speed would be reached at point p. When or before this speed is reached, it will be necessary to cut out some of the resistance if further acceleration is to take place. It is customary to cut out just enough to produce a second inrush n, equal to the initial inrush. The motor then accelerates along the curve na until point m is reached, where it is necessary to cut out another step. This will be selected to give a third equal inrush h and permit the motor to accelerate along the curve ha. At point g the last step is cut out and the motor is across the line.

The choice of the initial inrush value s determines the location of point p, and obviously, if the inrush is increased, the speed at p will be higher and the length of the line bp will be shorter. Line bc represents the voltage drop in the motor and leads, and cp that across the external resistance. It will be evident that kp represents the drop across the first step of resistance, fk that across the second step, and cf that across the third step. Since these voltages are proportional to the resistance values, the current being the same in all steps, the lines kp, fk, and cf are proportional to the ohmic value of the resistance steps. The curve, therefore, gives a graphical method of determining the value of the resistance and of dividing it properly. The total ohmic value is found by dividing the line voltage by the initial inrush current s. The first step is then

$$\frac{kp}{bp} \times \text{Total ohms}$$

The other steps may be found similarly.

Note that the sum of the steps will be less than the total ohms by the amount $bc/bp \times$ Total ohms, which is the armature and lead resistance.

Practically all methods of automatic acceleration fall into one of two general classes known as current-limit acceleration and time-limit acceleration.

Current-limit Acceleration. This method of acceleration makes use of the fact that, as a motor increases in speed, the current taken from the line decreases. Relays or other devices operating on current are used to control contactors which cut out the resistance steps. The relays are set to permit operation of the contactors successively as the current approaches the full-load value. Obviously, the relays must be set to close above the value of load current to insure that they will always operate. If the load is variable, the relays must be set high enough to insure acceleration under the heaviest load encountered. If the load at any time requires a current higher than the relay setting, the relay will not operate, the resistance will not be cut out, and the motor will not accelerate any farther.

With current-limit acceleration the time required to accelerate will depend entirely upon the load and will be constant only when the load is constant. When the load is light, the motor will accelerate quickly, the current will drop rapidly, and the relays will permit the resistance commutating contactors to operate quickly. When the load is heavy, the motor will require a longer time to accelerate, the current will fall more slowly, and a longer time will be required for short-circuiting the resistance.

Time-limit Acceleration. Time-limit acceleration may be defined as a starting method which permits short-circuiting the starting resistance and connecting the motor to the line in the same time for each start, regardless of the load on the motor and of the time which it actually takes for the motor to accelerate that load. The accelerating relays or devices are entirely independent of motor current. The timing should be adjusted so that under normal load conditions each resistance step will be cut out just as the motor has reached its maximum acceleration with that step in circuit.

Comparative Advantages. With time-limit acceleration properly adjusted the current peaks will be lower than with current-limit acceleration, because the operation of the accelerating device is independent of current, and the motor may be allowed to accelerate on each step as far as it will. With time-limit acceleration, and a variable load, the resistance may be made high enough to limit the current to just enough to start a light load smoothly. Then on a heavy load the motor will not start on the first point, or perhaps not on the second point. The accelerating device will continue to cut out resistance until the motor does start. In either event the motor will be connected to the line in the same time, but power will be saved with a light load.

In many instances a controller is adjusted to work properly when first installed, and when the machine is new and relatively hard to drive. With current-limit acceleration the relays will have to be set high enough to take care of this condition. Later, when the machinery is worn in, much less current may be required to start it, and the relays could be set to operate at a lower value. The chances are, however, that this adjustment will not be made, since there will be nothing to call the operator's attention to the possibility. The controller will then be wasteful of power during starting.

For the reasons given, time-limit acceleration has the advantage of saving power during acceleration.

The time-limit controller generally has the advantage from the standpoint of simplicity, as fewer relays and electric interlocks are required. The series lockout contactor requires no interlocks or auxiliary interlocks, and so provides a simple current-limit control, but it can be used only in the simple form for single-speed applications.

The time-limit controller has an additional advantage which is a strong argument for its use on motors subject to a large number of operations in a manufacturing process. This advantage is that, since it always accelerates the motor in the same time, it is possible to time a number of operations definitely with respect to one another. For instance, an operator in a steel mill may control a number of motors driving various parts of the mill. Since the response of each motor is always the same, he soon discovers just when to operate the starting switch for each drive to obtain the results he desires. The sequence and time of operating the various levers become almost automatic; and the operator's efficiency is improved. If he had current-limit controllers, the time of response would vary with changes in load, and it would be difficult, if not impossible, to arrive at the same efficiency of operation.

It would appear that the time-limit controller has a definite advantage when employed with drives having varying loads. The chief obstacle to its general use was, for many years, the lack of any simple, reliable form of timing device. This difficulty has been overcome, and the use of time-limit acceleration is almost universal.

Forms of Control. The principal forms of current-limit acceleration are those using

Counter-emf acceleration.
Series relay acceleration.
Lockout contactors.
Voltage-drop acceleration.

The principal forms of time-limit acceleration are those using

Time of contactors only.
Individual dashpot relays.
Multicircuit dashpot relays.
Magnetic drag relays.
Escapement timing.
Inductive time-limit acceleration.
Motor-driven timers.
Capacitor discharge.

Counter-emf Acceleration. A controller using counter-emf acceleration is shown in Fig. 43. The run button is pressed to start, energizing the closing coil of the main contactor M. When M closes, it connects the motor to the line through the starting resistance and also provides a maintaining circuit for its own coil by closing an auxiliary interlock to bypass the run button. The accelerating contactors have their closing coils connected across the motor armature. The coil of the first contactor, $1A$, is designed to close the contactor on approximately half of normal voltage. The coil of the next contactor, $2A$, is designed to close the contactor at, say, 80 per cent voltage, and that of the last contactor, $3A$, at approximately 90 per cent voltage. Consequently, the first contactor will close when the motor has reached approximately 50 per cent speed, and the third at 90 per cent speed. Contactors for this purpose are provided with an adjustable tension spring or some other means of adjusting the closing point.

This simple method of acceleration is satisfactory for controllers of small capacity. It is not generally used above 3 horsepower. Larger contactors, when closed on a low rising voltage, will close slowly and

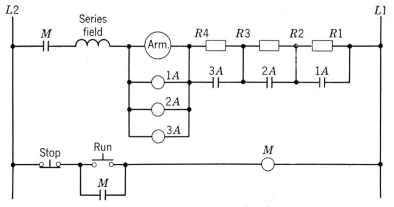

Fig. 43. Counter-emf Acceleration.

with light pressure. Under these conditions, the contacts are likely to weld together so that they cannot be opened.

Series-relay Acceleration. Figure 44 shows a controller using series-relay acceleration. The relays have normally closed contacts connected in series with the coils of the accelerating contactors. The coils of the relays are connected in the main motor circuit as shown. The relays are designed to be very fast in operation. They are provided with an adjustment, so that they can be set to close on a selected value of current. Figure 39 shows a relay of this type.

When the run button is pressed to start, the main contactor M closes. Its main contacts connect the motor to the line, and current flows through the coil of relay $SR1$. An instant later the auxiliary contacts of M close to provide a maintaining circuit around the run button and also to energize the closing coil of contactor $1A$. However, the series relay is fast enough to open its contacts before the auxiliary contacts of M close, and so contactor $1A$ is not energized. When the motor has accelerated enough to bring the line current down to that for which the relay is set, the relay will close. A circuit is now provided for 1A, which closes, cutting out the first step of resistance and short-circuiting the first series relay. Current now flows through contactor 1A and relay SR2. This relay opens its contacts in the interval between the closing of the main contacts of 1A and the auxiliary contacts. Consequently, no circuit is provided for coil 2A until the motor has accelerated enough to reduce the current to normal again. At this point relay SR2 closes, providing a circuit for coil 2A. Contactor 2A, in closing, cuts out the second step of resistance, short-circuits relay coil SR2, and allows current to flow through relay coil

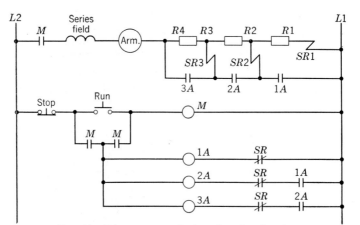

FIG. 44. Direct-current Series-relay Acceleration.

SR3. This relay operates in the above-described manner, finally allowing contactor 3A to close and connect the motor directly to the line.

At first thought it may seem difficult to insure that the relay will operate in the relatively short time between the closing of the main contacts and the auxiliary fingers of a contactor. When it is considered, however, that the speed of the relay may be as high as 100 times that of the contactor, the matter does not seem so difficult. In fact, this method of control is very reliable and has been widely used for many years. Its chief disadvantages are that it requires a relatively large number of electric interlocks, which are undesirable from a maintenance standpoint, and that the relays themselves must be light to insure speed.

Lockout Acceleration. Figure 45 shows a controller using one form of series-lockout acceleration. The contactors are shown in Fig. 35, and their operation is described in Chapter 5. Contactors 1A and 2A are each provided with two series coils, one being a closing and the

other a lockout coil. Contactor 3A has in addition a small shunt coil
to hold it closed if the running load is light and the pull of the series
coil is low. Referring to the diagram, the initial inrush current flows
from line L1 through both coils of contactor 1A, locking it open, and
then through the resistance and the motor to line L2. The current
also flows through the lockout coil of contactor 3A. This arrangement
prevents any tendency of 3A to close on the pull of the shunt holding
coil. When the current falls to normal, 1A closes, short-circuiting step
R1–R2 and also its own lockout coil. Current now flows through the

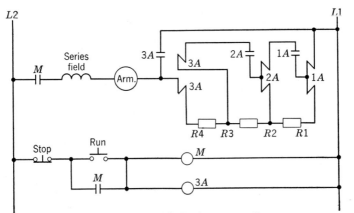

Fig. 45. Acceleration with Lockout-type Contactors.

closing coil and the contacts of 1A, and through both coils of 2A.
Contactor 2A is locked out until the current inrush, resulting from the
closure of 1A, has fallen to normal, when it closes. The closing of 2A
short-circuits step R2–R3 and the lockout coil of 2A. Current now
flows through the closing coils only of 1A and 2A, and through both
series coils of 3A. When this inrush has fallen to normal, 3A closes,
short-circuiting all the resistance, and also all series coils, on all
contactors. Contactor 3A is now held closed by its shunt holding coil
until the stop button is pressed.

There are other forms of lockout contactors, some having only one
coil and obtaining the lockout effect by means of a restricted iron
circuit which becomes saturated on inrush current. The chief advantage of lockout acceleration over series relays is its simplicity, as no
relays or interlock fingers are required. Its chief disadvantage is that
it is not very adaptable to multispeed controllers because of the series
coils. Another disadvantage is that, as the coils must carry motor
current, they must often be wound of heavy copper strap or bar, and
a number of different windings will be required to take care of different

motor sizes. It is possible to use shunt closing coils, and also shunt lockout coils, without electric interlocks, and this is sometimes done.

Voltage-drop Acceleration. Figure 46 shows a current-limit controller using the voltage-drop method of acceleration. The accelerat-

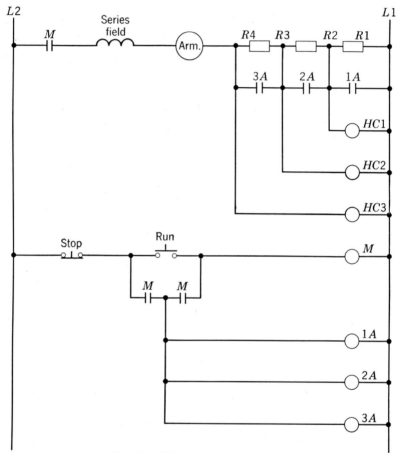

Fɪɢ. 46. Voltage-drop Acceleration.

ing contactors are provided with two coils, one for closing and the other for holding the contactor open. The closing coils are connected to line voltage through interlock fingers on the main contactor. The holdout coil of 1A is connected across the first step of resistance, and it is designed to permit the contactor to close on the voltage obtained when normal full-load current is flowing through the resistance. Similarly, contactor 2A is arranged to close when normal current flows through step $R2$–$R3$, and $3A$ when normal current is flowing in step $R3$–$R4$.

The initial starting inrush, being higher than normal current, holds all accelerators open. When the current falls to normal, contactor $1A$ closes. Contactor $2A$ does not close because its holdout coil is connected across both steps $R1$–$R2$ and $R2$–$R3$. The closing of $1A$ short-circuits step $R1$–$R2$, and the resulting inrush of current increases the voltage across $R2$–$R3$. The holdout coil of $2A$ is now connected across that step only, and, when normal current is reached, $2A$ will close.

Step $R2$–$R3$ is now short-circuited, and the holding coil of $3A$ is connected across step $R3$–$R4$ only, so that, when the inrush has again fallen to normal, contactor $3A$ will close. This method of connecting the contactors avoids the necessity of using any electric interlocks between them. If each holding coil were initially connected across its own step of resistance, it would be necessary to connect each closing coil behind interlocks on the preceding accelerator, as otherwise all accelerators would close as soon as the initial inrush had fallen to normal.

Time-limit Acceleration with Contactors. The simplest means of time-limit acceleration is the use of contactors only, without any auxiliary devices. Of course, the time required for a contactor to close is short, but the time required for acceleration is sometimes only a fraction of a second. If the accelerating time required were half a second, and the accelerating contactor required one-tenth of a second to close, then the use of five contactors would give the required time and would provide a very simple and dependable control. Though this method is not common, it has its application in high-speed drives, particularly in steel mills.

Individual Dashpot Relays. A number of forms of small timing relays utilize the dashpot principle. The relay consists of a piston, or plunger, operating in a dashpot, and provided with a valve to allow a rapid reset. A check valve or other means of time adjustment is also provided. The dashpot may be filled with oil or mercury, or may use air. The piston is mechanically attached, through a spring, to a contactor. When the contactor closes, the spring is stretched and pulls on the piston. The piston moves slowly, against the action of the dashpot, and after a given time reaches the end of its stroke. At this point the auxiliary electric contacts of the relay are closed. Generally, a bypass is provided in the dashpot, near the end of travel, so that the final closing of the contacts is accomplished with a snap action. When the contactor opens, the piston is released and falls to its original position instantaneously, the valve permitting the oil to flow past the piston in that direction of travel. Reliable timing up to approximately 30 seconds can be obtained from relays of this type.

Although the dashpot timing relay is widely used because of its relative simplicity and low cost, it has serious disadvantages. The timing is likely to vary with temperature and will be affected by any dirt or dust which gets into the dashpot or the adjustment valve. Since any oil used as a medium must have a uniform viscosity over a wide temperature range, a special oil is required. Some dashpots have a tendency to pump and splash out the oil. If air is used as a

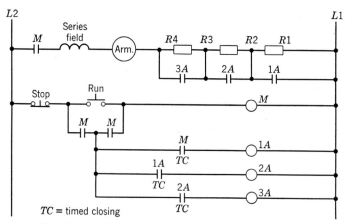

Fig. 47. Acceleration Using Individual Timing Relays.

medium, leather washers are generally required on the piston. These must be properly oiled for successful operation. Too little oil will cause them to dry up and crack; too much oil makes the piston sluggish in resetting. Many liquids have been tried in dashpots with more or less success. A properly designed dashpot using mercury will give good results.

A controller with dashpot timing relays is shown in Fig. 47. Pressing the run button closes the main contactor M. The first timing relay is mechanically tied to this contactor. After a set time the piston of the relay completes its travel and the contacts close, completing a circuit for the coil of the first accelerator 1A. The second timing relay is operated by 1A and controls the coil of 2A; in like manner any desired number of accelerators may be controlled. The control is simple, easily understood, and inexpensive.

Multicontact Timing Relays. Where it is not required to open and close the accelerating contactors individually for speed regulation, a multipoint dashpot timing relay may be employed. A device of this type is shown in Fig. 40, and the connection for its use in Fig. 48. The relay consists of a solenoid, the plunger of which is retarded in its motion by a dashpot. The dashpot may be of the air, oil, or mercury type. The plunger of the solenoid is adapted to close a series of contact fingers, which are staggered so that they will close in a definite order. The contact fingers are individually adjustable, and the timing of the whole cycle may be varied by a valve adjustment on the dashpot. Since this device has its own operating coil, mechanical ties to the

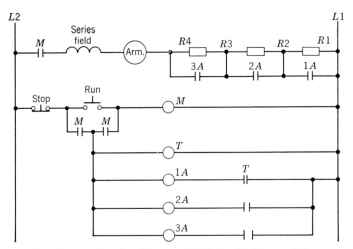

Fig. 48. Acceleration Using a Multi-circuit Timing Relay.

contactors are avoided. There is also an advantage in having only one dashpot to maintain and adjust.

The control circuits are simple. Interlocks on the main contactor energize the coil of the timing relay. The relay closes slowly, making circuits for the coils of $1A$, $2A$, and $3A$, in order and at desired time intervals. When the stop button is pressed, the relay resets itself immediately.

A device of this type, if properly designed, is sturdy and reliable. For small motors up to approximately 15 horsepower, the contacts of the relay may be built heavy enough to commutate the resistance directly, without the use of contactors.

Various devices have been adapted to relays of the type just described, to replace the dashpot. One such device has an escapement and pendulum similar to those for clocks. The time is varied by changing the length of the pendulum. Another device utilizes magnetic drag to get time delay. A small electromagnet is used, and the motion of the relay plunger is made to revolve a metal disk in the field of the magnet. The rotation of the disk is retarded by magnetic induction. A device of this type is shown in Fig. 49. It is reliable and trouble-free, but relatively expensive.

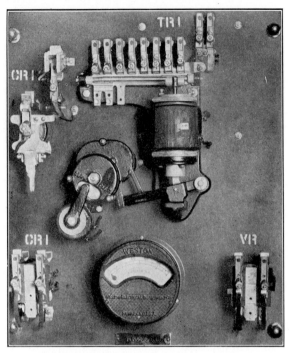

FIG. 49. Magnetic Drag Timing Device.

Motor-driven Timers. Motor-driven timers find application where long time is required, and where the starting is infrequent. A small pilot motor drives a contact cylinder, through reduction gearing. Figure 50 shows a scheme of connections in which the contact fingers control the coils of accelerating contactors. When the run button is pressed, the main contactor M closes, and through its electric interlock it energizes the pilot motor. The motor runs and revolves the contact cylinder, making circuits to fingers 3 and 4 first. At this time contactor $1A$ is closed. When contact is made with finger 5, a circuit is made for $2A$, and, on finger 6, $3A$ is energized. A little beyond this point in the cylinder rotation, finger 2 is de-energized, stopping the pilot motor. The main motor has now been started and brought up to speed. When the stop button is pressed, contactor M drops out, stopping the main motor. Normally closed interlocks on M energize the pilot motor through finger 3, so that the pilot motor starts and runs until the contact cylinder has been returned to its original position. The motor is stopped at this point by the opening of the circuit to finger 3.

The reset time thus required prohibits the use of the device on drives requiring rapid operation.

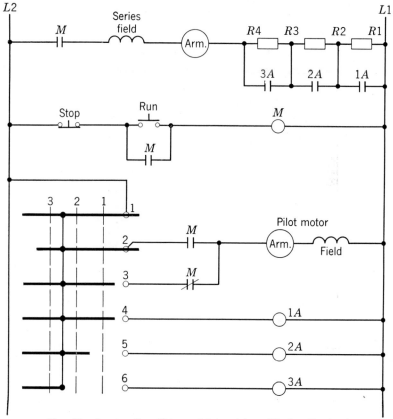

Fig. 50. Acceleration Using a Motor-driven Timing Device.

Motor-driven devices are often used to handle motor circuits directly instead of through contactors. The design is particularly adaptable where it is desired to make one starter serve for motors of different sizes. To accomplish this result, a number of contact fingers are provided, so that a relatively large number of resistance steps are obtained. The resistance is designed to have sufficient ohms to start the smallest motor satisfactorily, and sufficient current-carrying capacity for the largest motor. The starter will then be satisfactory for any motor in the range between those sizes. The larger motors may not start until several steps of resistance have been cut out, but there will be enough steps to insure good acceleration. The reason for a design of this kind is the desire to standardize, and to make one size and kind of controller serve as many sizes of motors as is reasonably possible. In one specific case, four sizes of controllers were designed to cover a range from 10 to 200 horsepower.

FIG. 51. Monitor Motor-driven Timer.

Figure 51 shows another form of motor-driven timing device for pilot circuits only, which is arranged to reset itself quickly. The current-carrying contacts are made in the form of rotatable disks, each carrying an adjustable contact point. These disks are loosely mounted on a sleeve, which is carried on a revolving hollow shaft. Each contact disk is between two other disks, keyed to the shaft, and equipped with carbon blocks, which bear lightly against the contact disks. The hollow shaft is driven by a continuous-running pilot motor. A rod extending through the hollow shaft is arranged to be moved lengthwise by means of a magnetic solenoid. Normally, the contact disks are stationary, held in place by weights mounted on them. To operate the timer, the solenoid is energized, causing the rod to be moved in the shaft and forcing all the disks together. The contact disks are then driven by friction until they come into contact with the stationary posts on the slate panel. These posts serve to complete the electric

circuit to the contactors which are being controlled; they also act as
stops for the contact disks. After making contact, the disks simply
slip between the driving disks. To stop, the solenoid is de-energized,
and the contact disks are immediately returned to their initial position
by the weights.

Inductive Time-limit Acceleration. An important development in
time-limit acceleration was the use of magnetic induction to give the
time delay. When a constant direct voltage is impressed on a circuit
having resistance, but neither inductance nor capacitance, the current
will instantly reach its maximum value, and any change in the voltage
will instantly produce a corresponding change in the current. When
the voltage is removed, the current will instantly drop to zero. However, if the circuit contains either inductance or capacitance, a period
of time will be required for the current to reach its final value when
voltage is applied, and also for it to drop to zero after the voltage
is removed. This is the basic principle of the inductive time-limit
control.

The accelerating contactors used have two coils, one for closing the
contactor and the other for holding it open. The closing coil operates
on line voltage, but the holding coil is connected across one or more
steps of the starting resistance. The iron circuit for the holding coil
is highly inductive, and the air gap is small. The strength of the coils
is so proportioned that, with full line voltage in the closing coil and
only 1 per cent of line voltage on the holding coil, the contactor will
be held open.

A simple form of this control is shown in Fig. 52. The coils marked
$HC1$, $HC2$, and $HC3$ are holding-out coils. Those marked $1A$, $2A$,
$3A$, are closing coils. In the off position the holding coil of $1A$ is
energized, as it is connected to the line through a resistance $A-B$.
When the run button is pressed, the contactor M is energized, connecting the motor to the line through the starting resistance. The motor
current, flowing through the resistance, produces a voltage drop across
the steps $R1-R2$ and $R2-R3$, so that contactors $2A$ and $3A$ are held
open. Interlock fingers on M provide a circuit to energize the closing
coils of the accelerating contactors, but they remain open because of
the holdout coils. The interlock fingers of M also short-circuit the
holding coil of $1A$. Because of the inductance of this coil, the current
flowing in it does not drop to zero immediately but requires a period
of time to do so. The contactor is held open until the current has
dropped to practically zero, after which it closes. When $1A$ closes,
the first step of resistance is short-circuited, and also the holding coil
of contactor $2A$. Time is again required for the current in this coil

to drop low enough to allow $2A$ to close. When $2A$ closes, the holdout coil of $3A$ is short-circuited, and after a time $3A$ closes, completing the accelerating cycle.

When an inductive contactor of this type is open, the magnetic gap between the core and the armature of the closing circuit is relatively large, and that of the holding circuit relatively small. The ratio is about ⅜ inch for the closing gap, as against a few thousandths of an

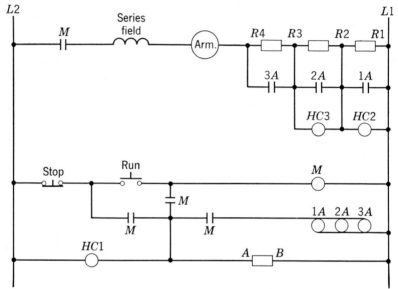

Fɪɢ. 52. Inductive Time-limit Acceleration.

inch for the holding gap. Consequently, the holding coil is able to keep the contactor open with a very low current in the coil. When the contactor has closed, the magnetic gap of the closing circuit is zero and that of the holding circuit large, so that the holding coil, if energized, would have very little effect. It follows that, as the contactor closes, the pull of the closing coil increases and that of the holding coil decreases, so that the closing is definite and the closing pull strong.

Adjustment for the time is made by changing the magnetic gap in the holding coil circuit, a small gap giving the greatest inductance and the maximum time.

Separate Inductors. The time which can be obtained with the inductive method is limited by the amount of inductance which can be included in the holdout coil circuit. There is a limit beyond which it is impracticable to make the holdout coils any larger, and, if the time required is longer than can be obtained, some other method of increasing the inductance must be found. A separate inductor has been used. The inductor is simply a closed iron circuit upon which coils are mounted. The iron circuit and the coils are large, so that the device has a considerable inductance.

One method of using the inductor is shown in Fig. 53. The coils $HC1$, $HC2$, and $HC3$ are holdout coils for contactors $1A$, $2A$, and $3A$,

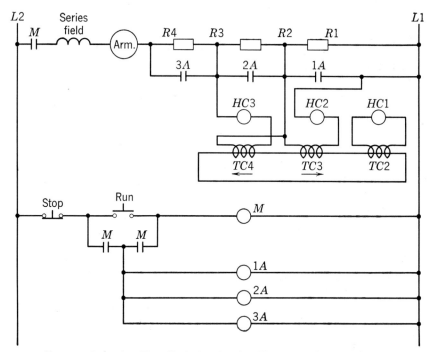

Fig. 53. Inductive Time-limit Acceleration Using a Separate Inductor.

respectively. Coils $1A$, $2A$, and $3A$ are the closing coils. Coils $TC2$, $TC3$, and $TC4$ are the coils of the inductor, all of the same strength. It will be noted that coils $TC3$ and $TC4$ are reversed in polarity. The initial inrush current causes a voltage drop through the resistance, and, since the resistance steps are tapered, the voltage across coils $TC3$ and $HC2$ is higher than that across coils $TC4$ and $HC3$. Magnetic flux is therefore set up in the inductor in the direction of $TC3$, which we will call positive. The building up of this flux causes an induced current to flow in the loop formed by coils $TC2$ and $HC1$, which current continues to flow as long as the flux is changing. When the flux has completely built up, current is no longer induced in $TC2$ and $HC1$, and contactor $1A$ closes. The closing of $1A$ short-circuits the first step of resistance and also the two coils $TC3$ and $HC2$. Coil $TC3$ no longer produces flux in the inductor, all the flux now produced being due to $TC4$. The total flux therefore changes from positive to negative, and this change induces a current in the loop formed by coils $TC3$ and $HC2$. During the time required for the flux to drop from its positive value to zero, and build up in the negative direction, the contactor $2A$ is held open. When the flux is again constant, current is no longer induced in $HC2$, and $2A$ closes. The closing of $2A$ short-circuits step $R2$–$R3$ and also the two coils $TC4$ and $HC3$. There are now no inductor coils connected to a voltage source, and the flux in the inductor drops to zero. During the time required for the flux to die down to zero, contactor $3A$ is held open by induced current in the coil $HC3$. When the flux is again constant, the induced current becomes zero and $3A$ closes.

With an inductor of this type the greatest time is always obtained by reversing the flux. The control scheme must be varied with different numbers of accelerating contactors and with different time tapers between contactors. The required variations may be obtained by connecting the inductor coils across different steps of resistance, or by using coils of different strength or additional inductor coils to accomplish a specific result.

Reversing Inductive Control. Since the inductive method of acceleration has found its greatest application in connection with the auxiliary drives in steel mills and on cranes, it seems proper to include here a description of a reversing plugging control of the type used for that purpose. An additional contactor and resistance step are used to keep down the inrush when the motor is plugged, that is, connected to the line in the reverse direction while it is running full speed in the forward direction. Under this condition the armature countervoltage, which has been opposed to the line voltage, is added to line voltage, so that the total voltage across the resistance is approximately 180 per cent of line voltage. As the motor decelerates, the voltage drops, until at zero speed only line voltage is left. The motor then accelerates in the reverse direction, just as if it were starting from rest. The plugging contactor should, then, remain open until the motor stops, and close at the instant of reversal.

When the motor is started from rest, the plugging contactor should close at once, without any time delay. Figure 54 shows the connections for such an arrangement. The holding coil of the plugging contactor is connected at the midpoint of a circuit which consists of two small rectifiers and two resistors A and B. When the motor starts from rest, there is no countervoltage across the armature, and contactor $1A$ closes at once. When the motor is plugged, the countervoltage is high at the instant of plugging and causes current to flow through one of the rectifiers, holding out the plugging contactor. As the motor decelerates, the voltage decreases, finally becoming low enough to allow the plugging contactor to close at, or near, zero speed. The rectifiers are used to insure that the current in the holding coil will pass through zero.

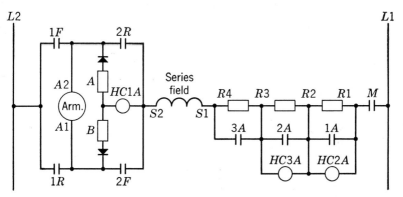

FIG. 54. Reversing Plugging Inductive Time-limit Controller.

General Electric Type MT Control. Figure 55 shows the connections for the General Electric Company's mill type, or MT, control, which is of the inductive time-limit type. In starting up from rest in the forward direction, the directional contactors close, and, through an interlock on the $1M$ contactor, the relay $TR2$-F is energized. This is a normally open relay, which closes immediately on the voltage drop across the armature and the resistor $R1$–$R2$. Closing of the relay provides a circuit for the plugging contactor $1A$, which closes immediately. This is the operation desired when starting up from rest. The relays $TR3$ and $TR4$ are small, normally closed relays similar to a series relay, except that they are provided with a core of a type which permits the flux to die down slowly. When the coil of the relay is short-circuited, the relay does not drop open immediately but delays for a short time. The time can be varied by changing the spring tension on the relay armature.

Referring again to the diagram, the coil of one of these relays, $TR3$, is connected across the first step of resistor, and the coil of the other relay, $TR4$, is connected across the first and second steps of resistor. After the plugging contactor $1A$ has closed in starting from rest, the coil of relay $TR3$ is short-circuited. A short time delay takes place, and then the relay armature opens, closing the contacts and permitting the contactor 2A to close. When contactor 2A closes, it short-circuits the coil of relay TR4, and after a time delay this relay closes its contacts, permitting contactor 3A to close. In this way the accelerating time is obtained. It will be noted that, if the controller is started

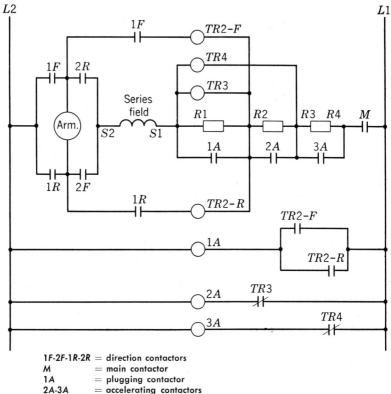

1F-2F-1R-2R = direction contactors
M   = main contactor
1A   = plugging contactor
2A-3A   = accelerating contactors
TR2-F   = forward plugging relay—normally open
TR2-B   = backward plugging relay—normally open
TR3-TR4   = accelerating relays—normally closed

FIG. 55.   Diagram of General Electric Type-MT Mill Controller.

from rest in the backward direction, the contactors 1R and 2R close, and plugging relay TR2-B is energized to bring in the contactor 1A, after which acceleration proceeds just as in the forward direction.

When the equipment is plugged, the voltage across the plugging relay, either TR2-F or TR2-B, is the algebraic sum of the counter-voltage across the armature and the voltage drop across the first step of resistor. On plugging, these voltages are opposed, and their difference is practically zero. The plugging relay does not pick up until the motor slows down to such a point that its countervoltage has dropped to practically zero. Then the algebraic sum of the two voltages mentioned is high enough to close the relay. In this way time is obtained on the first accelerator in plugging, but is not obtained when starting from rest.

Clark Contactor. Figure 56 shows the Clark Controller Company's delayed time contactor. With this control neither inductor nor any auxiliary relays are used, and the time is obtained by means of a special core in the accelerating contactor. The rest of the accelerating contactor is the same as the direction and line contactors. The sketch shows the construction of the core, which is a hollow cylinder containing a movable iron plunger. This plunger is held to the rear by means of a spring. The core is filled with a very light oil, and is soldered up so that it is completely air-tight. When voltage is applied to the coil of the contactor, the inner plug of the core is pulled to the front, against the action of a spring, so that a certain time is required for the core to move. When the plug reaches the front of the core, the reluctance of the main magnetic circuit is decreased, and there is then sufficient pull to close the armature of the contactor. The time may be adjusted by moving the armature of the contactor in or out to vary the magnetic gap.

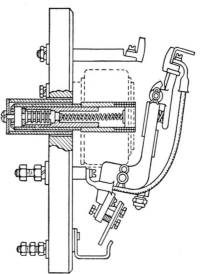

FIG. 56. Clark Delayed-time Contactor.

Combined Current and Time Limit. It is sometimes desirable to use a combined current- and time-limit acceleration, and so obtain the advantages of time-limit acceleration, but with a time that is short with a light load and long with a heavy one. For instance, a drive might be lightly loaded and normally require a short time to start, but might sometimes be required to start a very heavy load. One means of acceleration would be a motor-driven timer in combination with a current relay. The coil of the relay would be connected in the main motor circuit, so that the relay would open on high currents. The contacts of the relay would be connected in series with the pilot motor. Normally the timer would start up and accelerate the motor in the set time. However, if the load were unusually heavy, the relay would operate to stop the pilot motor until the main motor had a chance to accelerate and the current to fall to a safe value.

Electric Controller and Manufacturing Company's Time Relay. Figure 57 shows a relay used by the Electric Controller and Manufacturing Company in their current-time control. This equipment is similar to a series-relay controller in that the relays have series coils and are connected into circuit, in regard to both coils and contacts, exactly as if the controller were for straight current-limit control.

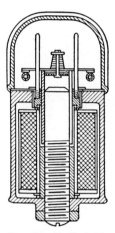

FIG. 57. E. C. & M. Time-current Relay.

There is a relay for each contactor, and each contactor is interlocked behind the previous contactor and through the series relay. However, the relays are different from straight current relays in that they will eventually close regardless of the load. The time for closing varies with the load.

Briefly, the construction of the relay is as follows:

There is an iron core through the center of the coil, and also an iron structure around the outside of the coil. A sleeve of ⅛-inch wall thickness extends about half way up the core inside the coil. Above this sleeve, which is permanently fastened in place, is a movable aluminum sleeve of the same wall thickness and approximately 2 inches long. The contacts of the relay are mounted on the aluminum sleeve. When current is applied to the coil of the relay, eddy currents are induced in the aluminum sleeve, and the flux produced by these eddy currents causes the aluminum sleeve to be repelled up out of the coil. If the steel core of the relay were long enough the aluminum sleeve would rise perhaps a couple of feet. However, since the steel core stops at the top of the coil, and since, as soon as the aluminum core goes past the end of the steel core, it begins to cut the main flux, which is crossing the gap between the steel core and the outside steel structure, the rise of the aluminum sleeve is stopped. The current in the main coil now becomes steady, or nearly steady, and the aluminum core begins to fall by gravity. As it falls, it again cuts the main flux of the coil and so sinks slowly into place. If the load is light, the flux is low, and the aluminum sleeve will fall rapidly. In this way the time required for the relay to close varies with the load, but the relay will always definitely close, even though the motor is stalled and does not accelerate.

Timing with Capacitors. It has long been known that timing could be obtained by allowing a capacitor to discharge through a contactor coil, but the principle has been widely applied only in recent years. One reason for this is the fact that the development of radio equipment, and of capacitor motors for refrigerators and other applications, resulted in the development of dry-type electrolytic capacitors suitable for motor-control work.

Fig. 58. Capacitor-timed Accelerating Relay.

The timing of a capacitor circuit is given by the equation:

$$T = KRC(\log E_1 - \log E_2)$$

where T = time in seconds.

K = a constant (0.00000230).

R = the circuit resistance in ohms.

C = the capacitance in microfarads.

E_1 = the initial voltage across the capacitor.

E_2 = the final voltage across the capacitor.

If logs are to the base e, $K = 1.0$. One method of timing with capacitors is to use a timing relay as shown in Fig. 58. This relay has a relatively large coil of high resistance, say, 20,000 ohms for 230 volts.

It has three independent armature members, which close when the relay is energized. One member has a fixed magnetic gap and operates normally open contacts. The other two members have independently adjustable magnetic gaps and operate normally closed contacts. Figure 59 shows the use of the relay for motor acceleration. In the off position of the controller, the capacitor is charged through the interlock

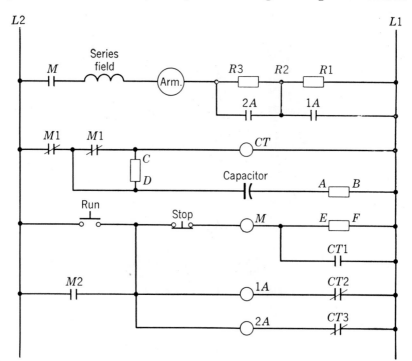

FIG. 59. Method of Timing Acceleration by Capacitor Discharge.

on M and the resistance $A–B$, which is a relatively low resistance, say 1000 ohms, to permit rapid charging of the capacitor. It is advisable to include such a resistor in series with the capacitor, partly to limit the surge through it, and also as a guard against short circuit if the capacitor should not be replaced before it deteriorates and fails, as it eventually will.

The timing relay CT is energized, closing contact $CT1$ and opening contacts $CT2$ and $CT3$. The resistor $E–F$ is high enough to prevent the closing of M, and so serves as an interlock to insure that CT is energized and closed, before M can be closed. When the run button is pressed, M closes, starting the motor and opening the circuit to CT by interlock $M1$. The capacitor then discharges through the coil of

CT, the resistance A–B, and the high resistance C–D, which might be 50,000 ohms for 230 volts. As it discharges, its voltage drops, and the pull of the coil CT is reduced. Contact $CT1$ opens, inserting resistance E–F, and then, after a few seconds, the armature member carrying contact $CT2$ drops open. This closes contact $CT2$ and energizes accel-

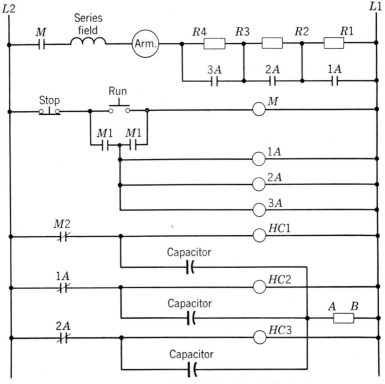

Fig. 60. Capacitor Timing of Double-coil Contactors.

erator $1A$. A few seconds later the armature member carrying contact $CT3$ drops open and accelerator $2A$ is energized.

A typical capacitor for this service will have a capacitance of about 25 microfarads. It should serve for a couple of years or longer, and it is inexpensive and easy to replace when it does wear out. Its timing will be constant, and, since it has no moving parts, it will not be affected by dust and dirt.

Larger controllers, having more than two accelerating contactors, require two timing relays with their associated condensors. The second relay would be operated by an interlock on contactor $2A$, just as the first relay is operated by the interlock $M1$.

Double-coil contactors, as used for inductive time-limit control, may also be timed by capacitors, as shown in Fig. 60. The circuit is similar to that of Fig. 52 except that the holdout coils are of high resistance and are connected across the line to hold the accelerating contactors open. The capacitors are charged in the off position of the controller. In starting, the interlock $M2$ opens the circuit to $HC1$, and the capacitor then discharges through that coil. When the condenser voltage has dropped low enough, the contactor closes, and an interlock on it opens the circuit to the next holdout coil. The timing may be adjusted by varying the magnetic gap of the holdout coil, just as for inductive time-limit acceleration. This method has largely replaced the separate inductor method of Fig. 53.

Calculation of Accelerating Time. For the method of calculating the time required to accelerate or decelerate a rotating body, see Chapter 15.

References

F. H. Winter, "Some New Uses of Capacitors in Control Circuits," *General Electric Review*, November, 1939.

C. Stansbury, "Capacitor Relay Timing in Industrial Control," *Electrical Engineering*, February, 1940, p. 65.

J. D. Burby, "Acceleration of Inertia Loads with a Varying Torque," *Product Engineering*, December, 1947.

E. J. Posselt, "Automatic Acceleration of D-c Motors," *Iron and Steel Engineer*, August, 1946.

R. B. Immel, "What Time-delay Starting for D-c Motors Involves," *Electrical Manufacturing*, December, 1943.

Problems

1. A 50-horsepower 230-volt 180-ampere motor has an armature resistance of 5 per cent of E/I. Plot a speed-torque curve similar to Fig. 42, for this motor, using four steps of resistance, equal inrushes on each step, and steps cut out at 100 per cent load.

2. What is the total resistance required (motor and controller) in per cent of E/I?

3. What is the resistance required in the controller, in ohms?

4. Calculate the ohms required in each step of the resistor.

5. Calculate the resistance of each step in per cent of E/I.

6. Using the values calculated in problem 5, determine the ohms required in each step of a resistor for a 15-horsepower 115-volt motor.

7. Using the curve prepared for problem 1, and the same resistances, determine the current inrushes which will be obtained on each step if current-limit starting is used, and the relays are set to cut out the steps when the current drops to 120 per cent of full load.

8. A capacitor having a capacitance of 100 microfarads is charged at 230 volts and then discharged across a resistor of 500 ohms. What is the time required to discharge to 20 volts?

9. Plot a speed-torque curve similar to Fig. 42, for a shunt motor, the starting peak currents being limited to a maximum of 130 per cent of full load current, and the contactors closing at 100 per cent of full load current. How many resistance steps are required?

10. Plot a speed-torque curve for a shunt motor driving a fan, assuming that the initial running torque required is 30 per cent of full rated torque and that the torque increases directly with the speed until it reaches 100 per cent at 95 per cent of full no-load speed. All accelerating peaks are to be 130 per cent of full-rated torque, and the contactors are to close when the torque is equal to the load torque required at the speed reached. How many resistance steps are required?

11. Draw an elementary diagram of a reversing controller for a shunt motor, including the following:

1 line contactor.
4 reversing contactors.
1 plugging contactor controlled by a series relay.
2 accelerating contactors controlled by mechanically operated timing relays.
Forward-reverse-stop pushbuttons.

12. Draw an elementary diagram of a non-reversing controller for a shunt motor, using three accelerating contactors, one a countervoltage contactor, one a lockout contactor, and one controlled by a series relay.

13. A controller having three resistor steps uses series-relay acceleration. If the adjustment of the second series relay is changed so that it closes at a higher current, what will be the effect on the inrush peak on each of the four starting points?

14. A controller having three resistor steps uses series-relay acceleration. If the resistor is changed so that there are more ohms in the first step and correspondingly less ohms in the second step, and the relay settings are unchanged, what will be the effect on the inrush peak on each of the four starting points?

15. Draw a speed-torque curve for a shunt motor driving a fan, assuming that the initial running torque required is 20 per cent of full-rated torque, and that the torque increases directly with the speed until it reaches 100 per cent at 95 per cent of full no-load speed. Each accelerating peak is to be 50 per cent more than the required running torque at that point, and the accelerating contactors are to close at 100 per cent of the torque required.

16. If the total resistance required for this controller is 2.5 ohms, determine from the curve how many ohms will be required in each resistor step.

17. A shunt motor equipped with a series-relay controller is driving a machine which has a flywheel. It is found that at certain points in the machine cycle the overload on the motor is too great, and it is desired to increase the flywheel effect. Will it help to

(a) Increase the ohms of the starting resistance?
(b) Set the series relays to close at a lower current?
(c) Connect a small amount of resistance permanently in series with the motor?
(d) Drop out the last accelerating contactor when the peaks occur?

18. A 250-horsepower motor has a full-load speed of 420 rpm, and a WR^2 of 900 lb-ft². Calculate the rated torque of the motor, and determine how long it will take to accelerate to full speed if it is provided with an electronic controller which will hold the accelerating torque constant at 150 per cent of rated torque (see Chapter 15).

19. If the motor of problem 18 is geared directly to a flywheel which is a solid cylinder having a diameter of 4 feet, and weighing 2000 pounds, how long will it take to accelerate?

20. If the speed of the flywheel is doubled by gearing it through a 2-to-1 gear train, how long will it take to accelerate the motor?

21. If the motor is provided with a contactor-type controller which allows an average accelerating torque of 25 per cent, how long will it take to accelerate under the conditions of problem 19?

22. Under the conditions of problem 19, how long will the accelerating period be if the 250-horsepower motor is replaced by two 125-horsepower motors, each having a WR^2 of 300 lb-ft²?

23. Under the conditions of problem 19, calculate the accelerating time if the speed of the flywheel is increased 30 per cent by the use of gearing, and the 250-horsepower motor is replaced by two 125-horsepower motors.

7

THE DIRECT-CURRENT SHUNT MOTOR

General Description. Direct-current motors are made in many forms, and with many types of windings, but they all fall into one of two general classes. When the main field winding is designed for connection in parallel with the armature, the machine is a shunt motor.

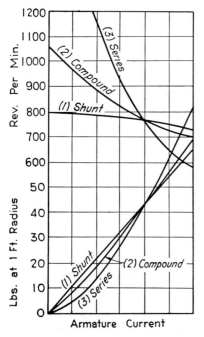

When the main field winding is designed for connection in series with the armature, the machine is a series motor.

The field of the shunt machine is not affected by changes in the armature current, and the motor speed is relatively constant with different loads.

The armature current of a series motor also passes through the field, and so the field strength, and the speed, will vary widely with the load.

Many motors are built with both shunt and series fields, and their characteristics may fall anywhere between those of the shunt machine and those of the series machine, depending upon the relative strength of the two fields. Figure 61 shows the general characteristics of shunt, series, and compound types.

FIG. 61. Speed-torque Characteristics of Direct-current Motors.

Motors having a predominating shunt field and a relatively light series field are called compound motors. The light series field is supplied to increase the starting torque and to cause the speed to drop off a little under heavy load. Compound motors are used for the same general purposes as shunt motors and are controlled in the same manner. They are treated in this chapter.

123

Motors having a predominating series field and a relatively light shunt field are called series-shunt motors. The light shunt field is supplied to prevent excessive speed under light load. Series-shunt motors are used for the same general purposes as series motors and are controlled in the same manner. They are treated in the chapter on series motors.

Shunt Motor Ratings. NEMA standard ratings for shunt motors are given in the tables below.

Standard horsepower ratings for constant-speed motors are as given in Table 9. Table 10 gives the minimum, or base, speeds.

TABLE 9

STANDARD HORSEPOWER RATINGS FOR DIRECT-CURRENT
INTEGRAL-HORSEPOWER MOTORS

1	7½	30	100
1½	10	40	125
2	15	50	150
3	20	60	200
5	25	75	

TABLE 10

STANDARD MINIMUM SPEEDS (RPM) FOR DIRECT-CURRENT
INTEGRAL-HORSEPOWER MOTORS

3500 *	575	300
1750	500	250
1150	450	200
850	400	150
690	350	100

* 3500 rpm is not standard for 1 horsepower.

Construction. A direct-current shunt motor has a stationary field member and a rotating armature member. The frame of the motor may be cast or fabricated steel, and to it are bolted steel pole members, around which the field coils are placed. The pole pieces are usually laminated to reduce the inductive effect and to make the field flux build up quickly when the field is energized. The main field coils are wound of insulated wire, either in a form or on a bobbin, and are mounted on the pole members. Figure 62 shows the general construction. It also shows a stabilizing winding, which is a light series field wound on the ends of the main pole pieces, next to the armature. The stabilizing winding is used on adjustable-speed motors, to insure stable operation when the main field is weakened. If it were not used, arma-

ture reaction at heavy loads might nullify the main field flux. Between
the main field poles are mounted commutating field poles, which are

Fig. 62. Stator of a Direct-current Shunt Motor. (Courtesy Reliance Electric &
Engineering Company)

wound with a bar or strap winding connected in series with the
armature; they are used to improve commutation by opposing the
armature reaction.

The armature is made up of laminations bolted together on a shaft,
and having slots parallel to the shaft, in which formed coils are placed.

A commutator is mounted on one end of the shaft, and the ends of the armature coils are connected to the bars of the commutator. Carbon brushes, mounted to the motor end frame, ride on the commutator bars, providing a means of connection to the armature coils.

The resistance of the shunt field is relatively high, since it is connected across the supply lines. The resistance is a matter of motor design, and the value must be obtained from the motor manufacturer.

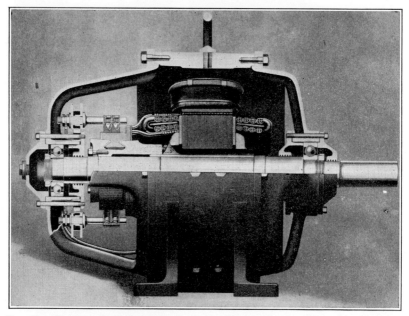

Fig. 63.   Construction of a Direct-current Shunt Motor.   (Courtesy Reliance Electric & Engineering Company)

Motor Torque.   The motor field winding sets up a magnetic field, in which the armature is located.   The armature windings and brushes are so arranged that, when the armature is energized, it becomes a magnet with its poles offset enough from the field poles to cause maximum attraction between field and armature, and so provide maximum turning torque.   As soon as the armature starts to turn, the connections are changed through the commutator, so that the magnetic poles of the armature are set back enough to compensate for the movement of the armature.   In other words, the commutator serves to change continually the portion of the armature winding which is energized, and to keep the north and south magnetic poles of the armature in a fixed position relative to the field poles.   The armature therefore has a practically constant turning torque, which is proportional to the magnetic strength of the field and that of the armature. For any direct-current motor, then,

$$T = I_a F \qquad [1]$$

T is the torque in percentage of full rated torque, where F is the field strength or magnetic flux in percentage of normal.
I_a is the armature current in percentage of full rated current, I_n.

In this equation it is permissible to use the armature current as a measure of the armature magnetic pull, because the armature winding is a relatively low-resistance low-inductance circuit, and the magnetic field produced by it is directly proportional to the armature current. This is not true of the field circuit, which is a highly inductive circuit, and in which the magnetic field is not directly proportional to the field current. It is therefore necessary to use the field magnetic strength F in calculations, and to determine the field current required to produce F from a curve of field current versus field strength which is called a field saturation curve. For accurate work a curve of the actual motor in question should be used, but for most work a typical curve is sufficiently accurate. Such a curve is shown in Fig. 82.

Motor Speed. When a motor armature is first energized, the only factor limiting the current is the ohmic resistance of the armature. As soon as the armature begins to turn, its conductors start cutting through the magnetic field produced by the field winding, and by so doing generate in the armature conductors a voltage opposite in direction to the applied line voltage. This countervoltage is proportional to the speed S of the armature and to the strength of the field, or, if we work with the values in per cent of their normal or full rated values,

$$E_a = KSF \qquad [2]$$

K is a constant. The voltage which forces current through the armature is the difference between line voltage E and countervoltage E_a. Therefore, as the motor speed increases and the countervoltage rises, the armature current drops, and, as it drops, the motor torque drops with it. The final speed of the motor can never quite reach the speed required to generate line voltage, because there would then be no armature current and no torque.

The final speed reached will be just enough below that value so that the difference between line voltage and countervoltage will send enough current through the armature to provide the torque necessary to turn the armature. This torque will depend on the load on the motor. The voltage $(E - E_a)$, which forces the current through the armature against the motor resistance, is, by Ohm's law, equal to $I_a R_m$, and, therefore,

$$E - E_a = I_a R_m \qquad [3]$$

or

$$E_a = E - I_a R_m$$

but

$$E_a = KSF \qquad [2]$$

and, by substitution,

$$S = \frac{E - I_a R_m}{KF} \qquad [4]$$

All of these values are in percentage of normal. To determine the constant K, assume that $I_a = I_n$ or full load. Then, by definition, S and F become 1.0, and

$$K = E - I_n R_m$$

Then,

$$S = \frac{E - I_a R_m}{F(E - I_n R_m)} \qquad [5]$$

To determine the speed when there is external resistance in series with the armature, let R = the total resistance of the motor and external resistor. Then,

$$S = \frac{E - I_a R}{F(E - I_n R_m)} \qquad [6]$$

With equations 1 and 5 for the torque and speed, respectively, the procedures necessary to control the motor may be determined.

Starting. Inspection of equation 5 will show that the speed will vary with the motor voltage drop $I_a R_m$, and therefore it is necessary to make the armature resistance low to prevent wide speed changes with changes in load. A high motor resistance would also result in too high a resistance heat loss in the motor. If a motor having a resistance of $0.05E/I$ were connected directly to a supply line, the resulting inrush current would be 20 times the normal full-load motor current. The resulting torque would be 20 times normal, and the initial heating of the motor would be at the rate of 400 times normal. Probably neither motor, driven machine, nor power line would stand this punishment. The voltage across the motor must be reduced in some way, and the simplest and commonest way is by connecting a resistor in series with the armature. The resistor must allow more than full-load current to flow, so that there will be some excess current to accelerate the load. With large motors a usual value is 150 per cent of normal, and with small motors as much as 300 per cent may be allowed.

The ohms required may be determined by Ohm's law, from the equation

$$R = \frac{E}{I_s} \qquad [7]$$

where R = the total ohms required in circuit.
E = line voltage.
I_s = desired starting current in amperes.

From this total the motor resistance may be subtracted, but, since this resistance is so low as to be negligible, R is commonly considered the value required in the controller.

Acceleration. When the motor starts to turn, it will accelerate in speed as long as its torque is greater than that required by the load. As the motor accelerates, its countervoltage rises, and its armature current drops, with a corresponding drop in torque. It is then necessary to reduce the resistance, as the motor speed increases, by cutting out, or short-circuiting, a step at a time, until finally all the resistance is out of circuit. The acceleration process is described in detail in Chapter 6.

A graphical method of designing the resistor for acceleration is shown in Fig. 64. Since the countervoltage developed is proportional to the speed, the ordinates represent both percentage of speed and percentage of countervoltage. The base line is percentage of full-load current. Assuming that 175 per cent inrush is allowable, the total resistance, including motor and line, will be

$$R = \frac{E}{1.75I}$$

The point a represents the first inrush, and the motor will accelerate along a line drawn from a to 100, but if fully loaded will not accelerate beyond point b, as full torque requires 100 per cent current. Therefore, at b a step of resistance must be cut out. Point c is selected to give an inrush equal to a, and a line is drawn from c to 100. This procedure is followed until a point is reached at which a line drawn to 100 will fall either directly on point h or very close to it.

The line gh represents the motor characteristic curve, and the line kh is the drop in speed between no load and full load, due to the resistance drop in the armature and leads. The point h then represents the maximum speed to which the motor will accelerate under full load. It is only necessary to provide resistance to accelerate the motor to that point. If the last curve falls directly on point h, the design is correct, and with three steps the desired inrushes will be obtained.

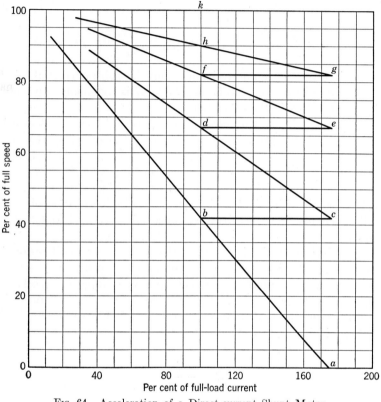

Fig. 64. Acceleration of a Direct-current Shunt Motor.

If it falls between k and h, the inrushes may be reduced slightly. If it falls between f and h, the inrushes must be increased, or, if this is not permissible, another step will be necessary. In that event the inrushes would be reduced until the final accelerating curve passed through point h.

Each of the curves ab, cd, and ef represents a characteristic curve of the motor with a certain amount of resistance in series. gh is the curve of the motor alone plus line resistance, ab is the curve with all resistance in series, cd the curve with one step cut out, and ef the curve with two steps cut out. The line gh represents the voltage drop across the motor at full load. Similarly bd is the drop across the first step of resistance, df that of the second step, and fh that of the third step. The ohms required are then

$$\text{First step} \quad = \frac{bd}{bk} \times \frac{E}{1.75I}$$

$$\text{Second step} = \frac{df}{bk} \times \frac{E}{1.75I}$$

$$\text{Third step} \quad = \frac{fh}{bk} \times \frac{E}{1.75I}$$

Under full load the motor will run at speed b with all resistance in circuit, at point d with one step cut out, at point f with two steps out, and at point h with all resistance out. If the load varies, the speed will vary also, always falling on one of the curves.

To design a resistance graphically in the manner described, it is necessary to know or to assume the motor resistance. The base current, or point at which the resistance steps are cut out, will be known. Then, if the inrush is known, the number of steps can be found, or, if the steps are known, the inrush can be found, and in either event the taper of the resistance steps can be determined.

The following example will illustrate a non-graphical method of calculating an accelerating resistor:

Assume a 50-horsepower 230-volt motor having a full-load current of 180 amperes, and assume that it is desired to limit the starting inrushes to 175 per cent of full-load current, or 315 amperes. The resistance steps are to be cut out when the inrush current has dropped to normal. The resistance of the motor and the leads to it may be assumed to be approximately 11 per cent of E/I, or

$$\text{Motor resistance} = \frac{0.11 \times 230}{180} = 0.14 \text{ ohm}$$

The total resistance including the motor is

$$R = \frac{230}{315} = 0.73 \text{ ohm}$$

When the circuit is closed, an inrush of 315 amperes occurs and the motor starts to accelerate. As it accelerates, it generates a countervoltage, so that the voltage across the resistance and the current from the line decrease. When the current has dropped to normal full-load value, the voltage across the resistance is

$$E_2 = 0.73 \times 180 = 131 \text{ volts}$$

At this point the first step of resistance is cut out, and the remaining resistance, to give a second inrush equal to the first, is

$$R_a = \frac{131}{315} = 0.418 \text{ ohm}$$

Further acceleration of the motor causes the current to drop to normal again, when

$$E_3 = 0.418 \times 180 = 75 \text{ volts}$$

Proceeding in the same manner, the rest of the calculation is carried through.

$$R_b = \frac{75}{315} = 0.238 \text{ ohm}$$

$$E_4 = 0.238 \times 180 = 42.8 \text{ volts}$$

$$R_c = \frac{42.8}{315} = 0.136 \text{ ohm}$$

This value is practically that of the motor resistance. The controller resistance steps may now be calculated:

$R_1 = R - R_a = 0.73 - 0.418 = 0.312$ ohm or 53 per cent of the total

$R_2 = R_a - R_b = 0.418 - 0.238 = 0.180$ ohm or 30 per cent of the total

$R_3 = R_b - R_c = 0.238 - 0.136 = 0.102$ ohm or 17 per cent of the total

Allowance for motor and leads = 0.136 ohm

Total = 0.730 ohm

Three steps of resistance are therefore necessary. If lower inrush peaks are desired, or if the steps are cut out at a current higher than normal, more steps will be required. In other words, the number of steps is inversely proportional to the ratio of the peak value and the base value.

In this discussion the acceleration curves of the motor have been assumed to be straight lines. Actually they follow the shape of the motor characteristic curve, and bend slightly, so that the current peaks obtained in practice will not be quite so high as those calculated above. The taper which has been determined in the example will be correct for any resistor of three steps having inrush peaks of 175 per cent and base currents of 100 per cent. That is, the total ohms required having been calculated, the first step will be 53 per cent of the total, the second

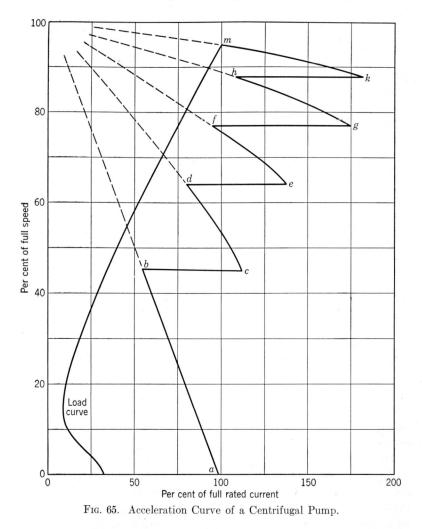

Fig. 65. Acceleration Curve of a Centrifugal Pump.

step 30 per cent, and the last step 17 per cent, regardless of the horse-power of the motor.

Taper tables may be worked out for any number of steps and for different values of inrush and base currents. The base current will generally be 100 per cent for time-limit controllers, and 110 or 120 per cent for current-limit controllers. The relays of current-limit controllers must be set to close above full-load current, to insure that the motor will have torque enough to accelerate. The starting torque required by some machines is higher than normal, and the inrush and base currents must then be high enough to allow the necessary torque. If the starting torque is low, as in a fan or a centrifugal pump, it is advantageous to reduce the inrushes, applying only as much torque as is necessary. This will give a smoother acceleration and will not apply so severe a shock to the machine. Also it will reduce the power required for starting and will generally result in some saving in resistance material.

Figure 65 illustrates the acceleration of a motor driving a centrifugal pump. The load curve shows the torque required to drive the pump at any speed. At low speed the pump is not delivering much water, and the torque is low. As the speed increases, the torque increases also, until full torque is reached at full speed. The rise in the load curve at zero speed is caused by the addition of the torque required to overcome friction at starting. Obviously the application of 150 per cent torque to this drive would be excessive and unnecessary. The acceleration curves have been laid out graphically to give increasing torque as the speed and load increase, and the base currents have been selected safely above the value required to insure acceleration. Since the average current carried by the resistor is less than it would be if the base currents were at normal or above, less resistance material will be required.

Reversing. Equation 1, for torque, shows that the motor may be reversed by reversing either the armature or the field but not both. It is customary to reverse the armature because the high inductance of the field windings makes them relatively hard to open and slow in response. Motors are often plugged for quick reversal, which means opening the armature circuit and immediately reconnecting it in the reverse direction before the motor has stopped.

Plugging. When a motor is plugged, or connected to the line in the reverse direction while still running full speed in the forward direction, the countervoltage of the armature is added to that of the line in forcing current through the armature and series resistance. The series resistance must be increased to limit the current to the same value obtained in starting from rest. This requires an additional step of resistance and a contactor to short-circuit it just before the motor reaches zero speed and reverses. The total resistance is

$$R_t = \frac{E + (E - I_a R_m)}{\text{Inrush current}}$$

A convenient formula for general use is

$$R_t = \frac{1.8E}{1.5I} = \frac{1.2E}{I}$$

where E = line voltage and I = normal current.

The plugging step is determined by subtracting the value of the accelerating resistance from R_t.

If the motor has speed regulation by field weakening, and the control is arranged to strengthen the field during acceleration, the counter-voltage will be increased in proportion to the field strength. For instance, for a 2-to-1 motor,

$$R_t = \frac{2.7E}{1.5I}$$

and for a 3-to-1 motor,

$$R_t = \frac{3.6E}{I}$$

However, it is usually not essential to plug motors having speed control by field, and such controls may be arranged to prevent plugging. Some motors, particularly those for high-speed metal planers, are designed to stand plugging at weakened field.

Shunt Motor. Dynamic Braking. The purpose of dynamic braking (Fig. 66) is to obtain a quick stop. The armature is disconnected from

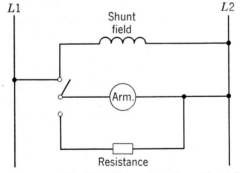

Fig. 66. Dynamic Braking Connections for a Shunt Motor.

the line, and a step of resistance is connected across it. The field remains on the line. Since the motor is turning, it acts as a generator and forces current around the loop formed by the armature and the braking resistance. At the start of the braking period the armature voltage is $E - I_aR_m$, and the ohmic value of the braking resistance is

$$R = \frac{E - I_aR_m}{I}$$

The value of I is dependent on the severity of the braking desired. It is usually set at 150 per cent of normal current, but, where very quick stopping is desired, the current may be allowed to go as high as 300 per cent of normal. As the motor slows down, the generated voltage falls, and consequently the braking current and braking effect are reduced. At zero speed there is no braking effect, and the final stopping of the motor is due to friction. For very quick stopping the braking resistance is sometimes cut out in two or more steps as the voltage falls, thus keeping the current high. It is not unusual to stop a large machine in 1 second or less.

Shunt motors having speed regulation by field control will commutate heavy braking currents better if the field is at full strength. It is customary to provide means to strengthen the field during the braking period by short-circuiting all or a part of the field rheostat. If this is done, the braking resistance must be increased to compensate for the increased countervoltage of the motor. For a motor having 2-to-1 speed increase by field, the resistance would be doubled. In any event

$$R = \frac{E - I_aR_m}{I} \times \text{Speed range by field}$$

Speed Regulation below Normal. Equation 4 will show that the speed of a shunt motor may be reduced below normal by reducing the voltage across the armature or by increasing the strength of the shunt field. Since the field is already across the line, there is no practical way to increase its strength. The voltage to the armature may be reduced by reducing the voltage of the generator supplying it, but the use of resistance in series with the armature to obtain speeds below normal is wide spread because of the simplicity of the method:

Let E = line voltage.

R_m = motor resistance.

R = controller resistance.

I = current.

S_n = normal speed.

S = reduced speed.

E_n = countervoltage at normal speed.

E_a = countervoltage at reduced speed.

Then,

$$E_n = E - IR_m$$

$$E_a = E - (IR_m + IR)$$

Since the shunt field strength is constant, the speed is proportional to the countervoltage, and

$$\frac{S}{S_n} = \frac{E_a}{E_n} = \frac{E - IR_m - IR}{E - IR_m}$$

$$\frac{S}{S_n}(E - IR_m) = E - IR_m - IR$$

$$IR = E - IR_m - (E - IR_m)\frac{S}{S_n}$$

$$IR = (E - IR_m)\left(1 - \frac{S}{S_n}\right)$$

Since S/S_n is the reduced speed in percentage of normal speed, $1 - S/S_n$ is the percentage speed reduction, and

$$R = \frac{(E - IR_m) \times \text{Per cent reduction}}{I} \qquad [8]$$

R_m may be assumed to be approximately $0.05E/I$. The current I is not the full-load rated current of the motor but the actual current taken by the motor when running at reduced speed. The load characteristics of most machines will fall into one of two classes, either machine-type or fan-type load. Experience shows that with a machine-

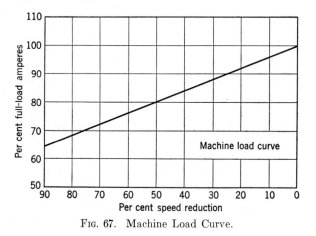

Fig. 67. Machine Load Curve.

type load the current follows approximately the curve of Fig. 67, being 80 per cent at 50 per cent speed, and 65 per cent at zero speed. The machine takes less power to drive it at reduced speeds, because of the reduction in friction and windage losses. With a fan-type load, the power required to drive the load varies as the cube of the speed. In addition, the friction varies with the speed. The resultant curve

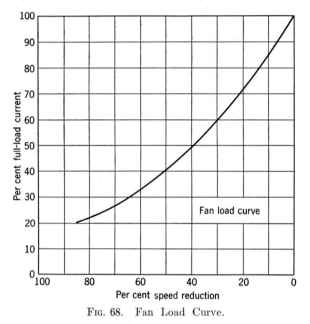

FIG. 68.   Fan Load Curve.

of current versus speed is shown in Fig. 68. The two curves of fan and machine load characteristics will be applicable to the majority of installations, and the results obtained by employing them will be sufficiently accurate. Of course, if information about the actual load is available, calculations should be based on that load, and, if accuracy is essential, data on the load should be obtained. There are two disadvantages in the use of series resistance for speed reduction, both of which grow more serious as the speed reduction is increased. The first is the fact that, if the load is variable, the speed will vary with it, and the second is the fact that considerable power is wasted in the resistor. From equation 8,

$$\text{Per cent reduction} = \frac{IR}{E - IR_m}$$

Since IR_m is so small as to be practically negligible, the speed reduction varies almost directly with the load current. Reference to the curve of Fig. 64 will show that this variation will not be serious with a small speed reduction but may be quite serious with a large one. If sufficient resistance is in circuit to give a small reduction at full load, so that the motor will run on curve *ef*, a 20 per cent increase in load will cause a speed change from 81 to 77, or 5 per cent. With a higher resistance and a greater reduction at full load, the motor will run on curve *cd*, and a 20 per cent increase in load will cause a speed change from 67 to 60, or 11.5 per cent. With still higher resistance, and the motor running on curve *ab*, a 20 per cent increase in load would cause a speed change from 43 to 31, or 28 per cent.

Because of this variation of speed with load, regulation by series resistance is usually limited to 50 per cent speed reduction.

If the motor resistance is neglected, the speed reduction is proportional to the voltage drop across the controller resistor. At 50 per

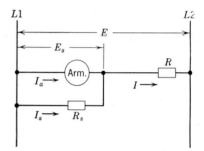

Fig. 69. Armature-shunt Connections for a Shunt Motor.

cent reduction the voltage across the resistor is approximately equal to that across the motor, and, since the current is the same in both, the power lost in the resistor is equal to the power used by the motor. At 75 per cent reduction the power loss in the resistor is three times the power taken by the motor. This method of speed regulation is, therefore, very inefficient. It should be used where the required reduction is 50 per cent, or preferably less, and where the slow speed is infrequently used.

Armature Shunt Resistance. Variation of speed with changes in load may be reduced by means of an armature shunting resistor. The resistor is connected in parallel with the armature, and its purpose is to increase the current flowing through the series resistor. If the current flowing through the shunt is high in proportion to that in the armature, changes in the armature current will have relatively little effect on the current in the series resistance. Consequently, the voltage across the series resistor will not change very much with changes in load, and the speed will remain more nearly constant. The armature shunt method is of particular value for speed reductions greater than 50 per cent and may be safely used to obtain reductions up to 90 per cent without danger of stalling. The method, however, is even more wasteful of energy than the straight series-resistance method.

When designing an armature shunt resistance, the series resistance must be known. The other known factors are the desired speed reduction and the load at the reduced speed. Referring to Fig. 69,

E = line voltage.

I_a = the armature current required to drive the load. If the load is unknown, use the ampere rating of the motor.

R = the series resistance. This usually will be the accelerating resistance but sometimes will be determined by the load at the speed required.

R_a = the resistance of the armature. For speeds above 20 per cent of normal speed, and for motors larger than 200 horsepower, this may be assumed to be zero. In other cases average values are:

$$5 \text{ hp } R_a = 0.10E/I$$

$$50 \text{ hp } R_a = 0.05E/I$$

$$200 \text{ hp } R_a = 0.04E/I$$

E_a = the countervoltage of the armature at the desired speed. For constant field strength the countervoltage is directly proportional to the speed.

$$\text{Full speed countervoltage} = E - I_a R_a$$

The desired speed being known,

$$E_a = \frac{\text{Desired speed}}{\text{Normal speed}} \times (E - I_a R_a)$$

E_s = the voltage across the armature (and the armature shunt resistance). This is the sum of the countervoltage and the resistance drop in the armature.

$$E_s = E_a + I_a R_a$$

I = the current in the series resistance.

$$I = \frac{E - E_s}{R}$$

I_s = the current in the shunt.

$$I_s = I - I_a$$

R_s = the resistance of the shunt.

$$R_s = \frac{E_s}{I_s}$$

The current-carrying capacity of this resistor is easily determined, as the current is practically constant at the calculated value I_s.

Speed Regulation above Normal. Equation 4 shows that speeds above normal may be obtained by increasing the armature voltage, which is impracticable, or by weakening the strength of the field. The field is readily weakened by connecting resistors or rheostats in the field circuit. Most standard motors will permit a speed increase of 10 to 25 per cent by field weakening, but for anything beyond that range a specially designed motor is required. A range of about 6 to 1 by field weakening is considered to be about the upper limit. This method of speed control is efficient, because the power lost in the field rheostat is negligible. The speed at any given field current is practically constant for all loads.

Wide Speed Ranges. Where extremely wide speed ranges are required, they may be obtained by a combination of speeds below and above normal. The normal speed might, for instance, be reduced to 20 per cent by a combination of series and shunt resistance, and increased to 4 times normal by field weakening. The whole range would then be 20 to 1. Adjustable voltage is often combined with speed increase by field weakening to give a wide speed range.

Overhauling Loads. As the load on a motor decreases, the speed increases, until, at zero load, there is no current in the armature, and the countervoltage is equal to the line voltage. If the load is negative, or overhauling, the countervoltage will be higher than the line voltage, and the motor will return power to the line. When the load is positive,

$$\text{Countervoltage} + \text{Resistance drop} = \text{Line voltage}$$

When the load is negative,

$$\text{Countervoltage} - \text{Resistance drop} = \text{Line voltage}$$

The increase in speed of a shunt motor, when the load is overhauling, is not very great, as the resistance drop is usually not more than 10 per cent. However, if external resistance is inserted in the armature circuit, the speed will increase instead of decreasing.

Special Adjustable-speed Motors. There are two types of direct-current motors whose speed can be adjusted by varying the reluctance of the field circuit instead of by changing the field current. In one construction the armature and the field poles are slightly tapered, and the armature is shifted along the axis of the shaft by means of a hand wheel. By thus shifting the armature, the air gap between the armature and the field poles is changed. With a small air gap the flux is greater and the motor speed is lower; and with a large air gap the speed is higher.

The other motor of this type has hollow field poles with movable plungers, and the reluctance is varied by moving the plungers in and out. Comparatively few motors of this type are used.

Multivoltage Control. Motors are sometimes controlled by varying the supply voltage to the armature, instead of having resistance in series with the armature. The advantage of this method is, of course, that less power is wasted on the low speeds. The use of two voltages is quite common, and some installations have been made with a number of different voltages. However, more than two voltages are infrequent because such voltages are not usually available except in laboratories. Controllers of this type may be constructed with armature and field resistance control in addition to the multivoltage control, and the combination will give a very wide range of speed variation.

Adjustable-voltage Control. Adjustable-voltage control is a combination of multivoltage control and field control. A motor-generator set is required in addition to the driving motor, and the first cost of the equipment is therefore high. Speed is controlled by varying the generator field to obtain low voltages on the armature of the motor, and by varying the motor field to obtain speeds above normal speed by field weakening. The advantages of the arrangement are that the power losses in the resistor are practically negligible and that it is possible to obtain wide variations in speed and very finely graduated increments. Adjustable-voltage controllers are discussed in detail in Chapter 9.

Motor Protection. In addition to its principal function of controlling a motor, a controller usually includes devices to protect the motor and its driven machine. Protection against overload is included as a part of most controllers. Thermal overload relays are used to some extent for direct-current motors, but a more common practice is to use a magnetic relay which has a time-delay action on ordinary overloads but will trip out instantaneously if the motor stalls. The instantaneous trip feature is desirable because the stalled motor current may be as high as 20 to 40 times normal, and the motor might be burned out before a thermal relay would trip.

Shunt motors are often protected against loss of field, and against too rapid acceleration or deceleration, by field control. The methods are described in Chapter 8.

Manually Operated Controllers. Manually operated controllers for shunt motors are made in three principal forms: face-plate controllers, multiple-switch controllers, and drum controllers.

Face-plate Type. Figure 70 shows a typical face-plate-type controller, and Fig. 71 is a diagram of it. Connection is made from one side of the line to a lever, which carries a contact brush, or shoe. The brush rides on a series of stationary contact buttons to which resistance is connected. When the lever is moved to the first button, the circuit is closed, and, as the lever is moved on across the buttons, the resistance is gradually short-circuited. The last contact is connected directly to

Fig. 70. Westinghouse Direct-current Face-plate Starter.

the motor. The lever is provided with a spring which will return it to the off position if it is released at any time during the starting period. When the lever has reached the final contact button, it engages a pivoted armature, or keeper, which closes the magnetic circuit of a small magnet. The magnet holds the lever in the on position as long as there is voltage on the line. In the event of voltage failure, the lever is released and returns to the off position. This avoids the danger of connecting the motor directly to the line when power returns.

When it is used with shunt motors, the common practice is to connect the release coil in series with the shunt field, so that any failure of the field circuit will release the lever and stop the motor. The shunt field is energized on the first contact button, insuring full field from the moment of starting, and a connection is also made from the first button to the frame of the release magnet so that the starting resistance will not remain in the field circuit when the motor is running. The use of the release coil in series with the field requires that the coil be selected to suit the current of the motor with which it is to be used. Usually, when these release magnets overheat or fail to hold properly, the trouble is that the field current is not what it was expected to be. The release coil may be connected directly across the line if desired. With small series motors, the coil is connected in series with the line, but above 10 amperes a shunt coil connected across the line is used.

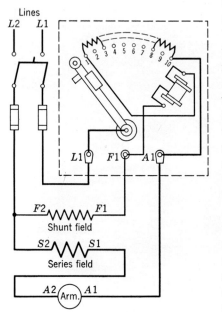

FIG. 71.   Diagram of a Direct-current Face-plate Starter.

Several types of contact buttons are used. The cheapest, made from brass rod, is simply a headed stud, the head being the contact and the shank passing through the slate to permit the resistor connection. The renewable contact is a better construction. It consists of a stud to which the head is threaded. The head is hexagonal, and the contact is an hexagonal cap attached to the head. This type of button may be renewed when worn, without disturbing the stud or the wiring to it. Button contacts are used up to 40 amperes. Above that rating segment contacts are used. These are copper segments, held in place by a screw at each end. The screws fasten to shouldered studs through the panel, so that the segments are raised from the slate. The segments may easily be removed for replacement without disturbing the rest of the panel. Segments are made in various sizes and are generally employed up to 50 horsepower.

When buttons are used, the last one, which carries the current continuously, is made larger than the others. In the larger controllers with segments, the additional capacity at the continuous-duty point is obtained by means of a laminated bridging brush, which makes contact on two posts. One of these posts is connected to the bearing point of the lever, or hub post, and the other to the last segment. The running current, then, does not flow through the lever and sliding brush.

The operating lever may be cast steel, but more frequently it is of drawn steel. The shoe is of brass and is backed up by springs so that it is always under pressure. Follow-up, or wear allowance, is provided, and the shoes are also renewable when worn out.

Most of the present-day face-plate controllers are enclosed and arranged for operation by a lever on the outside of the case. The lever has a bearing in the door of the case, and half of a coupling is mounted on the inside end of the lever shaft. The other half of the coupling is mounted on the lever of the controller. The coupling halves are provided with pins and corresponding holes, so that the door can be closed only when the inside and outside levers are in the proper relation to each other. The enclosure is usually dust-proof in front and ventilated in the rear where the resistor is mounted. Dust-tight or water-tight enclosure may be obtained.

The resistance material for face-plate starters may be cast-iron grids, in the larger sizes, or some form of wire-wound unit for the smaller sizes. The resistance is usually designed to allow the maximum inrush that the motor and fuses will stand and still have the fuses protect the motor properly. This varies from 200 per cent inrush with motors of fractional horsepower down to 150 per cent with motors of 5 horsepower and larger. The number of steps can be determined from the inrush value selected. However, more steps are required for a manually operated controller to keep down arcing on the contacts and also as a safeguard against too rapid operation of the lever. The operator is sometimes provided with an ammeter which he can use as a guide in starting, but generally he must simply depend on his judgment. The capacity of the resistor depends on the service requirement. For plain starting, NEMA class 115 is used, and for heavy-starting duty class 135. For speed regulation the resistance must have capacity for full-load current continuously.

Overload protection is built into some types of face-plate starters. The overload relay has a series coil connected in the line circuit, and so carrying motor current. If the current becomes excessive, a plunger is pulled up to open an electric contact. This contact opens the circuit to the release magnet and allows the lever to return to the starting position. These starters are also built with a self-contained knife switch and fuses, the knife switch being operable from the outside of the enclosure. They are also built with the addition of a circuit breaker. Some types may be obtained with a magnetic main line contactor for remote control. Direct-current face-plate controllers are built in four types:

1. Plain starting by armature resistor.
2. Starting by armature resistor, regulating by field resistor.
3. Plain regulating by armature resistor.
4. Regulating by armature and field resistor.

The starter of Fig. 70, which has been described, is typical of the first class. It is built up to 30 horsepower for 115 volts, and 50 horsepower for 230 and 550 volts. Seven steps of resistance are used through 1 horsepower, 8 steps through 5 horsepower, 10 steps through 20 horsepower, and 13 steps above 20 horsepower.

Starters of the second type combine the functions of starting by armature resistor and speed regulating by resistance in the field circuit. A compound lever is used. The mechanism consists of two contact-carrying arms mounted on the same hub post. The shorter lever carries a brush, which makes contact on the buttons to which the armature resistor is connected. The longer lever makes contact on a row of buttons mounted outside of the first row and connected to a resistor in the field. The operating handle is attached to the field control lever, and movement of this lever in a clockwise direction carries the starting lever up to the normal speed position, where it engages the low-voltage protective magnet. At this point all armature resistor is cut out and the shunt field is at full strength. To increase the speed, the operating lever is moved back, in a counterclockwise direction. The armature lever remains in the full on position, held by the magnet, and the field lever moves back to insert the field resistor.

Figure 72 is a diagram of the starter. Full voltage on the shunt field during the starting period is provided by means of a small auxiliary switch, adjacent to the hub post, which serves to short-circuit the field-regulating resistance until the levers reach the normal speed position. At this point the switch opens, but full field is still provided by a circuit through the field lever. As the lever is moved back, the switch remains open, and the resistance is gradually cut into the field circuit.

The low-voltage magnet coil is connected across the line, as the variation in field current between normal speed and maximum speed is generally too great to permit connecting the coil in the field circuit.

The starting resistor is designed on the same basis as that for a plain starting controller.

The starter is built in ratings up to 20 horsepower for 115 volts, and 35 horsepower for 230 volts, and for a speed range up to 4 to 1 by field control.

The third class of direct-current face-plate starters is that used for speed regulation below normal speed, by the insertion of resistance in the armature circuit. The controllers for this purpose are very similar to those for plain starting, except that all the buttons or segments must be large enough to carry the full-load current continuously. Another difference is in the arrangement of the low-voltage magnet, which must hold the lever on any point. To accomplish this, the lever is provided with a pawl, or star wheel, and the magnet armature operates to latch the lever wherever it may be placed. The coil is generally in series with the motor field but may be connected across the line.

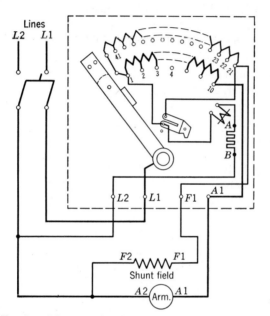

Fig. 72. Diagram of a Compound Face-plate Starter.

The speed of the motor is, within commercial accuracy, proportional to the voltage impressed on the armature. This voltage is the difference between line voltage and the voltage drop in the controller resistance. The drop in the resistance depends upon the value of the motor current. Speed regulation by armature resistor is, therefore, not satisfactory where the load is variable. Where the load is constant, the value of the load should be known and the regulator selected to suit it, as otherwise the desired speed reduction will not be obtained.

The characteristic of the load is usually expressed as "machine" duty or "fan" duty. Machine duty is that in which the torque is practically constant throughout the speed range, and the armature current is also practically constant. There is some reduction in torque at the lower speeds, owing to lower friction losses in the machine, and the current is usually considered to be 80 per cent at 50 per cent speed. Fan duty is that in which the torque varies with the square of the speed, as it does in fans and centrifugal pumps. Theoretically the torque varies with the cube of the speed, but, when the friction losses are taken into account, the armature current will be found to vary approximately as the square of the speed. With this type of load the current at 50 per cent speed is approximately 40 per cent of normal current.

The regulating resistance is tapered to give an equal change in speed on each step, although it is sometimes necessary to modify the taper to avoid detrimental arcing at the contacts when a step of resistance is inserted into the circuit. The practical limit of speed reduction by armature resistor is 50 per cent of normal speed, although a greater reduction is sometimes used. Ratings are 10 horsepower, 115 volts, and 20 horsepower, 230 volts.

The fourth type of direct-current face-plate controller is that combining speed regulation below normal speed by means of resistance in the armature, and regulation above normal speed by means of resistance in the field circuit. These controllers are made in two styles, one having a relatively small number of field-regulating steps and the other a large number. The first style is used with standard constant-speed motors of liberal design, which will generally stand an increase in speed of 25 per cent by field weakening. About five steps are provided up to 15 horsepower, and eight steps for larger motors. The majority of compound regulators are made this way. Where a wide range of speed by field is required, the number of steps must be larger, and a regulator built for such service would have as many field steps as a controller of the second class described.

Multiple-switch Starter. The multiple-switch controller is used where the current to be commutated is beyond the capacity of the face-plate type of controller. This mechanism consists of a number of individual toggle-operated levers. Each lever carries a laminated brush contact which bridges across two copper contact blocks mounted on the slate. A resistance step connected across these contact blocks is short-circuited when the lever closes. The lever also carries an auxiliary tip which closes before the main brush closes and opens after the brush opens. The auxiliary tip makes contact with a carbon block contact and serves to prevent arcing on the laminated brush. The levers are mechanically interlocked so that they can be closed only in the proper order, and, since each lever must be held in until the succeeding lever is closed, it is necessary to use two hands in operating the controller. The necessity of closing the levers hand over hand is desirable, as it introduces a time element which prevents the operator

from closing the levers too rapidly. When the last lever has been
closed, it is held in place by a magnetic latch, or low-voltage release
magnet, and, because of the mechanical interlocking, all the other
levers remain closed. Figure 73 shows the general construction of the
controller.

For speed regulating, the switch mechanism is essentially the same,
but the mechanical interlocking is modified to permit any desired

Fig. 73. Multiple-lever Starter.

number of levers to be closed. To accomplish this, each lever is
provided with a latch which engages a rod running across the width
of the slate. The rod has a flat side which is normally held parallel to
the slate by the release magnet. The levers must be operated in order,
but any desired number may be left open. Failure of voltage releases
the holding magnet and permits the rod to rotate. This releases all the
individual latches, and all the levers are opened.

The release coil may be connected across the line, or, for a shunt
motor, it may be connected in series with the motor field.

Controllers of this type may be either open or enclosed, the enclosure
usually consisting of a sheet-metal cover over the greater part of the
mechanism but not over the operating handles of the levers.

The multiple-switch controller has much better arc-breaking facilities than the face-plate type, because of the wide arc gap and the
auxiliary arcing tip. For this reason, and because of the time element

introduced by hand-over-hand operation, it is possible to have a smaller number of resistance steps. Table 11 gives the approximate number of levers (resistance steps), the inrush currents obtained, and the resistor class used for various sizes of motors.

TABLE 11

MULTIPLE-SWITCH CONTROLLERS

Horse-power	Number of Steps	Inrush Current in per cent of Full Load	NEMA Resistor Class
75	4	165	135
115	5	165	135
150	6	150	134
200	7	125	133

For regulating service the resistor is designed for continuous duty. Cast-iron grids are used for almost all sizes. In the lower horsepower ratings the grids are mounted in a frame at the rear of the panel; in the higher ratings they are separately mounted in mill-type boxes.

Drum-type Controllers. The drum type of manually operated controller has a number of advantages over both the face-plate and the multiple-switch types. These advantages are principally due to the method of construction, which is radically different from that of either of the other types of controller.

The essential parts of a drum controller are:

(a) The case.
(b) The contact fingers.
(c) The cylinder.
(d) The blowout magnets.
(e) The driving mechanism.

The case may be of iron, cast in one piece—a common construction for small drums; or it may consist of cast-iron end pieces joined by a back piece of boiler plate. In the second type, the back piece is welded to the end pieces. This is a flexible arrangement, as one design of end piece will do for drums of different lengths. A cover of sheet metal fits over the end pieces, to protect the sides and front of the drum. The cover may be provided with rubber gaskets to make it dust-tight. The wiring is brought into the drum through bushed holes, or conduit fittings in the back plate or in the end casting.

The fingers are the stationary contacts to which the supply lines, the motor, and the resistor are connected. Each finger consists of a copper tip riveted to a supporting channel of steel or brass. The finger is mounted so that it is pivoted at the back end and held in contact under the pressure of a spring. An adjustment is provided to permit changing the arc gap to compensate for wear. There are a number of methods of mounting the fingers. A common construction is shown

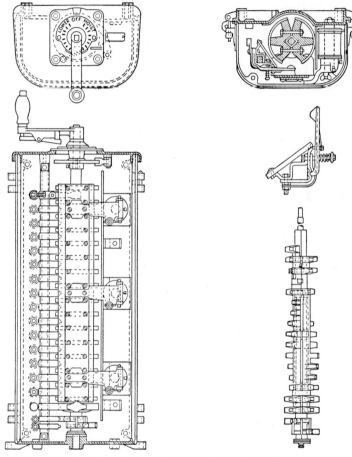

Fig. 74. Construction of a Drum Controller.

in Fig. 74, where the fingers are mounted on a square steel shaft which extends the length of the drum. The shaft is insulated by being wrapped with an insulating material or covered with a tube of insulation. Over this insulation steel brackets are mounted, and on them the finger is supported. The brackets also serve to mount a small insulating board which prevents copper dust from falling on the shaft and eventually causing a short circuit.

The cylinder provides the moving contacts that make connections between various fingers. No wiring is brought to the cylinder. An insulated square shaft is generally used, on which cast-iron or brass sections are mounted. Rolled copper contact segments are screwed to the cylinder castings. These segments may be of any desired length and may be arranged to make contact with a finger at any desired position as the cylinder is rotated. The segments may be easily renewed when worn out.

One of the principal differences between the drum-type controller and the face-plate type is that a magnetic blowout can readily be incorporated in the drum structure but cannot be easily built into a face-plate controller. This is a decided advantage, as much heavier currents can be commutated with the aid of the blowout magnet. The blowout coil is made of copper wire or bar, the size and number of turns being determined by the motor current. The coil is wound on a steel core fastened to the drum case. The circuit for the magnet flux is through the core, through the drum case, then to the cylinder. From the cylinder the flux crosses the air gap in the path of the contact finger and completes its circuit through the core support to the core. Assuming that the drum cylinder has just been moved to the off position, and that there is an arc hanging between the end of the segment and the tip of the finger, the reaction between the magnetic field due to the arc and the magnetic field of the blowout coil will cause the arc to be deflected either up or down, depending on the direction of current in the arc. The arc, in deflecting, will strike the barrier either above or below the finger, and will be cooled and dissipated.

The simplest type of drive for a drum is the radial handle, which is similar to the handle of a coffee mill. It is broached to fit on the end of the shaft, or it may be keyed to the shaft. Straight-line motion of the operating lever is secured by gearing the lever to the shaft through a bevel gear. Rope drive is obtained by mounting a sheave wheel on the drum shaft. Any of these drives may be arranged to return to the off position when released or to remain in any selected position.

The self-returning action is accomplished by means of a coiled spring that is wound up as the drum lever is moved to a running position and unwinds when the lever is released. If spring return is not used, the lever is held in any desired position by a star wheel and pawl. The star wheel is a toothed cam keyed to the drum shaft. The pawl, or roller, is arranged to roll over the surface of the star wheel as the cylinder is moved, and it is held in contact with the surface by a tension spring. The spring is strong enough to move the cylinder, so that the cylinder always stops in a position where the roller is in one of the star wheel notches. This is an important feature of the drum controller as it insures stopping the cylinder at definite positions which can be selected so that the fingers are squarely on the segments and making good contact. If it were not for the star wheel, the operator would be unable to feel the speed points and might pause during the operation in such a position that a finger would be making poor contact with a segment. This would produce heating or arcing between the finger and the segment, which would shorten the life of the contacts. The relation of the star wheel and the contacts can also be arranged so that the finger tips do not rest directly on top of one of the screws which hold the segment to the cylinder casting.

These advantages of the star wheel also apply to spring-return drums, and star wheels are sometimes used with that type of drive, but it is rather difficult to obtain a positive spring return and at the same time a star-wheel action that is strong enough to indicate definite positions. For this reason the star wheel is generally omitted with spring return.

Advantages of Drum Controllers. The drum controller has a number of advantages over the face-plate controller and the multiple-switch controller. In the first place, the drum has a better mechanical construction. It is stronger and able to stand more abuse than either of the other controllers. The construction of the drum also is favorable to good insulation, which is an important point.

Another advantage of the drum controller is that, owing to its construction and method of operation, heavy pressures can be maintained between contact surfaces without causing undue strains or making the operation difficult. If the contact pressure of a face-plate controller is increased very much, there will be a severe bending strain on the bearing shaft and a tendency to crack the slate at that point. Heavy pressure between the contacts will also increase the friction and make the operation of the starter difficult. These limitations do not apply to the drum construction.

Blowout magnets and arc barriers can readily be applied to the drum, as has been mentioned.

The drum structure lends itself more readily to complete enclosure than either of the other types. This is an important advantage as it affords safety to the operator and protection to the drum itself.

Complicated circuits, like those for reversing a motor or for handling both the primary and secondary windings of a slip-ring motor, are more easily handled in a drum controller than in any other manually operated controller. It is a simple matter to have the segments of the proper length so that contacts are made in any desired position. Sections of the cylinder may be insulated from each other, if necessary, by having separate castings for the two sections and mounting them on the insulated shaft separately.

The space required by a drum controller is usually less than that required by a face-plate or multiple-switch controller of the same rating and providing the same functions.

A drum controller is easier to operate than the other types of manual controllers, and the wide variety of drives for a drum is an advantage in adapting it to a particular service condition.

Auxiliary Functions. Contactors and relays are used in connection with drum controllers to obtain protective functions.

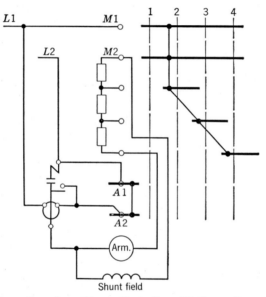

Fig. 75. Connections for a Drum Controller with Low-voltage Protection.

Low-voltage protection (Fig. 75), which is inherent in the face-plate controller, necessitates a contactor with the drum. The coil of the contactor is energized through a pair of auxiliary fingers in the drum, arranged to close the circuit in the off position of the drum only. When the contactor has closed, the pick-up circuit in the drum is paralleled by interlocks on the contactor, so that the contactor will remain closed when the drum is moved to a running position. The main circuit to the motor is fed through both the contactor and the drum. If the voltage fails during running, the contactor will open, and it will be necessary to return the drum to the off position in order to energize the contactor coil again. It will be noted that with this arrangement the contactor, once closed, will remain closed unless the power supply is interrupted. All making and breaking of the current is done in the drum.

Since a contactor is specially adapted to the opening and closing of heavy currents, it is often desirable to use one for that purpose in

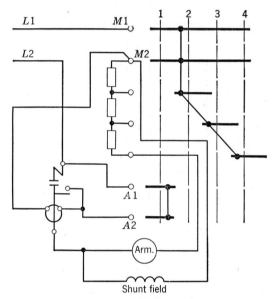

Fig. 76. Connections for a Drum Controller with a Line Contactor.

connection with a drum, energizing the contactor coil on the first point of the drum instead of in the off position (Fig. 76). This does not give true low-voltage protection, as it only requires that the drum be brought to the first position after a voltage failure. If the drum is in that position when power fails, the motor will be restarted upon return of power. However, the arrangement has the advantage of using the contactor to open the circuit and the further advantage that the contactor coil is energized only when the motor is running. Both the low-voltage protective arrangement and the low-voltage release arrangement are common. The advantages of both may be obtained by the use of a relay in connection with the contactor, the relay being energized in the off position and the contactor in the first position of the drum.

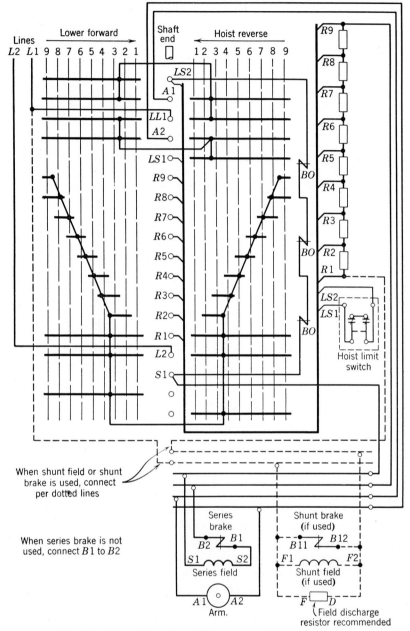

FIG. 77. Connections for a Direct-current Drum Controller.

Limit switch protection in two directions of travel may be secured by a single contactor in connection with a reversing drum controller. In the forward direction of travel the coil of the contactor is energized through the forward limit switch. When the switch trips, the circuit to the coil is broken and the contactor opens, stopping the motor. The drum may then be moved to the reverse position, when the contactor coil is energized again, this time through the reverse limit switch, and the motor will run in the reverse direction until that limit switch trips.

Drums for shunt motors are built in several forms, as follows:

1. Across-the-line, rated to 3 horsepower, 115 volts, and 5 horsepower, 230 volts.

2. Starting only, by armature circuit resistor.

3. Speed regulating, by armature resistor, to 50 per cent speed reduction.

4. Starting only, by armature resistor, and speed regulating by field resistor.

5. Speed regulating, below normal by armature resistor, and above normal by field resistor.

All types are built either reversing or non-reversing. They can also be built with armature shunt for 90 per cent speed reduction, and with dynamic braking circuits. All except type 1 are rated as shown in Table 12.

TABLE 12

NEMA DRUMS FOR SHUNT MOTORS

8-hour Ampere Rating	8-hour Ratings, Horsepower at		Intermittent Duty, Horsepower at	
	115 Volts	230 Volts	115 Volts	230 Volts
50	5	10	7½	15
100	10	25	15	30
150	20	40	25	50
300	40	75	50	100

Continuous ratings apply wherever any point on the drum switch will be used for any period exceeding 5 minutes. Intermittent ratings should be used for crane, hoist, or other duty where the running time is not over 50 per cent of the total time, and the maximum running time is not more than 5 minutes.

The resistance material used with drum controllers for armature starting or speed regulation is made up of cast-iron grids or units mounted separately from the drum. Resistors for connection in the shunt field circuit are sometimes mounted in the drum case, as they occupy a relatively small space.

Magnetic Controllers. Some small shunt motors, up to $1\frac{1}{2}$ horsepower, 115 volts, and 2 horsepower, 230 volts, are designed so that they can safely be started by direct connection to the power supply. Magnetic controllers are made for that purpose, both in reversing and non-reversing forms. These controllers are very simple, being just a magnetic line contactor, or pair of reversing contactors, and an overload relay.

Controllers for larger motors are made in a number of forms to suit the requirements of the machines which they control. They may be:

1. Non-reversing, starting service.
2. Non-reversing, starting service, plus dynamic braking.
3. Non-reversing, starting service, with speed regulation by field control.
4. Non-reversing, starting and dynamic braking, with speed regulation by field control.
5. Reversing, with dynamic braking.
6. Reversing, with dynamic braking, with speed regulation by field control.

The control devices used for these controllers are:

A line contactor or a set of reversing contactors.
A set of one to four accelerating contactors.
An accelerating means, usually of the time-limit type.
An overload relay.
A dynamic braking contactor.
A field accelerating relay for speed-regulating controllers.
A field discharge resistor.

In addition, the controllers may include a field failure relay, field decelerating relay, and control-circuit fuses. The armature resistor, NEMA class 135 or 136, is made up of wire-wound units, or cast-iron grids, and is contained in the case which mounts the control panel. Operating pushbuttons, or master controllers, are separately mounted. Standard ratings for these controllers are shown in Table 7, Chapter 5.

Figure 78 shows a typical controller of the reversing type, with speed regulation by field control. The cover of the enclosing case has been removed. The four reversing contactors are shown at the top of the panel. They are mechanically tied together in pairs, and the pairs are mechanically interlocked against each other. The two outer contactors have normally closed contacts, which provide a dynamic braking circuit when both contactors are open. Directly below the reversing contactors are three capacitors used with the relay in the lower right corner to time the acceleration. Two accelerating contactors are located below the capacitors, and the overload relay is below them. The relay in the lower left corner is a field accelerating relay, and the small relay to the right of the accelerators is used to prevent plugging and to strengthen the field during dynamic braking. This controller is master-operated, and the resistor for the field circuit

Fig. 78. Definite-time-limit Automatic Reversing Starter with Dynamic Braking.

is mounted in the master and commutated by contacts in the master. The armature-circuit resistor is mounted on straps at the top of the panel, and the panel may be tilted forward in the case, so that the resistor is accessible for maintenance.

Shunt motors are built in sizes much larger than those listed above for controllers, and, of course, it is possible to build magnetic controllers for them in any required size. For very large motors, whose current is above the rating of available contactors, magnetically operated circuit breakers are used as line-closing devices. The starting resistor for such motors is connected in parallel instead of series steps, so that the accelerating contactors each carry only a portion of the total current.

Application of Shunt Motors. Direct-current shunt motors are particularly applicable to those machines requiring a wide range of speeds, or a large number of operating speeds. The ability to obtain a quick stop by dynamic braking is also an advantage. Pumps, fans, some machine tools, printing presses, paper mills, elevators, and electric power shovels all use shunt motors. If a machine requires a constant speed at varying loads, a shunt motor will be selected. If rapid acceleration is desired, and relatively constant running speed, a compound motor should be used, and the series field might be cut out of circuit after the motor has accelerated. This is the usual practice for elevator installations.

Motors having speed adjustment by field control are larger and more costly than constant-speed motors, and these factors increase as the range of speed control is increased. Motors with high base speeds are smaller and less costly than slow-speed motors. For example, a 40-horsepower 1150-rpm motor weighs about 1360 pounds, whereas a 40-horsepower 575-rpm motor weighs about 2450 pounds. A 7½-horsepower 500- to 1500-rpm motor weighs about 79 per cent as much as a 7½-horsepower 400- to 1600-rpm motor. Totally enclosed motors are much heavier than partially enclosed motors, and they, in turn, are heavier than open motors.

References

H. D. James, "Consider the Shunt Motor," *Electric Journal,* 1935, Vol. 32, p. 319.

G. F. Leland and L. T. Rader, "Industrial Control—Shunted Armature Connection for a D-c Shunt Motor," *Electrical Engineering,* September, 1944.

G. Fox, "The Blast Furnace Skip Hoist," *Iron and Steel Engineer,* March, 1943.

Problems

1. Write an equation for the torque of a shunt motor.

2. Write an equation for the speed of a shunt motor.

3. A 25-horsepower 230-volt direct-current shunt motor has a full-load current of 100 amperes. Neglecting armature resistance, how many ohms will be required in the starting resistance to limit the starting torque to 200 per cent of normal torque?

4. Again neglecting armature resistance, what would be the running speed of this motor when operating without resistance in its circuit and at half load?

5. Suppose that this motor were running with resistance in series with its armature limiting the voltage across the armature to 70 per cent of line voltage, and suppose the motor is drawing 50 amperes from the line, what will the torque be in per cent of normal?

6. Under the conditions of problem 5, what will the speed be in per cent of normal?

7. A 50-horsepower 230-volt motor has a full-load current rating of 180 amperes, and its armature resistance is 5 per cent of E/I. What is the armature resistance in ohms?

8. A 75-horsepower 230-volt 268-ampere motor is driving a centrifugal pump. The controller is designed for starting characteristics like those of Fig. 65. What is the ohmic value of the controller resistor?

9. If it is desired that the pump run at 45 per cent speed with all resistance in circuit, what will be the controller resistance required?

10. A 35-horsepower 230-volt 128-ampere motor is equipped with a 3-step controller and a resistor which gives starting characteristics like Fig. 64. What is the ohmic value of the starting resistor?

11. If this motor is plugged, what current inrush will be obtained at the instant of plugging?

12. What is the ohmic value of the additional resistor step which must be added to hold the plugging inrush current to the same value as that obtained when starting from rest?

13. If the speed of this motor was increased 50 per cent by field weakening, and the field rheostat was short-circuited during starting, what would be the ohmic value of the plugging resistor step?

14. A 10-horsepower 230-volt 38-ampere motor has an armature resistance of 10 per cent of E/I. What is its countervoltage at full load, in per cent of the applied line voltage?

15. Calculate the ohms in a dynamic braking resistor which will limit the braking current to a maximum of 300 per cent of the motor rating.

16. If the braking is to be done in two steps, each limited to 300 per cent of motor rating, and the first step cut out when the braking current has dropped to 100 per cent, how many ohms will be in each step?

17. What will be the approximate speed of the motor when the first step is cut out?

18. A 50-horsepower 550-volt 75-ampere motor has an armature resistance of 5 per cent of E/I. How many ohms will be required in a series resistor to obtain 20 per cent speed reduction below full-load speed, when the motor is operating at 70 per cent load?

19. How many amperes must the resistor of problem 18 carry continuously?

20. Referring to Figs. 67 and 68, if a resistor is designed to produce 50 per cent speed with a machine-type load, what speed will the same resistor produce with a fan-type load?

21. If the motor of problem 18 is used with a resistor designed to give 50 per cent speed reduction with a machine-type load, how many additional ohms will be required to give the same speed reduction with a fan-type load?

22. Referring to Fig. 64, what per cent of no-load speed will be obtained on each of the four controller points if the motor is loaded to 140 per cent of rated load?

23. If this motor is running with all resistance in circuit, how much will the speed change if the load changes from 140 per cent to 90 per cent?

24. If the motor is running with only the last step of resistance in circuit, how much will the speed change if the load changes from 140 per cent to 90 per cent?

25. A 40-horsepower 230-volt 146-ampere motor has a series resistor designed to give 50 per cent speed reduction below normal full-load speed, when the motor is operating at full load. How many ohms are required in an armature shunt resistor which will give 80 per cent speed reduction at full load?

26. With the series resistor and the armature shunt resistor in circuit, what will the motor speed be at zero load?

27. Under the conditions of problem 25, how many horsepower will the motor be delivering, and how many horsepower will be lost in the resistor?

28. What are the delivered horsepower and the lost horsepower under the conditions of problem 26?

29. A 25-horsepower 230-volt 92-ampere motor is running with a series resistor of 1.6 ohms and an armature shunt resistance of 6.8 ohms. The motor armature current is 20 amperes. What is its speed?

30. What would be the speed of the motor if the load dropped to 10 amperes?

31. What would be the ohmic value of an armature shunt resistor which would produce the speed of problem 29, with a load of 10 amperes?

32. How many watts are lost in the resistor under the conditions of problem 29?

33. If the series resistance is reduced to 0.8 ohm, calculate the ohms in the armature shunt to produce the speed required by problem 29.

34. What is the wattage loss with the combination of series and shunt resistors of problem 33?

8

SHUNT FIELD RELAYS AND RHEOSTATS

When a shunt motor or compound motor is used to drive a machine, the handling of the shunt field introduces a number of factors into the control problem. Some of these will be present whenever a shunt field is involved; others may or may not need to be considered.

Discharge Path. When the shunt field circuit is opened, the high inductance of the field windings tends to oppose the opening of the circuit and to keep the current flowing. Opening the circuit abruptly may damage the insulation of the field windings. It is advisable, therefore, to supply a discharge path, so that the generated voltage may be limited to a safe value. With non-reverse controllers, it is customary to connect the shunt field behind the line contactor, so that when the circuit is opened a discharge path is provided through the armature of the motor and the starting resistance. With reversing controllers, the field cannot be connected in this manner, and a separate discharge path must be provided. The same is true of controllers having dynamic braking, for then the shunt field must be kept energized after the armature circuit has been opened.

In general, a discharge resistance is not essential on 115-volt equipment but should be provided for 230-volt motors rated at 7½ horsepower or higher, and for 550-volt motors rated 5 horsepower or higher.

The recommended ohmic value for a discharge resistor is between one and three times the ohmic value of the shunt field. The discharge voltage will depend upon the resistance of the discharge path, so that, if a resistance of three times the field ohms is used for the discharge path, the generated voltage will be four times normal line voltage.

Where the wattage consumed by the discharge resistor is relatively low, it is good practice to connect the resistor directly across the line, behind the service knife switch. The resistor must then have continuous capacity for the current flowing in it. For larger equipments, a discharge resistor is connected into circuit by a discharge clip on the knife switch, so that it is not consuming energy when the field is connected to the line. The capacity may then be figured on the basis of handling the discharge current for approximately 15 seconds.

163

If the field circuit may be opened at different points, as, for instance, by a set of reversing contactors, and also by a field knife switch, it is necessary to provide a discharge path to take care of each condition, or else to connect the discharge resistance permanently across the field itself.

Thyrite. Certain crystal materials have the characteristics of being good insulators at voltages below a critical value and good conductors at voltages above that value. One such material, developed by the General Electric Company under the name of Thyrite, is being used by control manufacturers as a field discharge resistor. Thyrite is a dark gray, dense, non-porous, ceramic compound, having mechanical characteristics somewhat similar to those of dry-process porcelain. It does not burn or disintegrate under red heat, and it is not affected by moisture, oil, or gases. It conducts current without arcing and is not dependent on ionization, de-ionization, or breakdown of gas. The resistance follows a definite law, and the critical voltage may be determined from the equation

$$E = RI^{1-a}$$

where E = the applied voltage.
    I = the current in amperes.
    R = the resistance in ohms when 1 ampere is flowing.
    a = a constant (approximately 0.76).

A typical block of this material for use as a 250-volt discharge resistor is cylindrical in shape, $1\frac{5}{8}$ inches in diameter and 1 inch long, with depressions in the ends to provide a conducting path of $\frac{1}{2}$ inch. The equation for such a block is

$$E = 1350\,I^{0.24}$$

If the block is connected across a 250-volt line, in parallel with a 1-ampere field, the continuous current taken by the Thyrite will be approximately 0.001 ampere. When the circuit is opened, and the field discharges through the Thyrite, the voltage will be limited to 1350 volts, on the assumption that the circuit will be opened instantaneously. Actually the arc on the interrupting device will not be extinguished instantaneously, and the peak voltage will be lower than the theoretical value. The losses in the resistor will be 0.24 watt, as against approximately 60 watts for an ordinary resistance-type discharge unit. Another advantage of Thyrite is the fact that it may be connected across a field without affecting the characteristics of a rheostat connected in the field circuit.

Field-failure Protection. With shunt or compound motors it is good practice to provide for shutdown in the event of failure of the shunt field circuit, as such failure means a runaway condition. Protection is obtained by means of a relay having its coil connected in series with the shunt field and its contacts in the stop circuit. Then, if the field fails at any time, the relay coil will be de-energized, and the relay in opening will shut down the motor. The coil of a field-failure relay must be able to carry the maximum field current continuously and at the same time must be able to close the relay at approximately 65 per cent of the minimum field current. The 65 per cent factor serves to take care of low-voltage conditions and of heating of the field and the relay coil. It is not difficult to design a relay to operate at these values, provided that field weakening is limited to a reasonable amount, but where the speed range by field is greater than 2 to 1 the current range may become so wide that it will be difficult to design a suitable relay. Under such conditions, it is generally satisfactory to assume that the field rheostat will be turned back sufficiently to permit picking up the field-failure relay when the motor is started. It is also generally satisfactory to connect the contacts of the field-failure relay in the maintaining circuit instead of in the pick-up circuit. Since the field rheostat is short-circuited during the accelerating period, the relay will receive sufficient current to close as soon as the motor starts to accelerate.

When field-failure relays are used with series shunt motors having a series field of more than 40 per cent, it is necessary to take special precaution to insure that the relay will remain closed during the acceleration period. During this period, the series field reacts upon the shunt field in such a manner as to greatly reduce, or even reverse, the current in the shunt field. If only a single-coil relay were used, the relay would drop out during the acceleration period and shut down the motor. One means of avoiding this is a double-coil relay, one coil being connected in series with the shunt field and the other in series with the armature accelerating resistance. The second coil then insures that the relay is held closed during the starting period. After acceleration, this coil is short-circuited.

Another method of obtaining the same result is to short-circuit the contacts of the field-failure relay by an interlock on the final accelerating contactor. With this arrangement, the field-failure relay may open during the accelerating period, but it will not shut down the motor.

After the acceleration is over, and the last accelerating contactor has closed, the relay is free to function as it normally should.

Economizer Relay. An economizer relay, or field-protective relay, is used to insert resistance in series with the shunt field whenever the motor is not running. It may be necessary to keep the shunt field energized when the motor is idle, for a number of reasons, and, since the ventilation of the field is greatly reduced when the motor is not running, it is necessary to insert a resistance to prevent the field from overheating. The relay is simply a single-pole shunt-type relay having its coil connected in parallel with the coil of the main line contactor. The resistance may be designed to reduce the voltage across the field to one-half of the normal value, which will reduce the wattage in the field to one-fourth of the normal value.

Reversing. Wherever rapid reversing is required, it is necessary to reverse the armature circuit; but a number of drives require only emergency reversing, and for such drives it is often advantageous to reverse the shunt field instead of the armature. If the motors are large, the cost of the control may be reduced by omitting the large armature-reversing contactors and using the smaller reversing contactors required by the field. Where field reversal is employed, it is the usual practice to interlock the controller, so that it cannot be plugged and so that the field cannot be reversed until the motor has stopped. When reversing contactors are used, they are provided with a normally closed contact, which serves to set up a discharge circuit when the field is opened. Where remote control is not particularly required, the field is often reversed by a knife switch provided with discharge clip. This knife switch is usually interlocked with the main control circuit, so that, if it is opened when the motor is running, the main contactors will immediately be de-energized and the motor disconnected from the line.

Plugging. When a shunt motor is plugged under full field conditions, the countervoltage of the armature is added to the voltage of the line, and additional resistance, nearly equal to the accelerating resistance in ohms, must be used to limit the inrush current. If the motor has some speed increase by field weakening, the field will be strengthened when the motor is plugged and the countervoltage of the armature will be increased in proportion to the strengthening of the field. For example, assume that a motor having a speed increase of 2 to 1 by field is running at maximum speed and is plugged. As soon as the circuit is closed in the reverse direction, the accelerating relay will close and short-circuit the field rheostat. The field strength is then doubled and the armature countervoltage correspondingly doubled. The total voltage is therefore three times the line voltage; and, if the inrush current is to be limited to that obtained when starting from rest, resistance equal to three times the value of the starting resistance will have to be used. With motors of greater speed range by field, the resistance must be still higher in ohms.

Frequently plugging is not essential to the proper operation of the drive, and the extra resistance is only a safeguard in case of accidental plugging. Then it is usually more economical to arrange the control so that the motor cannot be plugged, and so avoid the use of additional resistance. The method of doing this when dynamic braking is employed has been explained. Where there is no dynamic braking relay, a normally closed voltage relay, having the coil connected across the armature, will serve the same purpose. The contacts of the relay are connected in series with the direction contactor coils and are bypassed by normally open interlocks on the direction contactors. It is not necessary that the motor be entirely stopped before the voltage relay closes to permit plugging. The relay is usually set so that the speed is low enough to insure that the countervoltage of the motor will not be excessive.

Speed Increase by Field Control. In order to increase the speed of a motor by weakening the field, resistance is inserted in series with the field, either by means of a rheostat or by means of a set of magnetic contactors. Contactors are used in connection with the control of large motors, where the field currents are high, and also where rapid and frequent commutation of the resistance is necessary.

When the field strength is reduced by the insertion of a step of resistance, the countervoltage generated by the motor is also reduced, and the difference between line voltage and the new countervoltage causes an inrush of current to the armature. If the field strength is reduced 10 per cent, and the countervoltage correspondingly 10 per cent, the inrush which occurs will be in the neighborhood of 100 per cent of normal full-load current. This is on the assumption that the inrush is limited only by the resistance of the armature and leads to it, and that this resistance is approximately 10 per cent of E/I. Actually the inrush current will be less than this value, because of the inductance of the field windings which prevents the field current from changing instantly.

The amount of resistance which may be inserted in the field at any one time is limited by the characteristics of the motor. A motor with a slow field will permit of a greater field weakening without excessive inrushes. If the field characteristic is such that the field current changes rapidly, a greater number of steps will be necessary. The number of steps is influenced also by the amount of current inrush which may be permissible from the standpoint of line disturbances and also from that of good motor commutation. Other factors to be considered are the effect of the inrush on the machine which is being driven and the extent to which smooth acceleration is necessary. Adjustable-voltage-control equipment for large motors having a speed increase by field of 2 to 1 generally requires about ten steps as minimum. Automatic self-starters for control of continuous-running mill rolls, or similar machinery, may be safely accelerated with approximately four steps. Plate-type field rheostats have between thirty and sixty steps. The large number of steps is necessary because of the limited wattage which can be handled by any one step of a device of this kind, and it is an advantage because of the finely graduated control that is obtained.

Accelerating Relay. In order to obtain full torque for acceleration up to full field speed, it is necessary to short-circuit the field rheostat during the armature acceleration period. This is generally accomplished by means of a full field relay, the coil of which is energized during armature acceleration and the contacts of which short-circuit the field rheostat. If the field rheostat is left in a set position and the motor started from rest with some resistance in the field circuit, it is necessary to use a full field relay.

If the speed increase is greater than 25 per cent, it is also advisable to use an accelerating relay of the vibrating type as shown by Fig. 41. This relay acts to insert the resistance in the field circuit and short-circuit it again when the inrush reaches a predetermined limit. The coil of the accelerating relay is in the armature circuit and energized by the armature current. The contacts of the relay short-circuit either all the field rheostat or a portion of it. After the motor has been accelerated to full field speed, the full field relay opens, inserting the field resistor, and an inrush immediately occurs in the armature circuit. This inrush closes the accelerating relay, which short-circuits the field rheostat again. In the meantime, the motor has accelerated somewhat above full field speed. When the rheostat is short-circuited, the inrush current drops and the accelerating relay opens, again inserting the field resistor. A second inrush then occurs, and this action goes on until the motor has been accelerated up to full speed. The acceleration obtained is shown by the curve A of Fig. 79.

It is possible to combine the functions of the full field relay and the accelerating relay by having a second coil on the accelerating relay. This coil is connected in series with the last step of armature-accelerating resistance, and it is of sufficient strength to close the accelerating relay during the time of acceleration to normal speed.

When the armature resistor is short-circuited, the starting coil is also short-circuited, and the accelerating relay is then controlled by the running coil only and vibrates in the manner described.

The currents at which the accelerating relay will open and close can be determined by adjustments on the relay. Since these values are fixed, once adjustment has been made, the relay will always open at the same current, and consequently it is necessary that this current be above the full-load running current in order that the motor will accelerate. For this reason, the torque which is obtained during the first period of field acceleration is higher than necessary. For the majority of drives this does not do any particular harm and is perfectly satisfactory. However, if the driven machine has a high inertia, and particularly if it is belt-driven, the excess torque will be objectionable.

Curve *B* (Fig. 79) shows a method by which the accelerating relay may be made to vibrate in such a manner that the torque obtained will follow the torque required by the load. With this arrangement, one coil of the relay is connected in the usual manner in series with the armature, and the other coil is connected in series with the field. At the full field speed, the armature current is low and the field current is high; at the weak field speed, the armature current is high and the field current is low. Consequently, at full field speed the field coil is strong, and a relatively low armature current will close the relay. As the field is weakened, the effect of the field coil constantly decreases, so that more and more armature current is required to cause the relay to close. By properly proportioning the coils, an acceleration curve as shown in Fig. 79 may be obtained.

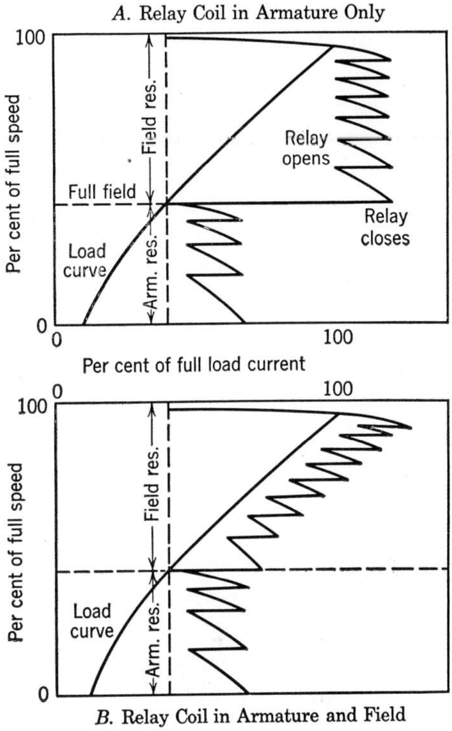

Fig. 79. Field Acceleration Curves.

Decelerating Relay. If the field is suddenly strengthened by removing resistance, the countervoltage of the motor will be increased and the current flowing from the line will be decreased. If the deceleration is too rapid, the armature current may even be reversed. It is possible to control the deceleration by means of a relay handling one coil in the armature circuit, and a second coil connected across the line. During normal operation these coils are arranged to oppose each other. The contacts of the relay are normally closed and are arranged so that in opening they will insert a step of resistance to weaken the field. As long as the deceleration is not too rapid, the decelerating relay remains closed. However, if the rheostat is moved too rapidly, so that the current in the armature reverses, then the two coils of the relay are accumulative in effect and cause the relay to open. Resistance is then inserted in series with the field to weaken it again. The relay vibrates in the same manner as the relay used for accelerating.

Miscellaneous Relays. The diagram of Fig. 80 shows all the devices which have been described, including the accelerating relay FA, decelerating relay FD, field-failure relay FL, and field-protective relay FP. It also shows a method of obtaining a desired speed in one direction of travel and a different speed in the other direction, both being adjustable. This control feature is of value for such machines as planers, where it is desired to cut at slow speed and to return at high speed. Two rheostats are used in series. The relay C, which has one normally open and one normally closed contact, is arranged to short-circuit one rheostat when energized and the other when de-energized. The relay is then energized in one direction of travel and de-energized in the other direction.

The diagram also includes a relay FF, which is used to short-circuit the field rheostats and to provide full field for dynamic braking. It is generally desirable to strengthen the field during the braking period in order to increase the braking torque and also to improve the commutation of the motor when handling heavy braking currents. When the master is moved to the off position, the line and direction contactors are open, and the dynamic braking contactor DB is closed. Current then flows through the armature, the braking resistor, and the coil of the relay FF. The relay closes and short-circuits the field rheostat. The relay remains closed until the current in the dynamic circuit reaches a low value, unless the motor is restarted, in which case the dynamic loop would be opened. The relay is usually interlocked with the rest of the control so that the motor cannot be restarted until the dynamic current has fallen to a value low enough to permit *FF* to open. In other words, the motor cannot be restarted, or plugged, until it has practically come to a stop. This feature is not shown in the diagram. It is secured by using a normally closed contact on relay *FF*, connected in series with the direction contactor coils, and

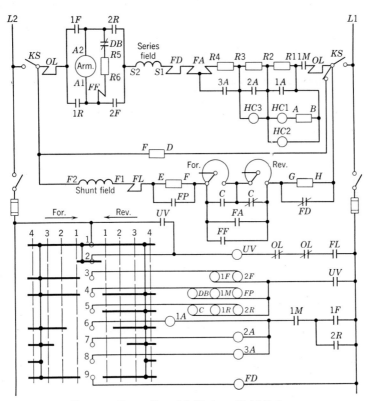

Fig. 80. Controller with Various Field Relays.

bypassed by normally open interlock contacts on the forward and reverse direction contactors.

Estimating Field Rheostats. It has previously been stated that the number of steps required for field regulation is determined by four factors:

1. The range of speed control.
2. The degree of fine regulation required.
3. The inrush current drawn by the motor as the speed is changed.
4. The commutation on the contacts of the starter.

Considering the first two requirements, which depend upon the nature of the driven machinery, it is evident that a large number of different rheostats would be necessary to meet each condition exactly. It is cheaper in the long run to design only a few types, using a sufficiently large number of steps to take care of the majority of applications. Commercial manual starters are designed to cover any speed range up to 4 to 1, as standard. They have approximately 14 field steps up to 5 horsepower, and 20 steps above that size. This number is sufficient to keep the motor inrushes well within a safe value. Plate-type rheostats have from 30 to 60 steps. Rheostats for large motors may have 100 to 150 steps.

The field current varies widely with different sizes and different makes of motors. The field-regulating resistance is tapered to give approximately equal percentage increments of speed with an average motor, and this should result in a design which will cause no arcing of the contacts. However, with wide speed ranges, or with unusual field characteristics, it is necessary to check the commutation, using a curve like that of Fig. 81. This curve shows the maximum resistance which can be inserted on a single step when no star-wheel action is provided, and the lever may remain with a very small gap between the contact brush and the button.

TABLE 13

ESTIMATED RHEOSTAT RESISTANCE

Per Cent Speed Increase	Per Cent Field Current Decrease	Rheostat Resistance in Per Cent of Field Resistance
25	40	66⅔
50	66⅔	200
100	75	300
200	83½	500
300	87½	700
400	97⅓	1500

Field-regulating resistors should not be designed from estimated or calculated field data. It is practically impossible to predict the field characteristics, unless data are available upon other motors of identical design. The designer is often forced to make an estimate of the field-regulating resistor which will be required, either to arrive at an approximate cost for sales purposes or to enable him to determine the space which will be required by the resistor. Tables 13 and

14 may be utilized for that purpose, but the final design should be based on actual test data obtained from the motor manufacturer. The figure given for summation watts is an approximation of the watts

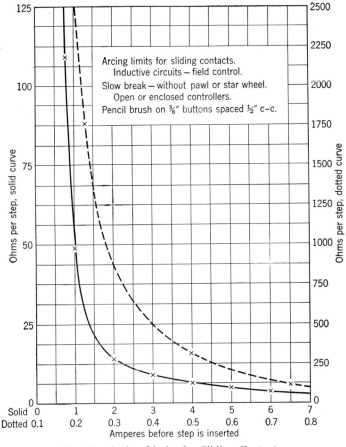

FIG. 81. Arcing Limits for Sliding Contacts.

dissipated in the rheostat; it is the product of the maximum field current, the minimum field current, and the rheostat resistance.

As an illustration of how this information can be used, let us suppose that we have under consideration a 4-horsepower controller calling for 25 per cent increase by field control. This would mean that

TABLE 14

Estimated Rheostat Summation Watts

Hp	25 Per Cent Increase		50 Per Cent Increase		100 Per Cent Increase	
	Maximum Field Current %I	Summation Watts	Maximum Field Current %I	Summation Watts	Maximum Field Current %I	Summation Watts
1	8.8	38	9.5	60	10.5	75
2	7.7	49	8.0	80	9.2	130
3	5.5	61	6.0	100	7.2	150
4	4.4	67	5.0	110	6	160
5	3.3	73	4.0	120	5	170
7½	2.8	80	3.5	130	4.5	230
10	2.2	85	3.0	140	4	260
15	2.1	110	2.5	180	3.2	310
20	1.9	150	2.2	240	2.7	350
25	1.8	170	2.0	280	2.6	420
30	1.7	184	1.8	300	2.5	480
40	1.7	250	1.8	400	2.3	560
50	1.7	310	1.8	500	2.2	650
60	1.7	370	1.8	600	2.1	750
75	1.7	430	1.8	700	2.0	920
100	1.7	610	1.8	950	2.0	1220
125	1.7	730	1.8	1200	2.0	1540
150	1.7	860	1.8	1400	2.0	1800
175	1.7	980	1.8	1600	2.0	2100
200	1.7	1200	1.8	1940	2.0	2400

Hp	200 Per Cent Increase		300 Per Cent Increase		400 Per Cent Increase	
	Maximum Field Current %I	Summation Watts	Maximum Field Current %I	Summation Watts	Maximum Field Current %I	Summation Watts
1	12	90	13	100	14.5	120
2	10.5	140	11.4	180	13	210
3	9	180	10.5	200	12	240
4	8	210	9.5	300	11	350
5	6.5	220	8.8	345	10	380
7½	5.2	250	7.0	400	8.5	500
10	4.6	280	5.9	440	7	525
15	3.9	350	4.7	520	6	660
20	3.4	410	4.1	600	5	750
25	3.1	480	3.8	700	4.5	840
30	3.0	550	3.6	780	4	880
40	2.9	690	3.5	960	4	1000
50	2.8	870	3.4	1200	3.8	1300
60	2.7	940	3.3	1400	3.7	1550
75	2.6	1120	3.2	1660	3.6	1880
100	2.5	1450	3.1	2170	3.5	2450
125	2.5	1800	3	2650	3.5	3100
150	2.5	2050	3	3150	3.5	3650
175	2.5	2600	3	3690	3.5	4300
200	2.5	2900	3	4200	3.5	4900

I = normal full-load current.

the motor fields would take approximately 4.4 per cent of the full-load current of the motor, and that approximately 67 watts would be dissipated in the resistance in series with the shunt field. Knowing this, and knowing the type of unit which would be used on the particular rheostat in question, the number of units can be determined. If the specifications call for 300 per cent increase, the approximate shunt field current would be 9½ per cent of the normal current, and the approximate watts to be dissipated in the rheostat would be 300. Watts given in Table 14 are summation watts.

Calculation of Summation Watts. The summation watts which a rheostat must dissipate may be calculated as follows:

Assume a rheostat of resistance R_1, connected in series with a field of resistance f. If E is the line voltage, the maximum current will be E/f, and the minimum current will be $E/(f + R_1)$. If the resistance of the rheostat is divided into an infinite number of steps, the resistance of one step will be dR and the wattage of the step will be $I^2 dR$. I is the current at any point, and R the resistance to that point

$$I = \frac{E}{f + R}$$

$$I^2 = \frac{E^2}{(f + R)^2}$$

$$W = I^2 dr = \frac{E^2 dR}{(f + R)^2}$$

$$\text{Summation watts} = E^2 \int_0^{R_1} \frac{dR}{(f + R)^2}$$

$$= -\left[\frac{E^2}{f + R_1} - \frac{E^2}{f} \right]$$

$$= \frac{E^2 R_1}{f(f + R_1)}$$

$$= \frac{E}{f} \times \frac{E}{f + R_1} \times R_1$$

or

Summation watts = Maximum current × Minimum current

× Resistance of the rheostat

As an example, assume that it is desired to determine the material required for a rheostat of 100 ohms for use with a 50-ohm field on 230 volts.

$$\text{Maximum } I = \frac{230}{50} = 4.6 \text{ amperes}$$

$$\text{Minimum } I = \frac{230}{150} = 1.52 \text{ amperes}$$

$$\text{Summation watts} = 4.6 \times 1.52 \times 100$$

$$= 710 \text{ watts}$$

The rheostat must have sufficient material to dissipate this wattage safely.

Rheostat Design. A motor field rheostat is usually designed to give either equal speed changes per step, or equal percentage changes per

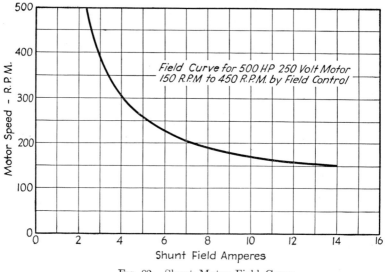

FIG. 82. Shunt Motor Field Curve.

step. A typical example of each design is presented to illustrate the method. Figure 82 is a curve giving field current against speed for a 500-horsepower 250-volt motor having a speed range by field of 150 to 450 rpm. The rheostat to be designed has 150 steps. Experience has shown that it is not necessary to calculate each step, which would be a very long process, but that it is sufficiently accurate to divide the rheostat into a number of groups of steps. In this case

fifteen groups of ten steps each have been used. The design calculations of Table 15 are for a rheostat giving equal speed changes per
step. The step numbers are given in the first column. The speed
change at each step is readily calculated by dividing the total speed
change by the number of groups of steps; that is, 300 divided by 15
gives 20 rpm per group.

TABLE 15

RHEOSTAT DESIGN

500 Horsepower 250 Volts—150–450 RPM by Field—150 Steps—
Equal Speed Increase per Step

Rheostat Step	Motor RPM	Field Amperes	Total Ohms	Rheostat Ohms	Group Ohms	Group Watts
0	150	15.9	15.7	0	0	0
11	170	10.2	24.5	8.8	8.8	915
21	190	8.0	31.3	15.6	6.8	436
31	210	6.75	37.0	21.3	5.7	269
41	230	5.9	42.4	24.7	5.4	188
51	250	5.2	48.1	32.4	5.7	155
61	270	4.65	53.8	38.1	5.7	123
71	290	4.25	58.8	43.1	5.0	90
81	310	3.97	63.0	47.3	4.2	66
91	330	3.70	67.6	51.9	4.6	63
101	350	3.50	71.5	55.8	3.9	48
111	370	3.28	76.3	60.6	4.8	52
121	390	3.08	81.2	65.5	4.9	47
131	410	2.90	86.2	70.5	5.0	42
141	430	2.80	89.3	73.6	3.1	25
151	450	2.70	92.6	76.9	3.3	24

These data are listed in column 2. The field amperes to give the
required speed at each point are then read from the field curve.
The total ohms of column 4 are obtained by dividing the line voltage by the field current at each point. The value obtained for point
zero is the resistance of the field itself, in this case 15.7 ohms. The
rheostat ohms, in the next column, are obtained by subtracting the
value of the field resistance from the total ohms of column 4. Column
6 gives the resistance in each group. The wattage which must be
dissipated by each group is calculated from columns 3 and 6. When
the ohms per group and the wattage per group are known, the resistor
material required for the group may readily be selected from the units
or cast grids available, whose resistance and current-carrying capacities will be known. Each group will be divided into ten equal steps.

As a check it is desirable to calculate the wattage on the first step of the group, particularly at the high-current end of the rheostat, to be sure that equal division of the resistance over the ten steps will not overload the first step. If that step has ample capacity, the rest of the group will be on the safe side.

With the rheostat arm at any setting the current at the last step cut in will be at the full capacity of that step, but all other steps up to that point will be working below full capacity. Only one step can be operating at full capacity at any one time. It follows that the step which is at full capacity is not subjected to as much heat from the rest of the rheostat as it would be if the entire resistor were operating at full rating. The continuous rating of resistor material is based on a number of units bunched together, and so helping to heat each other. It is possible, therefore, to rate the resistor material of a field rheostat approximately 15 per cent higher than its regular continuous rating.

The calculations of Table 16 are for a rheostat based on the same field but designed for equal percentage speed increases. The rheostat is again divided into fifteen blocks of ten steps each. It is then necessary to find a factor by which the low speed (150 rpm) can be multiplied 15 times to give the high speed (450 rpm). This factor is the fifteenth root of three, or 1.076. The speed at the beginning of the second block is then 150 multiplied by 1.076, or 161. At the beginning of the third block the speed is 150 multiplied by 1.076^2, or 173, and in this manner the speed at each point is calculated. The speeds required having been determined, the currents are read from the curve, and the rest of the design is calculated in the same manner as has been described for Table 15. The irregularities in the tables of group ohms and group watts are caused by slight errors in plotting and in reading the field current curve.

Any desired stepping of a rheostat can be worked out by the method described. Both the design giving equal speed increments and that giving equal percentage increments result in an unequal distribution of wattage over the rheostat. With a face-plate rheostat this does not make much difference, as the resistance material is separate, and any required amount may be used for any step. However, if the amount of material per step were fixed, as it is in a plate-type rheostat, these designs could not be used unless each step of the plate had capacity for the maximum step wattage. The use of equal percentage speed increments per step gives a more nearly balanced condition, but in order to get anything like equal wattage per step the resistance would have to be tapered much more steeply. The speed increases at the

TABLE 16

RHEOSTAT DESIGN

250 Horsepower 250 Volts—150–450 RPM by Field—150 Steps—
Equal Percentage Speed Increase per Step

Rheostat Step	Factor	Motor RPM	Field Amperes	Total Ohms	Rheostat Ohms	Group Ohms	Group Watts
0	.....	150	15.9	15.7	0	0	0
11	1.076	161	12.0	20.8	5.1	5.1	750
21	1.157	173	9.7	25.8	10.0	5.0	470
31	1.245	186	8.35	29.9	14.2	4.1	287
41	1.339	201	7.2	34.7	19.0	4.8	250
51	1.442	216	6.6	39.2	23.5	4.5	195
61	1.551	232	5.9	43.7	28.0	4.5	157
71	1.668	250	5.2	49.6	33.9	5.9	159
81	1.795	269	4.7	55	39.3	5.4	120
91	1.931	289	4.3	60	44.3	5.0	93
101	2.056	307	3.9	64	48.3	4.0	61
111	2.235	335	3.63	69	53.3	5.0	66
121	2.404	360	3.4	76	60.3	7.0	81
131	2.586	386	3.1	83	67.3	7.0	67
141	2.79	418	2.9	87	71.3	4.0	34
151	3.00	450	2.7	92.6	76.9	5.6	41

low-speed end of the rheostat would have to be smaller, and those at the high-speed end would be larger. For this reason plate-type rheostats may not always work out well for motor field control.

Constant-torque Drives. If the characteristic of the driven machine is such that it requires a constant torque, or nearly constant torque, at any speed, and if field control is used, these facts should be taken into consideration in designing the armature-accelerating resistance and in determining the capacity of the accelerating contactors. If the required torque is constant, armature current will vary in proportion to the speed increase by field, so that, for a 2-to-1 motor, the armature resistor may theoretically be designed on the basis of one-half of the full-speed horsepower. This permits of considerable saving in resistance material and in contactors. Also, the correct torque, and not excessive torque, is applied during the starting period. Instead of reducing the horsepower directly in proportion to the speed range, it is a common practice to reduce it in proportion to the square root of the speed range; that is,

$$\text{Accelerating horsepower} = \frac{\text{Maximum horsepower}}{\sqrt{\text{Speed range by field}}}$$

A resistor designed on this basis will give enough torque to insure acceleration but will not give excess torque, and at the same time it will permit of economical design.

A machine tool which takes a light cut at high speed and a heavy cut at low speed is essentially a constant-horsepower drive. When field control is used for any drive of this type, the armature resistor must be designed for full-speed horsepower. It is only in constant-torque drives that the accelerating resistance may be designed on a reduced-horsepower basis.

Small Field Rheostats. The smaller field rheostats are usually constructed in the form of circular plates from 6 to 15 inches in diameter. The base is of soapstone, or some other insulating material, on which contact buttons are mounted. Resistance wire is looped between the buttons and cemented into place. The short-circuiting lever is mounted on a bearing at the center of the plate and is turned by a knob. Such plates are commonly used for generator field control and for small motors. They are limited in capacity by the type of resistance material and by the general method of construction. The resistance wire for each step covers the same area of plate surface and therefore should dissipate the same wattage. To accomplish this it is necessary that the resistance be tapered in ohms rather steeply. It happens that such a taper is close to the resistance characteristic required for generator voltage control and will give approximately equal voltage changes per step, but the taper required for motor-speed regulation is much flatter. Plate-type rheostats therefore do not always work out efficiently in motor-speed control except in low capacities. However, they are so economically constructed that it is often advantageous to use them for motor-speed control, even inefficiently, rather than some other construction.

When the required wattage is beyond that of one plate, several may be used in series or in parallel, and their levers may be operated by a common handwheel. A series arrangement is preferable for several reasons. The resistance per plate will be lower, permitting the use of heavier wire and so reducing the danger of mechanical weakness or of breakage due to electrolysis. With plates in parallel, there is always the chance that, if one burns out, the others will be overloaded and all will burn out before the trouble is corrected. There is also the danger that the levers will not be exactly synchronized, and so the plates will become unbalanced, overloading one or more until a burnout occurs.

Large Field Rheostats. The larger rheostats consist of a series of buttons or segments mounted in a circle on a slate panel, and commutated by a lever which is usually double-ended. The resistance material is separate and may consist of any type of resistor unit or grid connected to the segments. The resistor is laid out in two duplicate portions, each half being connected to a half circle of segments. The two parts are then connected either in series or in parallel, depending upon the current capacity required. The lever is arranged to cut out the segments alternately in one half and the other, so that only one step is cut out at a time.

Motor-driven Rheostats. If it is necessary or desirable to control the speed from a remote point, a motor-driven field rheostat is used. The rheostat has a small motor which drives the rheostat lever through a reduction gearing. Split field motors are commonly employed, as they afford a simple means of reversal. Motor drives of this sort can be applied to rheostats of either the plate type or the segment type. The speed of the rheostat is controlled by the insertion of variable resistance in the pilot motor circuit. Limit switches are also supplied. These may be of the geared type and incorporated directly in the rheostat drive, or they may consist of interlock fingers operated by the rheostat arm in its travel. Motor drives are usually arranged so that the drive may easily be disconnected, and the rheostat moved by hand, if desired.

Potentiometer Rheostats. Potentiometer rheostats are connected directly across the line, and the field of the motor is connected across a portion of the rheostat.

Referring to Fig. 83,

E = line volts.
R = total rheostat resistance.
r = resistance of the field.
i = amperes in the field.
I = amperes in the portion of the rheostat which is in series with the field.
x = resistance of that portion of the rheostat which is in series with the field.

Then

$$R - x = \sqrt{Rr + \left(\frac{E - iR}{2i}\right)^2} - \left(\frac{E - iR}{2i}\right)$$

$$I = \frac{E}{\dfrac{r(R - x)}{r + R - x} + x}$$

The equations give the value of the resistance x in terms of quantities which are known (E and r) or which can be assumed (R and i). The total rheostat resistance R should be made as high as is possible within the limits of the resistor materials used, to keep the summation watts of the rheostat low. A good value for R is approximately $4r$,

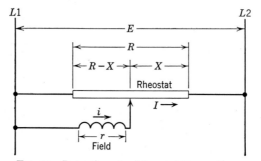

FIG. 83. Potentiometer Rheostat Connections.

and with this ratio the summation watts will be about $1.1E^2/r$. If $R = 2r$ the summation watts will be about $1.2E^2/r$.

Instead of calculating each step of the rheostat, it is simpler to calculate a few points and plot curves of field amperes and rheostat amperes against the position of the rheostat arm, x. The other steps

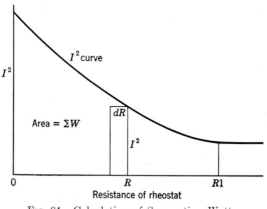

FIG. 84. Calculation of Summation Watts.

can then be read from the curve and be proportioned to give approximately equal current increments per step.

Summation Watts for Potentiometer Rheostats. The summation wattage equation for a potentiometer rheostat is somewhat more difficult to calculate than that of a series rheostat.

Referring to Fig. 84,

$$I = \cfrac{E}{\cfrac{r(R - x)}{r + R - x} + x}$$

$$= \frac{E(r + R - x)}{Rr + Rx - x^2}$$

$$d \text{ (watts)} = I^2\, dx$$

$$\text{Summation watts} = \int_{x=0}^{x=R} \left(\frac{E(r + R - x)}{Rr + Rx - x^2}\right)^2 dx$$

The steps involved in the solution of this equation are rather complicated and not of enough general interest to be included here. The equation reduces to

$$\text{Summation watts} = \frac{E^2}{r}\left(\frac{2r^2 + 4Rr + R^2}{4Rr + R^2}\right)$$

If the rheostat resistance is now expressed in terms of the field resistance,

$$R = Kr$$

Substituting this value in the summation watts equation,

$$\text{Summation watts} = \frac{E^2}{r}\left(\frac{2r^2 + 4Kr^2 + K^2r^2}{4Kr^2 + K^2r^2}\right)$$

$$= \frac{E^2}{r}\left(\frac{2 + 4K + K^2}{4K + K^2}\right)$$

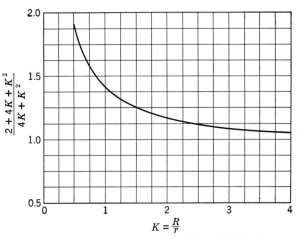

FIG. 85. Factors for Summation Watts Calculation.

Since the ratio of rheostat resistance to field resistance, K, is known, the summation watts can readily be determined. Figure 85 is a curve plotted between K and the expression of the equation in parentheses, as an aid in solving the problem when K is not a whole number.

References

S. B. Griscom, "How to Protect Motor and Generator Field Coils," *Power*, January, 1941.

Problems

1. The speed of a direct-current motor is to be varied by field control. If the line voltage is 250 volts and the desired range of speed control is obtained by varying the field current from 5 amperes to 2.5 amperes:

(*a*) What is the resistance of the motor field?

(*b*) What total resistance is required in the field rheostat?

(*c*) What is the summation watt rating of the rheostat?

(*d*) What is the current taper of the rheostat?

2. The resistance of the shunt field of a 230-volt motor is 55 ohms. The field current at maximum speed is 1.2 amperes. If the field rheostat is made up of resistor units having a continuous rating of 50 watts each, how many will be required?

3. If units of various continuous ratings are available, and if the rheostat has 10 steps of equal ohmic value, what will be the continuous wattage of the unit used for the first step of the rheostat?

4. What will be the ohmic value of the unit used for the last step of the rheostat?

5. Referring to Fig. 82, calculate a rheostat of 100 steps in 10 blocks, to give equal speed increases per step.

6. Referring to Fig. 82, calculate a rheostat of 100 steps in 10 blocks, to give equal percentage speed increases per step.

7. A 230-volt motor field having a resistance of 150 ohms is connected to a 600-ohm potentiometer rheostat at a point where the field is in parallel with one-third of the rheostat. What field current is obtained?

8. What will be the relative cost of the resistor material in the potentiometer rheostat of problem 7, compared with the cost of a straight series resistor that will give the same motor speed?

9. Referring to Fig. 102, and using a method similar to that of Table 15, calculate the ohms and watts for a generator rheostat of 100 steps, in 10 blocks, to reduce the voltage to 30 volts at full load, with a hot field.

10. A 230-volt shunt motor has a maximum field current of 7 amperes, and the field current at twice base speed is 2 amperes. Calculate a rheostat of 100 steps in 10 blocks, to give equal speed increases per step.

11. A 550-volt shunt motor has a shunt field resistance of 100 ohms, and the resistance required in a rheostat to give a desired speed range is 300 ohms. Calculate a 150-step rheostat, using blocks of 10 steps each, and giving equal speed increases per step.

12. How many resistor units, rated at 100 watts each, will be required for the rheostat of problem 10?

13. How many resistor units, rated at 100 watts each, will be required for the rheostat of problem 11?

14. Using the data of problem 10, calculate a rheostat to give equal percentage speed increases per step.

15. Using the data of problem 11, calculate a rheostat to give equal percentage speed increases per step.

16. A salesman is asked to quote on the resistor material required for a field rheostat for a 230-volt motor having a field resistance of 45 ohms. The field current at maximum speed is 1.3 amperes. If resistor units rated 75 watts each sell for $1.50 each, what is the price of the resistor?

17. A 230-volt shunt motor has a field having a resistance of 65 ohms. When the motor is standing still, the maximum voltage which the field can safely dissipate is 400 watts. Calculate the ohms and the wattage capacity of an economizer resistor to be connected into the field circuit when the motor is not running.

18. A 230-volt shunt motor has a field resistance of 50 ohms. The field current at the desired slowest speed is 3.5 amperes and at the desired highest speed is 1.5 amperes. Calculate the ohms and summation watts of the permanent resistor which is required, and also of the variable rheostat.

19. Calculate a 50-step rheostat for the motor of problem 18, using 10 blocks of 5 steps each, and giving equal speed increases per step.

20. If the motor of problem 18 is equipped with a field-failure relay, what is the current at which the relay must close, and what current must the relay coil be able to carry continuously?

21. A salesman has to quote on a resistor for a rheostat for a 100-horsepower 230-volt motor, whose field characteristics are unknown. The speed range required is 3 to 1. The resistor units to be used are rated 75 watts each and sell for $1.50 each. Using the data of Table 14, calculate the price which should be quoted.

22. A 30-horsepower 550-volt shunt motor which has not been designed is to have a speed increase of 100 per cent by shunt field weakening. Using Table 14, calculate the estimated field characteristics, that is: field resistance, rheostat resistance, maximum and minimum field currents, and rheostat summation watts.

23. A 230-volt shunt motor has a speed range of 2 to 1 by field control. If this motor is plugged when running at maximum speed, to a reversed direction with full field strength, what countervoltage will be developed?

24. A potentiometer rheostat of 400 ohms is connected across a 230-volt supply line. A motor field of 100 ohms is to be varied by this rheostat. If the potentiometer rheostat is divided into 10 equal steps, calculate the field current which will be obtained on each of the 11 points of the regulator.

9

ADJUSTABLE-VOLTAGE CONTROLLERS

Basic Principles. The speed of a shunt-wound direct-current motor has been shown to be proportional to the motor countervoltage. The motor terminal voltage is the sum of the countervoltage and the armature-resistance voltage drop, the last being a relatively low value. The motor may then be made to run at any desired speed below normal by applying a suitable supply voltage to the armature, at the same time maintaining full voltage to the shunt field. When the motor must be operated from the main power supply, it is obviously impractical to change the voltage of the supply lines, as that would affect the operation of every other motor connected to the lines. A resistor is then connected in series with the armature to reduce the applied voltage and so obtain a reduced speed. In order to be able to vary the supply voltage directly, it is necessary to have a generator supplying only the motor, or motors, of the drive in question. With that arrangement, the applied voltage may be varied by varying the strength of the generator field. The motor armature is connected directly to the generator, and the motor may be started without requiring accelerating resistor or contactors. Speeds above normal may be obtained by weakening the motor shunt field. Reversing is obtained by reversing the generator field, and so changing the polarity of the voltage applied to the motor armature.

The basic adjustable-voltage system, then, requires the following machines and devices:

A direct-current generator.
A means to drive the generator (Diesel engine, or a-c motor).
A direct-current motor.
A small direct-current generator to excite the motor and generator fields.
A rheostat, or other means, for varying the generator (and sometimes also the motor) field strength.

Variations. The basic system is subject to many variations and modifications, as determined by the requirements of the machine to be driven. The generator may be a single machine or a group of machines. The motor may also be a single machine or a group of motors connected to the same load or to different loads. The motor and generator fields may be excited from some available direct-current supply or from a small exciter. When a group of motors is being controlled, there may be separate exciters for each motor. The control may be manual or automatic. Motor-driven rheostats are widely used. Control for large motors and for motors subject to rapid speed change and reversal may use contactors to commutate resistance in the motor and generator fields. Separate exciters may be used for the generator and the motor, and the control may be in the exciter fields instead of in the fields of the main machines.

Characteristics. Since the controlling means operate in the field circuits of the machines, and the armatures of the motor and generator are directly connected to each other, the control is relatively simple, and large magnetic contactors are not required, although a single main circuit contactor is often used.

Armature-accelerating and -regulating resistors are eliminated, together with their associated contactors and timing devices. The power losses, which make speed regulation by armature-circuit resistance inefficient, are also eliminated. The power lost in the field-circuit resistors is relatively low.

Rheostats can readily be built with a large number of finely graduated steps to give a wide range of stable speeds. These speeds will be accurate and will be affected relatively little by changes in load. By suitable design of the generator, speeds may be held constant to within a few per cent under any load condition.

Because of the large number of speeds, the current and torque peaks during acceleration and deceleration are low, and the machine is started and stopped smoothly. This is important, for instance, on high-speed elevators and on paper-making machines. A smoothly applied regenerative braking for slowdown and stopping is obtained.

By suitable design of the generator it is possible to obtain automatically, and without the use of control devices, special speed-torque characteristics required by a machine. The electric shovel is a good example. Here it is desired that the machine slow down and stall when the shovel strikes an obstruction requiring more than a safe torque to move it. When the operator backs the shovel away, the speed should come back to normal. A three-field generator having a self-excited shunt field, a differentially connected series field, and a separately excited shunt field will give these characteristics.

The adjustable-voltage system affords a means of controlling the speed of a group of motors simultaneously. The roll-table drive described in Chapter 16 is an example; others are described in this chapter.

The adjustable-voltage system also offers a means of obtaining a wide range of speeds for a machine in a plant where only alternating current is available.

An obvious disadvantage of the system is the cost of the machines required to obtain the adjustable voltages.

Applications. Adjustable-voltage control is applied to machine installations to obtain one or more of the advantages mentioned, and the usual applications fall into one of the following groups:

1. Controllers for starting and speed-regulating duty:
   (a) Single-motor or multimotor.
   (b) Manually operated, or automatically operated.
   (c) Speed control by adjustment of generator field only or by regulation of both generator and motor fields.
2. Controllers arranged for presetting the operating speed:
   (a) Single-motor or multimotor.
   (b) Manual or automatic speed selection, automatic acceleration to preset speed.
   (c) Speed control by adjustment of generator field only or by regulation of both generator and motor fields.
3. Electric coupling between machines.
4. Helper drives.

Single-motor Manual Controller. Figure 86 is the diagram of a single-motor adjustable-voltage controller, using manually operated rheostats, and arranged for low-voltage starting and speed regulating. The motor armature is connected to the generator armature through a magnetic contactor M and an overload relay OL.

In the off position of the controller, the contactor M is de-energized and open, and the generator rheostat is disconnected by an interlock contact on M.

To start up the drive, the generator and exciter are brought up to speed and the exciter voltage is adjusted to the right value by means of its field rheostat. These machines continue to run as long as the drive is in use. The start button is pressed, and the contactor M is energized, provided that the generator rheostat is in the weak field position, in which position only the interlock contact on the rheostat is closed. When M closes, its main contact closes the circuit between the generator armature and the motor armature, but little or no current flows because the generator field is short-circuited. One interlock contact of M provides a maintaining circuit, and the other connects the generator field rheostat into circuit. The motor is now accelerated to any desired speed up to normal by strengthening the generator field.

A potentiometer rheostat is used for the generator rather than a series rheostat, so that the initial generator field current may be zero.

Speeds above normal are obtained by weakening the motor field. The motor is stopped by pressing the stop button, which de-energizes M. It is impossible to restart until the generator rheostat is returned to the weak field position to reclose the interlock switch.

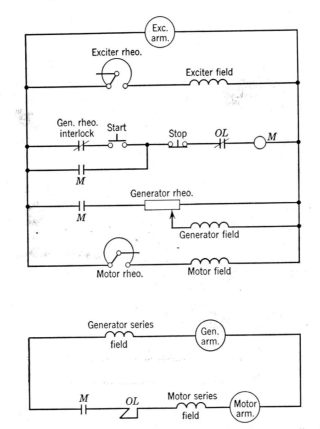

FIG. 86.   Single-motor Adjustable-voltage Controller with Manually Operated Rheostats.

This is a very simple form of controller, and no provision is shown for protection against too rapid acceleration or deceleration. Such provision, and other protective devices, disconnecting knife switches, etc., may be added to suit the requirements of a given installation. Figure 87 shows a manually operated generator rheostat of a type that might be used. The interlock switch is a pushbutton operated by the rheostat arm. The handwheel of the rheostat is not shown, as it is mounted on the shaft after the door has been closed. The exciter rheostat would probably be a small plate-type device. The motor rheostat might be a plate type, or, if the service were severe, it might be a duplicate of the generator rheostat. If the speed range of the motor above normal were very great, the motor rheostat might also be provided with an interlock switch to insure that it was in the full-field position before M could be closed. Motor and generator field circuits might be incorporated in one rheostat, or two rheostats

Fig. 87.   Manually Operated Rheostat.

might be mechanically connected, so that the generator would be brought up to full voltage before the motor field was weakened.

Single-motor Starting and Regulating Controller. When operation from a remote point is desirable, the rheostat may be driven by a pilot motor, which is controlled from pushbuttons. The pilot motor may be connected to the rheostat arm by gearing or through a chain and sprocket drive, or the rheostat arm may be mounted directly on the slow-speed shaft of a geared-head motor. Figure 88 shows a small rheostat of this kind.

The controller shown in Figs. 89 and 90 uses a reversible series-wound motor, specially designed for the purpose and having a gear reduction built into it. The motor is provided with a large flange for mounting to the panel, and the slow-speed shaft is extended through the panel to support the rheostat arm. The arm is not permanently fastened to the shaft but is driven through an adjustable friction clutch, so that it may slip a little when it strikes the limiting stops and so relieve strains on the gearing. The circuits for controlling both

FIG. 88. Small Motor-operated Rheostat.

motor and generator fields are combined in the one rheostat. Below the rheostat proper are the relays for controlling the pilot motor, the main motor circuit contactors, and the overload relay. The rear view shows the type of field resistors used. These are small coils of resistor wire, mounted directly to the rheostat buttons, which eliminate the wiring that would be necessary with conventional resistor units. One of the plate-type rheostats mounted on the panel is used in the exciter field circuit, and the other is an adjustable permanent resistor in the main generator field circuit. The normally closed contactor and the grid resistor are used for dynamic braking of the main motor. The round slider-type units regulate the speed of the pilot motor.

Figure 91 is a diagram of a motor-operated controller arranged for starting and speed regulation both below and above the normal

FIG. 89.   Motor-operated Adjustable-voltage Controller.

motor speed. To put this drive into operation, the main generator and the exciter are started and brought up to speed by their driving means, which would probably be alternating-current motors. The exciter voltage is adjusted to the proper value. The main generator voltage will be zero, as the generator field is short-circuited.   The motor field will be at its full strength to give normal, or base, motor speed.   To simplify the diagram, the rheostat circuits have been shown

Fig. 90.   Motor-operated Adjustable-voltage Controller.   Rear View.

as straight lines.   Actually they are arranged in circles as shown by the photographs.   The photographs do not correspond exactly with the diagram, as no photograph of a controller having these exact circuits was available.

To start the motor, the start button is pressed, energizing relay 1C, which maintains its own circuit around the start button and provides a circuit to energize the main contactor M. The starting circuit is available only when the rheostat arm is in the off position; in any

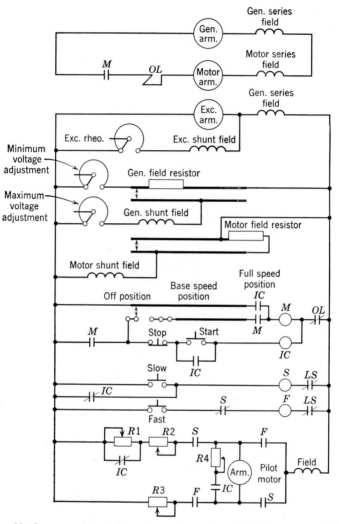

Fig. 91. Single-motor Adjustable-voltage Controller with Motor-operated Rheostats, for Starting and Speed-regulating Service.

other position $1C$ and M are energized through their maintaining interlock contacts. The motor may now be accelerated to any desired speed by holding down the fast button until that speed is reached. This button energizes relay F, which in turn energizes the rheostat pilot motor. The rate of acceleration is governed by the settings of the adjustable series resistor $R3$ and the adjustable armature shunt resistor $R4$. The main motor speed may be reduced by pressing the slow button, energizing relay S. This relay energizes the rheostat pilot motor in the reverse direction, the rate of deceleration being governed by the settings of the adjustable resistors $R1$ and $R2$. As the rheostat arm moves from the off position, it first strengthens the generator field by cutting out one step after another of the resistor. When the generator field has reached its full strength, resistance is inserted in the motor field to increase the speed further.

The main motor is stopped by pressing the stop button, which opens the circuit to $1C$. A normally closed contact on $1C$ bypasses the slow button, energizing relay S, and so causing the rheostat arm to return to the off position, where it is stopped by the limit switch LS. During this time M is maintained closed by its own interlock contacts and does not open until the rheostat arm returns to the off position and there breaks the maintaining circuit. The motor cannot be restarted or reaccelerated after the stop button has been pressed, as there is no circuit to the start button, and the circuit to the F relay is broken by one contact of the S relay. By so arranging the stopping circuits, the controller provides regenerative braking during deceleration. The pilot motor is usually adjusted to run much faster during deceleration than during acceleration, perhaps 60 to 90 seconds in one direction, and 3 seconds in the other.

For some applications this method of stopping is too slow. A normally closed dynamic braking contactor D, shown on the photograph, is then provided, and the stop button is arranged to de-energize M and D at once and so connect a step of resistance across the motor armature. The coil of D would be connected in parallel with that of M, and the maintaining interlock contact of M, which connects to the rheostat contact strip, would be omitted. The rheostat would automatically return to the off position as before. A combination of the two methods is often used, regenerative braking being used for slow-down and dynamic braking for the final stop.

Multimotor Drives. There are many applications, particularly in the paper and textile industries, in which it is necessary to control the speed of a group of motors simultaneously. Adjustable-voltage control is widely used for such applications.

Figure 92 is a diagram of a controller for a group of motors, which is arranged for starting them together and regulating their speeds as a group. Three motors are shown, but there might be any number in the group. For each motor there is a main contactor and an overload

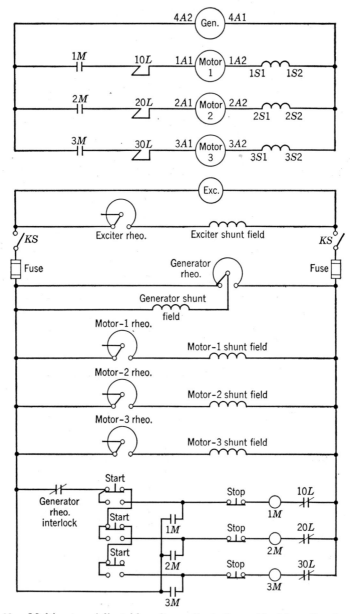

FIG. 92.   Multimotor Adjustable-voltage Controller with Manually Operated
Rheostats.

relay. A group of pushbutton stations, one for each motor, is arranged so that any one or more of the motors may be connected to the generator, provided that the generator rheostat is in the off position and the generator voltage therefore zero. If the number of motors in the group is fixed, the individual contactors and pushbuttons could be omitted and a single main contactor substituted. The individual motor rheostats are used to adjust the relative speeds of the motors, and they might have to be set differently at different operating speeds because the characteristics of the motors might not be alike. This would be particularly true if the motors were of different sizes. It will be apparent that a motor-operated generator rheostat could readily be applied to a group drive if remote control were desired.

Speed-setting Control. Many applications of adjustable-voltage control require speed setting, which means that it must be possible to stop the drive, and restart it from a pushbutton, having it automatically return to the speed at which it was running when the stop button was pressed. There are a number of ways of doing this. At first thought it might seem that an adjustable limit switch might be provided for the rheostat lever, but there are several objections to that arrangement. It is not a simple matter to design a limit switch which can be readily set at any point in the rheostat travel, particularly if the switch must be set from a remote point. The speed of a motor-driven rheostat is usually slow, so that the arm can easily be stopped on any desired button, and with slow operation it would take too long to restart the drive after a stop.

Controllers for large motors, such as those driving rolling mills for sheet steel, use a double-arm rheostat arrangement. A conventional motor-driven rheostat, having about 150 steps, is used for selecting the operating speed. A second motor-driven rheostat arm, having about 75 contacts, but without resistor, and running at a faster speed, is used for starting. The contacts of the starting arm are connected to alternate contacts of the regulating rheostat, so that the starting arm commutates the resistor two steps at a time. The control is then arranged so that the regulating arm is set from pushbuttons and left at the desired speed point. When the starting pushbutton is operated, the starting rheostat arm travels through its full cycle, cutting out resistance up to the point at which the regulating arm is set. The rest of its travel does not have any effect. In stopping, this arm moves back through its full travel to the off position. The drive may then be started and stopped as often as desired and will always return to the preset speed. Since the field currents of these large motors may be in the neighborhood of 100 amperes, a relatively expensive controller is not out of consideration, but for smaller installations other methods are generally employed.

A method used relatively infrequently is to preset the speed by means of a generator rheostat and to do the starting and stopping of

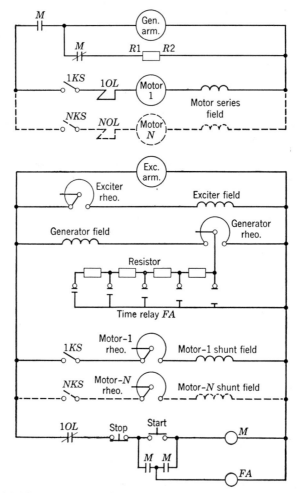

Fig. 93.   Multimotor Adjustable-voltage Controller with Manually Operated Rheostats.   Speed Setting by Generator Field Acceleration.

the whole drive by starting and stopping the alternating-current motor which drives the generator. This arrangement may be used with either a manually operated or motor-driven generator rheostat, and for either a single motor or a group of motors. It has the undesirable feature of requiring the starting and stopping of the alternating-current motor and the generator as well as the drive motor. Also the starting will not be so smooth as it might be, particularly if the alternating-current motor is started by direct connection to the lines.

Another method, and one frequently used, is to supply the conventional generator rheostat and in addition a starting resistor in the generator field circuit. Figure 93 shows the connections, and it will be evident that the method may be applied to either a single motor or a group of motors. In this diagram, a single main contactor has been shown, one having both a normally open contact for the line and a normally closed contact for dynamic braking. The latter feature is not always desired. Individual contactors for each motor could be used if it were desirable to be able to cut out some of the motors. The generator rheostat remains at the preset speed point, but the field is reduced to a low strength at the start because of the starting resistor. The relay FA has been shown as a multicontact timing device, which, when energized, closes its contacts one after another in sequence, until the starting resistor is short-circuited. When that has been accomplished, the generator field strength will be determined by the setting of the rheostat. The timing device is one of a type frequently employed for the purpose, but for larger motors it could be replaced by a set of magnetic contactors timed by this device or by some other form of timing relay.

The connections for still another common method of speed setting are shown in Fig. 94. Here armature circuit accelerating resistors are used, and the motors are started as if they were connected to a constant-voltage power supply. No means of timing the acceleration has been shown, but any of those in general use would be satisfactory. Here again many modifications of the general scheme are possible.

Synchronizing Motor Speeds. Several of the diagrams for multi-motor controllers show rheostats in the individual motor field circuits, and it has been said that these are for the purpose of adjusting the relative speeds of the motors. Manual adjustment is satisfactory for some applications, but, if a continuous strip of material, such as steel, cloth, or paper, is passing through a series of motor-driven machines, it is generally necessary to provide some means of automatically holding the motor speeds in the right relation to each other. In the textile industry, a device known as a dancer roll is common for that purpose. A dancer roll is a roller so mounted in slotted end supports that it is fixed in position horizontally but free to move vertically within limits. A motor field rheostat is mechanically connected to the dancer roll and operated by it as it moves up and down in its supports. The

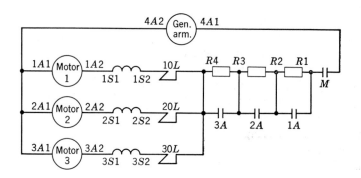

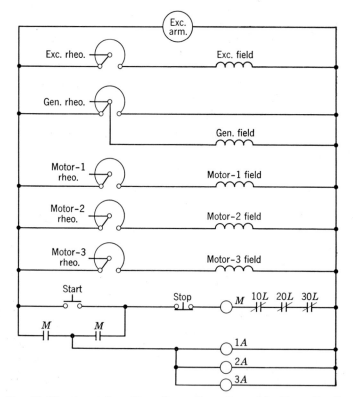

FIG. 94.   Multimotor Adjustable-voltage Controller with Manually Operated Rheostats.   Speed Setting by Armature Acceleration.

cloth is fed over a stationary roller at the top of the dancer roll, then down under the dancer roll, back up to another stationary roller, and from there into the next processing machine. Now, if the motor of the leading machine is running too fast, the slack in the cloth will begin to be taken up, and the cloth will pull the dancer roll up. As the roll moves up it operates the rheostat connected to it, resistance is cut out of the motor field circuit, and the motor speed is reduced. Similarly, if the leading motor is running too slowly, there will be a greater loop of cloth between machines, and the dancer roll will drop. The rheostat will then be moved in the opposite direction and will insert resistance to speed up the motor. Rheostats for this service must be well built, as the dancer roll is continually hunting, and the rheostat is in constant motion. A series of textile processing machines would have a dancer roll for each individual motor, with the exception of the leading motor, to which the speeds of the others would be synchronized.

While the dancer roll works well for cloth processing, it obviously would not work for sheet steel which is being processed under tension. Here the strip may pass through a number of tandem rolling mills, each driven by a large motor of perhaps several thousand horsepower in rating. The motors are designed for a very close speed regulation; that is, the speed at any load is almost the same. Even so, it is desirable to provide additional means of holding the speed constant, because two motors which will run at the same speed at one speed value will not necessarily run together over the whole speed range. One method of correction is to provide an auxiliary field winding in the motor and to vary its strength in different amounts, depending on the motor speed. The rheostat for varying the main field of the motor has an additional set of contacts to vary the resistance in the auxiliary field winding. The resistor values have to be carefully determined, generally by test after installation of the motor and mill.

A series exciter may be used to obtain approximately flat speed regulation over the speed range. The exciter is a small direct-current generator, which has its field connected in series with the armature of the main generator and its armature connected in series with the field of the main generator. Normally the speed of a motor decreases with an increase in load, because of the increased IR drop in both generator and motor. When the series exciter is used, an increase in load will strengthen the exciter field and increase the voltage at its armature. This, in turn, will increase the current in the main generator field and so increase the generator armature voltage. By proper adjustment it is possible to obtain very close speed regulation between no load and full load, and at all speeds (see Fig. 95).

A paper-making machine requires extremely close speed control because the paper is so weak that a very slight variation from the correct speed relation between sections of the machine would result in a break in the paper. In its wet state, newsprint paper has a tensile

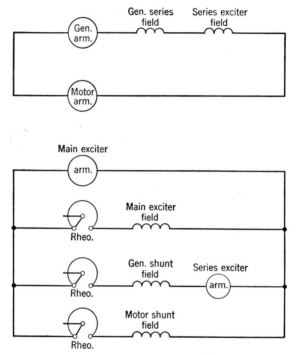

FIG. 95.   Connections for a Series Exciter.

strength of about 0.06 pound per inch of width, and, as the tension produced by its own weight is about 0.04 pound per inch, the margin of safety is rather small. Since the speed of the paper traveling through the machine may be 1000 feet per minute or more, it is evident that the control must be sensitive and accurate.

One form of control makes use of a mechanical differential, similar in principle to the differential gears of an automobile, but made with extreme accuracy. Such a differential has three shafts, one to each of the outer gears and one to the ring gear. When the two outer gears are rotated in opposite directions at the same speed, the ring gear remains stationary, but, if there is any slight difference in the speeds of the outer gears, the ring gear will begin to revolve. In applying this principle to a paper machine, one differential mechanism is used with each motor of the machine. A master speed-setting motor is arranged to drive a shaft which extends the whole length of the paper machine, and one outside gear of each differential is geared to this shaft. The other outside gears of the differentials are each driven from one of the motors driving a section of the machine. The ring gear shafts of the differentials are each arranged to drive a rheostat having a large number of finely graduated steps. These rheostats control the speed of the section motors. If the gearing were fixed in ratio, all the motors would run at the speed of the master shaft, since any attempt to run at another speed would cause a ring gear to turn, operate the rheostat, and correct the motor speed. Actually, it is necessary to have a slight speed difference between motors, to make up for the elongation of the paper between machines. This is accomplished by using a belt drive, through a pair of cone pulleys, between the motor and the differential. By suitable adjustment of the pulleys, the motor speed may be set at any desired value, and the differential rheostat will hold it there. The speed of the machine as a whole is adjusted by varying the main generator voltage, which affects all motors alike, including the master motor.

The differential function may also be obtained electrically, eliminating the necessity for the master shaft and mechanical differential gearing. The electrical differential consists of a stator and a rotor, so arranged that any relative motion between them will move a rheostat. One is used for each motor of the paper machine. All the stators are energized at the same frequency from a master alternator. Each rotor is energized from a generator belted through cone pulleys to one section of the machine. As long as the frequency of the individual generator matches that of the master generator, which would mean that the speed was correct, the rheostat would not be moved, but, as soon as any variation occurs, the rotor of the differential will start to turn to correct it. The torque of this type of regulator follows a sine curve, so that a slight displacement between rotor and stator will produce a strong torque, and to further insure sensitivity the device is designed to produce many times the torque required to turn the rheostat.

A third method of synchronizing the sections of a paper machine uses the mechanical differentials but substitutes for the master shaft a master alternator and an individual synchronous motor driving each differential. The three methods are illustrated in Fig. 96.

Electric-shovel Control. The contrast between the drives just described and the electric-shovel drive illustrates the flexibility of the

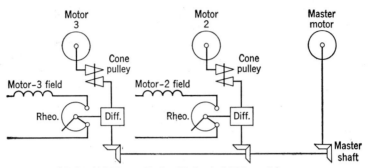

Mechanical Master Shaft – Mechanical Differential

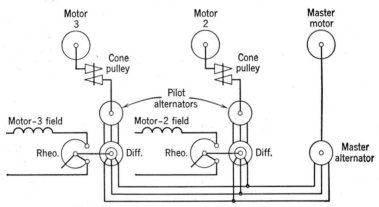

Electric Master Shaft – Electric Differential

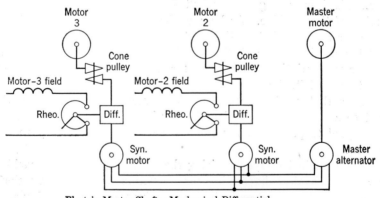

Electric Master Shaft – Mechanical Differential

Fig. 96.   Differential Speed-synchronizing Control Methods.

adjustable-voltage system. Instead of requiring a constant speed at all loads, the shovel requires a control which will allow it to slow down under heavy loads and stall if the load is too great. This is accomplished by means of a three-field generator. The machine has a

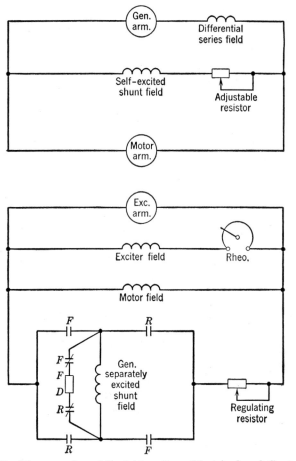

Gen. arm.

Differential series field

Self-excited shunt field

Adjustable resistor

Motor arm.

Exc. arm.

Exciter field

Rheo.

Motor field

F   R

F

F

D

R

Gen. separately excited shunt field

Regulating resistor

R   F

FIG. 97. Diagram of an Adjustable-voltage Electric-shovel Controller.

differentially connected series field, a self-excited shunt field, and a separately excited shunt field. The connections for the controller are shown in Fig. 97. The series field and the self-excited field are usually not varied in operation, the control being obtained from the separately excited field only, although sometimes the strength of the self-excited field may be changed by the controller. For electric shovels the controllers are usually of the drum type, including contacts for reversing the field, applying the field discharge resistor $(F–D)$ in the off position, and varying the regulating resistor for speed control.

The shape of the generator voltage curve will depend on the relative strength of the three fields, and with a constant motor field excitation the speed-torque curve of the motor will be of the same shape. Figure 98 shows typical curves obtained by varying the separately excited field. At no load, the effect of the series field is zero; and, when the motor is stalled, the effect of the self-excited field is zero. The effect

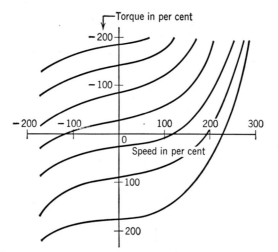

Fig. 98. Speed-torque Curves of an Electric-shovel Drive.

of the self-excited field is to maintain the load current nearly constant over a considerable voltage range.

The advantages obtained with this type of drive are that the maximum motor torque, maximum motor speed, and maximum motor armature current are limited. Good operating speeds are obtained at loads near the maximum torque value, and the maximum torque is exerted at standstill with little expenditure of power.

Prevention of Creeping. Not all adjustable-voltage systems are arranged so that the main armature circuit is opened when the motor is stopped. The motor and generator armatures may be permanently connected together, or, particularly with large motors, there may be a circuit breaker in the armature circuit for disconnecting and for protection against overload. The circuit breaker would not open in normal operation. Such drives are stopped by reducing the generator field strength to zero, but there is danger that enough residual field strength may remain to generate a low voltage and keep the motor turning at a low speed. To prevent this, the generator shunt field is disconnected from the exciter by suitable magnetic relays and reconnected across the generator armature, the polarity being such that any voltage generated by residual field magnetism will cause current to flow through the field in the reverse of the normal direction. The result will be to kill any remaining field magnetism, and for that reason the scheme is known as a suicide connection.

Electric Coupling. An adjustable-voltage system is sometimes used only to obtain an electric coupling between two machines. A reel for coiling strip steel as it comes from a rolling mill is a good example. The mill itself may be driven from a constant-voltage power supply but may operate over a range of speeds obtained by field control of its driving motor. The speed of the reel must basically follow that of the mill, and so the reel motor will be driven from a generator geared to the mill. Then any change in the mill speed will result in a change in the generator speed and voltage, with a corresponding change in the motor speed. The reel motor will be required to change its speed continually as the roll of steel builds up, in order to maintain a constant linear speed and a constant tension in the steel. The control devices for this purpose cannot be described here, but they operate by controlling the motor field, and the adjustable-voltage generator is needed only for the coupling described.

Helper Drives. When a machine includes a long endless belt, or an endless web of felt running over a number of rolls, it is desirable to

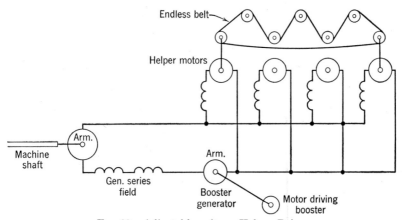

FIG. 99. Adjustable-voltage Helper Drive.

apply driving power at a number of points to equalize the stresses in the belt or web. The usual practice is to drive a generator from some shaft of the machine, and to utilize the generated power to

energize several motors applied to individual rolls. In this way the
entire driving effort need not be transmitted through the web, and the

FIG. 100.   Operator's Control Panel.

stresses may be equalized by adjusting the torque delivered by each
motor. It is generally necessary to have a small motor-driven booster
generator in addition to the main generator, to supply a constant

voltage to compensate for the motor voltage drop. This voltage drop is constant at all speeds, so that it cannot be correctly compensated for by the adjustable-voltage generator. Figure 99 shows the arrangement of a helper drive.

Fig. 101. Tandem Motor-operated Rheostats.

Operator's Panels. The operator of a machine driven by an adjustable-voltage system is likely to have to handle a good many pilot-control devices. There are usually several rheostats and a number of pushbuttons; there may be transfer switches or emergency switches. The operator may also have to watch a number of instruments, such as voltmeters, ammeters, and tachometers. These devices might be mounted individually at convenient points on the machine, but convenient places are not always easy to find, and the interwiring of the devices may be difficult. It is often a better arrangement to mount all the control devices and instruments on a steel panel, which will also contain the interwiring and be provided with a terminal board for the connections to the main control panel. Figure 100 shows such

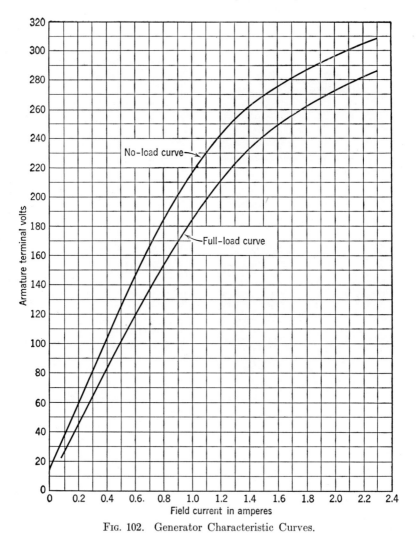

Fig. 102. Generator Characteristic Curves.

a panel, mounting meters, rheostats, and operating pushbuttons. The three acorn nuts, grouped around each rheostat handwheel, are the mountings for the rheostats, which are on the rear of the panel. The rheostats shown have a duplex concentric drive, for a main and a vernier rheostat. The panel is hinged to its supporting frame and may be opened for inspection of the rheostats and for wiring to the terminal board. Flexible hinge wire is used between the devices on the door and any devices mounted to the stationary frame. Some operator's panels are totally enclosed, requiring that the door be open for operation. This arrangement would be adopted only if access to the panel was not often necessary.

Tandem Rheostats. When more than one motor is to be controlled by a rheostat, the rheostat may include two or more sets of segments and field resistors. When the motors are large, and the field currents high, this may not be practical. For some applications it might be desirable to control the motors either individually or in tandem, and the multiple sets of contacts would not readily permit that operation.

Figure 101 shows the construction of a tandem rheostat for a pair of large mill motors, with motor-driven crossheads which move in a straight line. The pilot motor of each rheostat drives a screw shaft, through suitable gearing, and the crosshead operates as a nut on the shaft. Brushes on the crosshead contact the rheostat segments. The resistor is mounted in the frame behind the crosshead and is connected to the segments. The two screw shafts are connected at the top, through bevel gearing and a cross-shaft, and a magnetically operated mechanical clutch is included as a part of the cross-shaft connection. For individual operation, the clutch is open; for tandem operation, the clutch is closed by pressing a button which energizes its operating magnet, and then the rheostats will operate together. The control circuits are arranged so that the clutch can be closed only when the crossheads are in the off position, and so that both pilot motors are always operated when the clutch is closed. These rheostats were arranged for the future addition of a third unit in tandem with the two first installed. Figure 102 is a typical generator saturation curve.

References

L. A. Umansky, "Direct-current Drives for Runout Tables and Coilers," *Proceedings Iron and Steel Engineers*, 1938.

H. W. Rogers, "Regenerative Tension Control for Paper Winders," *Electrical Engineering*, September, 1938.

R. A. Geuder, "Speed Control by Voltage Control," *Iron and Steel Engineer*, July, 1939.

W. L. O. Graves and E. H. Dinger, "Three Control Systems for D-c Adjustable-speed Drives," *Electrical Manufacturing*, July, 1949.

E. L. Schwartz-Kast, "Selecting Drives for Speed Control," *Machine Design*, April, May, June, 1945.

E. E. Moyer and M. E. Cummings, "Basic Control Requirements of D-c Adjustable-voltage Drives," *Electrical Manufacturing*, November, 1949.

A. D. Howry, "The Operation and Maintenance of Variable-voltage Control Systems," *Iron and Steel Engineer*, May, 1948.

J. E. Jones, "Adjustable-voltage Control System," *Product Engineering*, February, 1948.

J. E. Jones, "Flexible Control Systems for Tandem Operation," *Product Engineering*, July, 1947.

P. S. Stevens, "Evolution of Ward-Leonard Control for Shovels and Draglines," *Transactions AIEE*, 1948, Vol. 67, p. 1491.

Problems

1. Using the curve of Fig. 102, calculate the ohms required in a rheostat which will reduce the generator voltage to 30 volts at no load, and with a cold field.

2. Calculate the summation watts of the rheostat of problem 1.

3. Calculate the ohms required in a vernier rheostat which will permit a minimum adjustment of 20 volts at full load, with a hot field.

4. Calculate the ohms required in a vernier rheostat which will permit an adjustment of a minimum of 20 volts under any condition of generator load and field temperature, and at any point in the voltage range up to 250 volts.

5. Calculate the maximum ampere capacity, minimum ampere capacity, and summation watts, for the vernier rheostat of problem 4.

6. With the rheostat of problem 4, what will be the maximum voltage adjustment obtained under any condition of generator load, field temperature, and generator voltage?

7. Make an elementary diagram similar to Fig. 91, except replace contactor M by a circuit breaker, and add relays for preventing creeping when the drive is stopped.

8. Make an elementary diagram similar to Fig. 92, except add relays and pushbuttons for selecting the direction of travel before the motors are started.

9. Make an elementary diagram of a controller like Fig. 93, for 5 motors.

10. Complete elementary diagram Fig. 97, adding the control circuits, and using a reversing master controller having five speeds in each direction. Use magnetic contactors to commutate the regulating resistor. Add overload and low-voltage protective relays.

11. A 230-volt 600-rpm shunt motor has a field resistance of 50 ohms, and for a 2-to-1 speed range has a field current range of 4 to 1. Calculate the ohms, maximum and minimum ampere capacity, and summation watts, of a rheostat for the motor.

12. Plot a curve of speed against field current, for the motor of problem 11, assuming that the speed varies inversely as the square root of the field current.

13. Using the curve of problem 12, calculate the ohms required in a dancer-roll rheostat which will give a minimum speed adjustment of 60 rpm.

14. What is the maximum speed adjustment which will be obtained with the dancer-roll rheostat of problem 13?

15. If the rheostat of problem 13 has a taper so that the last step is four times the ohms of the first step, and there are 20 steps, what is the ohmic value of each step?

16. If the dancer-roll rheostat is operating with the main motor rheostat all in circuit, what speed change occurs when the last step of the dancer-roll rheostat is inserted into the circuit?

17. If the dancer-roll rheostat is operating with the main motor rheostat all out of the circuit, what speed change occurs when the first step of the dancer-roll rheostat is inserted into the circuit?

18. A machine drive consists of two 230-volt shunt motors having a speed range of 600 to 1200 rpm, and a generator having a voltage range of 115 to 230 volts. If the motor armatures are arranged for series-parallel connection, what is the speed range of the machine?

19. A 230-volt motor field having a resistance of 150 ohms is connected in parallel with a permanent discharge resistor which limits the discharge voltage to 690 volts. What are the ohmic value and maximum and minimum ampere capacity of a rheostat which will provide a field current at high speed, of 0.50 amperes?

20. Referring to Fig. 102, and using the method of Table 15, calculate the ohms and watts for a rheostat of 150 steps, in 15 blocks, to reduce the voltage to 50 volts at no load, with a cold field.

10

AUTOMATIC REGULATING SYSTEMS

Closed-loop Regulators. Most regulating systems used in industrial motor-control applications are of the closed-loop type. A closed-loop regulator is an amplifying system, which operates from an error or difference between a reference quantity and an actual resulting quantity, in a manner tending to keep the error as small as possible.

Motor-control Applications. The need for automatic regulating systems in electric motor control has developed largely because of changes in manufacturing methods. Formerly, single operations were performed on materials being processed, and the materials were moved from one machine to another until finally completed. This method required cutting the raw materials into suitable sizes and handling them throughout the processing as individual pieces.

In keeping with improved manufacturing methods, the natural trend was to eliminate as much as possible the handling of materials between process operations. This has led to processing materials in continuous form, as coils of strip or sheet and rolls of wire or rod. When materials are handled in continuous form, and pass through a series of processing operations, control problems are encountered that often require automatic regulating systems for their satisfactory solutions. The several machines in a continuous processing line are usually driven by individual motors, the motors receiving their power from one or more adjustable-voltage systems. Individual motor drives are usually required because the length of the line makes shafting impractical, but a more important reason is the requirement for flexibility between process sections. This would be extremely difficult to provide by mechanical means.

The proper coordination of a number of motors driving separate machines, which process a continuous length of material, requires precise regulation of voltage, speed, current, tension, and position. Often, there is one section of a machine where the linear speed must be held constant, and this becomes the master section of the group. Other sections must be synchronized with it so the material does not pile up between sections, nor is torn because it gets too tight. Sometimes the tension in the material entering a machine is critical, and

214

this requires tension regulation. Other machines may require a slack loop in the material, and a regulator is used to maintain the loop at its proper form. Lateral location of the moving material is often important, and position regulators are used to compensate for irregularities in the edge of the material and other variables. Current regulators are usually used with helper motors and cause these motors to operate at constant torque output.

Continuous-processing methods require handling of the materials in roll, coil, or bobbin form. These coils must be wound under carefully controlled tension conditions for process reasons and to prevent damage to the coil in handling. Constant-tension winding is commonly done not only in the continuous-processing operations, but also in preparatory processes when getting the material ready for the final process or for sale. Properly wound coils or rolls will not telescope in handling and will not be damaged under normal storage or handling conditions.

Regulators used in industry must meet a wide range of performance requirements and, very often, the type of regulator used is determined by the requirement. Beyond the ability to do the job satisfactorily is the need for dependability. This is especially true in the case of high-speed processing lines, where the failure of one part or function may shut down the entire line and where down time is expensive in terms of lost production.

Basic Regulating Systems. The basic closed-loop regulating system is shown in Fig. 103. The regulated quantity is the end result and can be either electrical or mechanical in nature. For instance, the regulated quantity can be the output voltage of a generator, the rotational speed of a shaft, or the position of a strip of material being processed. The regulating system usually furnishes only a small portion of the total power involved, and this is often in the form of shunt-field excitation for a motor or generator. The regulated quantity has some principal power source, and this, too, can be in the form of electric or mechanical power.

The basic regulator has a source of power necessary to operate the regulating devices and to supply the control power for regulating purposes.

The reference can be mechanical, such as a calibrated spring, but the customary reference used is a known voltage. This reference voltage should be stable, and, where precise results are required, it is carefully regulated so it does not fluctuate with line voltage, load, and temperature changes. A sufficiently accurate reference for most industrial-control applications can be obtained from a constant-

potential transformer. The reference is used to preselect the performance level required of the regulated quantity.

The signal-sensing device is a means of measuring the actual performance level of the regulated quantity. It must be capable of
measuring the thing to be regulated and of producing a signal which
bears a fixed relationship to the measurement. The signal is usually
a voltage that is proportional to the level of the regulated quantity.

The error-sensing system is that portion of the regulator where the
comparison of the actual signal is made with the preselected reference.

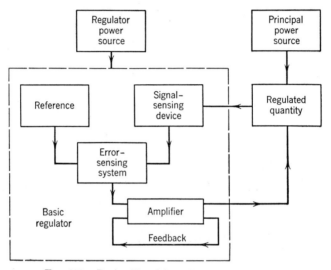

FIG. 103. Basic Closed-loop Regulating System.

The reference represents the wanted result, and the signal represents
the actual result. Any difference resulting from the comparison is
the error signal used to drive the amplifier system. The polarity,
or sense, of the error is in the direction to produce a correction that
tends to reduce the error.

The purpose of the amplifier is to enlarge the relatively weak signal
from the sensing system to the power level needed to control the performance of the regulated quantity effectively. The power gain in
the amplifying system, which is the ratio of the regulator output power
to the signal power, is dictated by the sensitivity required or, in other
words, by the allowable error. The principal difference in regulating
systems is in the type of amplifier used.

Circuits are usually employed which take off a portion of the
amplifier output and feed it back into the input end or at some

intermediate stage of the amplifier. If this feedback is additive, it is called regeneration, and, if subtractive, it is degeneration. In general, feedback is used to stabilize the system, and the usual arrangement is to feed back transients, rather than to use steady-state feedback. Stabilizing circuits are frequently called anti-hunt circuits, and their purpose is to prevent oscillations of the regulated quantity. In transient feedback anti-hunt circuits, the sense of the transient is in opposition to the change taking place in the amplifier output.

Sensing Devices. As pointed out previously, the function of the sensing device is to measure the actual performance of the quantity

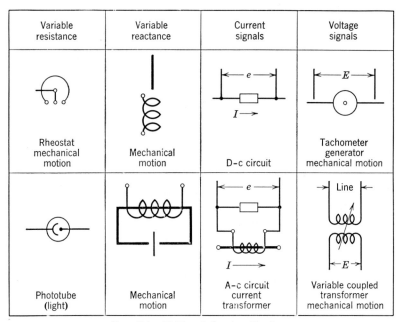

Variable resistance	Variable reactance	Current signals	Voltage signals
Rheostat mechanical motion	Mechanical motion	D-c circuit	Tachometer generator mechanical motion
Phototube (light)	Mechanical motion	A-c circuit current transformer	Variable coupled transformer mechanical motion

Fig. 104. Table of Sensing Devices.

that is being regulated. An axiom of the control industry is, "If you can measure it, you can control it." There are a great many devices that can be used for this purpose, and some of the more common ones are shown in Fig. 104.

The simplest device for converting mechanical motion into a signal is the rheostat, but because of the relatively short life of the sliding contact it has limited used. Signals from mechanical motions, and without objectionable wear, can be obtained from variable-reactance devices. This type is shown in the ordinary coil and plunger form, where the impedance varies with plunger position, and the bipolar reactor structure, where the impedance is varied by the introduction of an iron member between the poles. The mechanical motion is usually linear, but this is not a necessity.

High level alternating-current signals can be obtained from mechanical motions by using the variable-coupled transformer sensing device. The primary and secondary coils can be stationary, and the mechanical motion varies the coupling between them by changing the magnetic path characteristics. The movable iron structure can be designed so that very little or no forces are produced by the magnetic circuit, thus making it an extremely sensitive sensing device that can be operated from delicate mechanical apparatus.

Signals from rotating devices are usually produced by small tachometer generators. These generators are of the permanent-magnet field type and have voltage outputs that are linear with the rotational speed, over a wide speed range. They are used in both alternating- and direct-current outputs. The signal level obtained is relatively high and is advantageous where precise control of speed is a requirement.

Current regulators need signals which are proportional to the current flow in power circuits. In direct-current circuits, the signal e is produced across a resistor which carries the current being regulated. This is commonly used in tension systems, and the resistor can be a winding of one of the electric machines, rather than an additional voltage drop introduced for this purpose alone. The alternating-current sensing device uses a current transformer having a resistor load across its secondary terminals. The voltage e produced across the resistor is proportional to the load current.

The phototube is used as a variable resistor, to signal changes in light falling upon it. This sensing device is used on positioning regulator equipment. The device or material to be positioned cuts into or varies the beam of light that is directed on the phototube, and the variable-resistance characteristic of the phototube acts as the signal to the sensing system.

Error-sensing Systems. The function of the error-sensing system is to compare the signal from the sensing device with the reference and to transmit the error to the input of the amplifying apparatus. The two generally used methods are voltage comparison and magnetic comparison. Each method has noticeable advantages and disadvantages which must be taken into account when selecting one to use for a specific application.

Voltage-comparison Circuit. In this circuit, the voltage signal from the sensing device is electrically compared with the reference voltage, and any difference voltage is directly applied to the regulator or amplifier input. In Fig. 105, the error voltage e is shown applied to a coil on a magnetic structure, but it can be applied to a field of a rotating regulator, or to a grid in the input stage of an electronic amplifier.

The circuit makes efficient use of materials, especially where magnetic structures are used in the amplifier input. All of the copper in the input winding is active in producing ampere turns from the error voltage. The circuit is the most effective type to use for simple regulating systems where a single control or error voltage is employed.

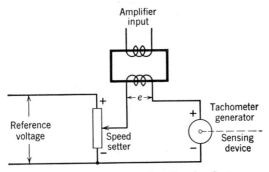

Fig. 105. Voltage-comparison Sensing System.

The principal disadvantage of the circuit is the necessity of making the reference circuit and the signal circuit electrically common. This means that the two circuits must be actually connected together, so that the voltage comparison can be accomplished. Some applications require that additional signals be fed into the sensing system and enter into the comparison. The circuit does not lend itself readily to the use of a multiplicity of signals, since these must also be made electrically common with the principal voltage comparison circuit. Sometimes, where a magnetic structure is involved in the input, an additional coil is used to feed in an isolated signal. Whatever signal is fed in, in this manner, is opposed by the voltage comparison circuit, with the net result that the new signal biases the regulator and forces it to operate at a somewhat different error voltage. If the isolated signal were exceedingly strong, it might bias the regulator to some extreme value, which would result in damage to one of the coils because of coil heating.

Magnetic Comparison Circuit. It is necessary to use some form of magnetic structure in the regulator input stage if magnetic comparison is to be used. This type of circuit is inherently present when rotating regulators and magnetic-amplifier regulators are used. It can also be accomplished with an electronic regulator if a saturable core reactor or similar device is used for the input, but this is not usually done because of the time delay introduced by the saturable reactor.

This circuit offers a great deal of flexibility because a variety of isolated signals can be introduced through separate coils. The signal sent in to the regulator from the sensing system is the result of the algebraic sum of the separate signals. In the circuit (Fig. 106) the reference

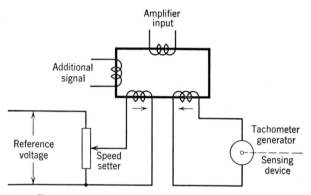

Fig. 106.   Magnetic-comparison Sensing System.

is established from the reference voltage and, through the speed setter, is connected to a coil on the magnetic structure. The sensing device shown is a tachometer generator used to measure rotational speed, and it is connected to another coil. The design of these coils is such that the ampere turns balance each other at any steady-state condition. In operation, the ampere turns of the reference coil and the signal coil are in opposition to each other. Any difference in the ampere turns of these two coils shows up as resultant ampere turns which are active on the magnetic structure and produce the error signal fed into the input of the regulator. Any number of additional signals can be fed in through isolated coil circuits on the magnetic structure, and the resultant ampere turns of all of the coils is the signal to the regulator.

The principal disadvantage of the magnetic comparison circuit is that it does not use material efficiently in the input circuit. The major portion of the reference and signal energy is dissipated in heating in the coils, rather than in producing effective ampere turns in the input unit. This inefficiency can be overcome by increasing the size of the magnetic structure and coils of the input unit appreciably.

Another method is to accept the performance obtained from a smaller magnetic input unit and regain the circuit amplification required by adding stages to the amplifying system.

Regulating System Stability. The closed-loop regulator action sometimes tends to overshoot when making corrections and may set the system into oscillation about the desired value. Such oscillation or hunting is damped out by the use of stabilizing or anti-hunt circuits. The design of system stability into regulating systems is the most involved part of the entire problem. The problem goes beyond the regulator itself, including time constants of the electric machinery and mechanical inertia of rotating elements in the electric machinery and the process machinery. Methods of calculation of stability problems have been derived, but in all of them complete knowledge of the mechanical and electrical factors external to the regulator is required. References to published information on stability are listed at the end of this chapter.

The designer is confronted by the time constants of all parts of the closed-loop regulating system. In many cases, the time constant of the regulated quantity is large in relation to all other time constants in the loop. When this ratio is large, the problem of stabilizing the system becomes easier. In general, the time constant of the regulator should be kept low, which, stated differently, means the regulator response should be fast.

Within the regulator, the gain and response time, in combination, are important factors. The regulator must have adjustments of sufficient range to adapt it to a variety of field applications. When it is used where high gain is necessary, the speed of response should also be high.

Regulators used for industrial-control applications usually have anti-hunt circuits that employ transient feedback signals. These feedback signals may be picked up at the regulator output and fed back into the input, or they may feed back around just a portion of the amplifier. Transient signals can be obtained from a direct-current output by feeding the output signals back through capacitors. The capacitors block out steady-state voltages but allow changes in voltage to be fed back. Another feedback method uses a transformer having its primary winding excited from the output circuit. The transformer design must avoid saturation of the iron when excited from the maximum output. Under steady-state conditions, there is no voltage induced in the transformer secondary winding. However, when the regulator output changes, voltages are induced in the secondary and are fed back.

The sense of the transient feedback signals is in opposition to the change that is taking place. This damps out the tendency of the system to oscillate. The amount of the anti-hunt feedback signal is usually made adjustable. Typical anti-hunt circuits are shown in the following paragraphs which deal with complete regulating systems.

Voltage Regulators. Automatic regulators are often used to maintain the output voltage of generators and alternators within certain required limits, for industrial-control applications. The generating equipment used for power purposes in mills and factories is subjected to wide variations in loads and temperature, both of which can cause the voltage to fluctuate enough to be objectionable.

Frequently individual processes may require closely regulated generator voltage, where an individual generator supplies all or a portion of the process. Typical examples are electroplating, some high-temperature ovens, high-cycle tools, automatic welding, and excitation generators used on continuous processing lines. The high-cycle alternators used to supply hand tools and for high-speed resistance welding inherently have relatively poor load regulation. This imposes heavy duty on the regulating apparatus, often requiring that the alternator excitation current be doubled to compensate for the sudden application of full load. The regulator response must be fast, to prevent an objectionable dip in voltage when the load is applied.

Most industrial-control applications use relatively small machines, having excitation requirements within the rating of regulators, so that the regulators can control the generator fields directly. Some larger generators require auxiliary exciters, and the regulators operate in the shunt fields of the exciters. Designers prefer to avoid auxiliary exciters, because they put an additional time delay in the system. This has led to the development of regulators capable of handling large kilowatt ratings of excitation power.

Speed Regulators. When precise control of rotational or linear speed is a process requirement, an automatic speed regulator is used. Paper-making machines must operate at carefully regulated speeds because speed variations result in variations of paper thickness. The speed of a strip of steel through a plating tank, where tin is electro-plated on the strip, must be constant if the plating is to be uniform.

The sensing device used is a tachometer generator, which is driven by the machine, and produces a voltage signal that is proportional to the speed. The speed regulator is, in reality, a voltage regulator, and operates to hold the tachometer generator voltage constant at some value determined by the desired speed. The output of the regulator is fed into some element which is capable of changing the speed. This element is usually the shunt field of the motor driving the machine or the shunt field of a generator that supplies power to the motor.

When high precision of control is required, a tachometer generator having relatively high volts per revolution is employed. The degree of precision, for a given regulator gain, is related to the ratio of the error voltage to the voltage level of the sensing device and reference. This makes it beneficial to operate at the highest tachometer voltage that is practical. Some processes require that the speed be maintained constant to within a small fraction of 1 per cent of the preselected value.

Position Regulators. Moving strips of material, particularly in continuous processing lines, sometimes require positioning regulators for process reasons or to guide them laterally in passing through the machines. Some applications, such as printing, require precise coordination of a moving strip of material with the machine. This is sometimes called "register control," referring to the requirement that the material and the machine must operate in register. Color printing, where several colors are applied, each in a separate printing unit, requires careful control of register. Register control usually employs marks or dots on the moving strip as the measuring medium, and a light system with photocells takes regulating signals from the register marks. The regulating system operates on some mechanical means that is capable of shifting the strip to maintain the required register.

When a moving strip of material, under tension, must be guided laterally, the regulating signal is picked up at the edge of the strip by means of a light and photocell system. The regulator can shift the strip by moving rolls over which it travels. When the signal is taken from one edge of the strip, regulation is about a point where the light beam is partially intercepted by the strip. Some systems use a light beam at each edge of the strip, and the automatic regulator action keeps the amount of intercept of the two beams equal.

Some processes require a slack loop in the continuously moving strip of material. Certain cloth-finishing ranges handle the cloth in completely relaxed form, which is attained by allowing it to hang freely in a festoon between process machines. In coating processes, such as paper coating, the material is not allowed to ride on rolls until the surface coating has dried. The material may be supported on air jets and allowed to form a slack loop before entering the next process. Steel-mill process lines require slack-loop control at certain slitters, in process tanks and other places.

When slack loops are used in continuous processing, the regulating problem involved is to synchronize the speed of one side of the loop with that of the other side, to maintain the length of the loop constant. The sensing device must be able to measure the length of the loop and send an appropriate signal into the sensing system. If the strip is of magnetic material, a variable inductance or variable coupled transformer can serve as the sensing device. In non-magnetic materials, the sensing device is usually one or more photocell systems.

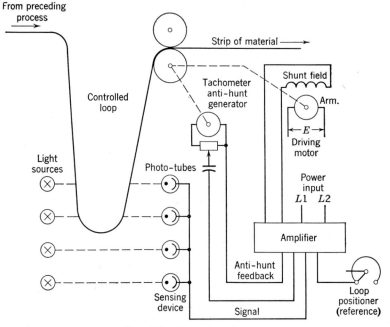

FIG. 107. Loop Regulator.

The regulator maintains the loop length in agreement with some pre-selected reference.

A slack-loop regulating system is shown in elementary form in Fig. 107. The strip of material is fed up to the loop from a process. It can be fed from rolls or might fall naturally from a supporting system of air jets. The next motor-driven process in line pulls the material from the loop at a synchronized speed, so as to maintain the loop at substantially constant length. The motor takes armature power from some source such as E, which is usually an adjustable-voltage system.

It is advantageous to use a wide zone of regulation for the bottom of the loop, because this desensitizes the mechanical system, resulting in less tendency to hunt. Figure 107 establishes a wide regulation zone by using four light sources and photocells. The combined effect of impedance change of the four photocells is the signal that is compared with the reference. The reference, in this case, selects the desired loop position in the light system. The output of the amplifier supplies excitation for the driving-motor shunt field. Any change in loop length changes the amount of light intercepted, resulting in a signal change from the photocells. The signal change is amplified and applies a correction to the motor shunt field, in a direction tending to restore the preselected loop length.

Sometimes, the process or space available will not permit a deep loop or festoon as illustrated in Fig. 107. A long shallow loop is a more critical mechanical system than a deep loop and, for that reason, usually requires effective anti-hunt methods in order to obtain stability. One such method is to measure speed changes with a tachometer generator, and feed the transient tachometer voltage changes into the amplifier in degenerative sense. A capacitor in the feedback circuit blocks out steady-state signals from the tachometer generator. A potentiometer across the tachometer output permits adjustment of the strength of the anti-hunt signal. This signal should be as small as possible, to avoid objectionable interference with changes in the basic process speed. This type of feedback is particularly effective on applications where high mechanical inertias are involved and where there is a tendency to oscillate at low frequency.

Constant-tension Regulation. Long strips of material, such as paper, cloth, steel, and others are usually wound at constant tension. This is important for handling and, in many cases, prevents damage of the material, both in handling and in storage. Considerable attention is given to holding the winding tension uniform all the way from the inner core to the outside diameter. Where the tension cannot be held uniform for one reason or another, it is customary to taper it, the turns being somewhat tighter at the core than they are at the outside.

The tension systems employed are roughly classified as surface winding and mandrel winding. Surface winders make use of winding drums which are driven so that their surface speed is the same as the linear speed of the material being processed. The roll of material is supported in such a manner that it rests in contact with the winding drum, and the winding effort is transmitted to the roll by the surface contact between the winding drum and the outside surface of the roll. Since the surface speed of the winding drum does not need to change as the roll diameter changes, and since the driving effort of the drum can be constant, the driving motor operates at constant torque and constant speed for a given linear speed of the strip. This type of winder does not usually require an automatic regulator.

In mandrel winding, the mandrel on which the roll of material is wound is coupled to the driving motor. When a roll is started, the strip is usually secured to the mandrel, and this firm connection permits winding at much greater tension than can be obtained from surface winding.

Basic Constant-tension Relations. In Fig. 108, the strip of material is fed up to the reel from a pair of tension rolls. These rolls can be

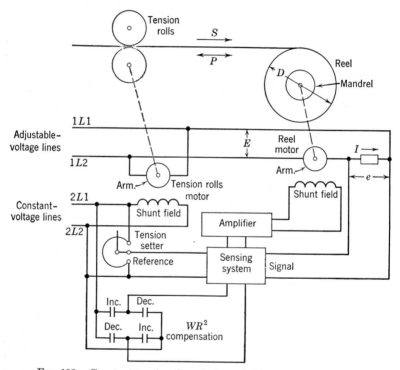

Fig. 108. Constant-tension Regulation of Mandrel-type Winder.

a portion of a processing machine, the only requirement being that some machine member must have a firm grip on the material to produce back tension, so the material can be wound at the desired tension.

The reel motor is directly coupled to the mandrel of the reel and is shown as receiving its power from adjustable-voltage lines. The reel motor can have a separate adjustable-voltage system, but the voltage applied to the motor should be proportional to the linear speed of the strip of material.

Because the length of turn varies with the diameter of the roll, the speed of the reel motor must vary inversely with the diameter of the roll, if the linear speed of the strip is constant. For a tension P in pounds and a linear speed S in feet per minute, the horsepower in the strip is

$$\text{Horsepower} = \frac{PS}{33,000}$$

Since the horsepower is in no way related to the diameter of the roll, it follows that the reel drive is constant horsepower.

The reel motor must be able to deliver constant-horsepower output to the reel over a speed range determined by the ratio of the outside diameter of the roll to the mandrel diameter. This requires an adjustable-speed constant-horsepower rated motor. The speed range of the motor by shunt field control should be somewhat greater than the diameter ratio of the coil, to allow some range at each extreme for regulating purposes. For instance, a $^{400}\!/_{2000}$ rpm constant-horsepower motor might be selected for winding a 4-foot-diameter roll on a 1-foot mandrel.

With the constant-horsepower output, the reel-motor power input EI is also constant. The voltage E is fixed by the linear speed of the process, so the product EI can be held constant for constant tension by regulating I to a constant value.

The motor torque must vary directly with the diameter of the roll, and this relationship is

$$\text{Motor torque} = \frac{PD}{2} = K_1 FI$$

where D is the diameter of the roll.

K_1 is a motor design constant.

F is the motor field flux.

Also, $$\text{Motor speed} = \frac{S}{\pi D} = K_2 \frac{E}{F}$$

where K_2 is a motor design constant.

The adjustable-speed motor performance for mandrel winding is shown by Fig. 109. The horsepower and armature input watts are held constant by holding the armature amperes constant. The motor flux must vary directly with the roll diameter. The motor torque and speed can be kept in the proper relation for constant tension by simply changing the motor field flux as the diameter of the roll changes. If the armature current I is to be a direct indication of tension, the following are the requirements:

1. The linear speed changes of the strip must be made by changing the applied voltage E.
2. Tension adjustments must be made by adjusting the motor armature current I. The regulator then maintains the preset value of I.

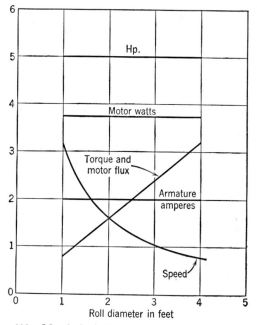

FIG. 109. Mandrel-winding Motor Performance Curves.

3. Motor speed variation with change in roll diameter must be accomplished by motor field-flux variation. The important point here is that for each increment of roll diameter there is a value of motor field flux that is independent of the linear speed setting and substantially independent of the tension setting.

Constant-tension Control System. As shown in Fig. 108, the customary constant-tension system makes use of an automatic regulator to supply the shunt field excitation of the reel motor. The tension-setting device usually operates from constant-voltage direct-current lines. It presets the desired tension by selecting a reference voltage which is fed into the sensing system of the regulator. The regulating signal e is produced by a voltage drop which is proportional to the reel-motor armature current I. In the sensing system, any difference between the signal and reference voltage shows up as an error, which is fed into the amplifier system and results in a correction of the shunt field current of the reel motor.

Assuming stable operation at the desired tension, the regulator action responds to the signal voltage e with the material being wound at constant linear speed and the roll getting steadily larger in diameter. As the roll diameter tends to increase, the motor momentarily tries to drive the roll faster than required and, in so doing, tends to take a slightly greater armature current. This increases the signal voltage e fed into the sensing system and sends an error signal into the amplifier calling for more shunt field excitation. This greater field flux tends to slow down the motor and to increase its torque, in keeping with the increase in roll diameter. Thus, by holding the armature current constant, the regulator varies the motor flux and keeps the motor speed and torque in a proper balance with the roll diameter at all times, thereby producing constant tension.

The foregoing discussion assumes constant linear speed operation. When the linear speed of the material is changed during the winding operation, the horsepower input to the reel must be changed, to compensate for mechanical inertia effects. During process speed acceleration, the motor must be allowed to take more armature current than the value needed for the desired tension, to supply the horsepower for acceleration. The reverse condition is true for deceleration, and the system must be made to operate at lower than the armature current needed for constant tension. The usual method employed is to have some form of bias that can be fed into the regulator, which can add to or subtract from the reference, to produce a fixed increment of armature current for WR^2 compensation. In Fig. 108, the WR^2 compensation signal is fed into the sensing system, and its polarity is reversible by means of the increase and decrease relay contacts of the associated control.

Figure 108 illustrates a constant-tension winder taking material from a process. It is sometimes necessary to feed material, at constant tension, into a process. This is referred to as "unwinding" or "payoff."

During unwinding, the process pulls the material from the roll. The unwind motor operates as a generator and generates power into the adjustable-voltage system. Constant tension holdback is obtained by regulating constant current in the unwind motor armature. The control equipment is much the same as is used for winders. However, since generating action, rather than motoring action, is controlled, the sense of the amplifier output and the polarity of the WR^2 compensation signals are the reverse of the winder requirement.

Solenoid-operated Regulators. In this general classification are included those regulators which convert electric signals into mechanical motions, the motions being capable of changing the electric characteristics of circuits of the controlled machines.

The reference is usually mechanical and in the form of a spring and linkages, which, in combination, provide a fixed mechanical bias for the complete throw of the regulator mechanism. The signal is a voltage from the regulated quantity. This signal voltage furnishes the power to operate a solenoid having a movable plunger. The solenoid pull on the plunger balances the pull of the reference spring when the regulator is in operation. The solenoid is designed for a pull characteristic to match the reference spring characteristic, so that a small change in solenoid ampere turns can swing the regulator over its entire range. The solenoids usually have straight-line plunger motions, but some regulators use rotary-motion solenoids or torque motors to set up the operating forces.

The precision of this type of regulator is intimately related to the efficiency of the mechanical system employed to translate the sensing signal into a regulating quantity. The regulators built by the different manufacturers differ mainly in the types of mechanical motions used, to eliminate friction and to employ the signal forces to the best advantage. The anti-hunting means is also mechanical and operates to damp oscillations of the mechanical system.

The control output of this type of regulator is a variable resistor or rheostat, which is connected in series with a shunt field of the machine to be regulated, so that it can automatically change the machine excitation. Regulators differ in the type of variable resistor or rheostat output mechanisms used. Some use carbon-pile resistors, while others use tapped fixed resistors with almost frictionless commutating elements.

Typical of this class is the Allis-Chalmers rocking contact regulator (Fig. 110). The output variable resistor is the tapped type, with the taps connected to segments. These segments are arranged in the form of a sector of a circle. The photo shows a two-sector regulator, one sector at each side of the device. The commutating element for each sector is a rocking contact, which is formed at a somewhat smaller radius than the stationary sector. An extremely small amount of work is required to roll the rocking contact over the sector to commutate the output resistor.

The operating solenoid is shown at the upper right portion of the mechanism. The diagonally mounted spring opposes the solenoid and is the reference. The black cylinder, which partially covers the left-hand sector, is the air dashpot used for anti-hunting. A piston inside the cylinder forces air through a restricted passage and damps out any tendency of the mechanism to oscillate.

Figure 111 shows, in simplified form, the rocking contact regulator connected to maintain constant the output voltage of a self-excited direct-current generator. The generator output voltage is the signal applied to the solenoid coil. The pull of the solenoid is opposed by

Fig. 110. Allis-Chalmers Type-VD2 Rocking Contact Regulator.

the reference spring, and any resulting motion rocks the contact sector. The plunger system transmits motion to the dashpot piston through an elastic member. This permits fast initial corrections, but its damping action tends to limit the amount of regulator movement for a given disturbance.

If the generator output voltage drops for any reason, the pull of the solenoid decreases somewhat, allowing the spring to pull the plunger down and rocking the contact sector downward. The contact sector commutates the resistor in the direction to reduce the resistance in the shunt field circuit. The increased field excitation restores the generator output voltage to the preselected value. The voltage-adjusting rheostat is connected in the signal circuit, in series with the solenoid coil. Inserting resistance in this rheostat requires an increase in generator voltage, to supply the necessary solenoid ampere turns to balance the regulator.

Rotating Regulators. Under this general classification are several specific types, which differ in the detailed principle of operation of the amplifying elements. They are alike in the broad sense that the amplifying elements are rotating direct-current electric machines. These rotating amplifiers, or generators, are usually driven from the alternating-current power lines by induction motors. The reference

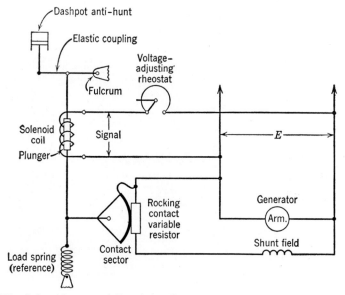

FIG. 111. Solenoid-operated Regulator Connected to Maintain Constant Voltage on a Generator.

and signal power is applied to low-energy shunt-field windings, and the amplifying generator armature output is the regulator output used for control purposes. The power gain is the slope of the curve of regulator output watts plotted against signal watts.

The differences in the amplifying generators sold under various trade names are, in general, in the circuits employed to increase the power gain. Special attention, in all cases, is given to obtaining fast rates of response, because the regulators must have low time constants in order to give stable operation in many applications. One method of getting high gain from a direct-current generator is to supply most of its excitation from a self-excited field circuit, whose resistance is adjusted to the critical value that just allows excitation to be supported. Low power signals, applied to other fields on the generator, can then readily change the generator output over its entire range.

Another method is to operate two direct-current generators in two stages. These can be built as two stages in one machine, or in two machines.

It is not within the intended scope of this treatment to go into a detailed description of each of the types of rotating regulators. The

Fig. 112. Reliance Electric and Engineering Company VSA Rotating Regulator.

separately excited rotating regulator, known as the Reliance VSA, is selected to represent this group, because its circuits are similar to those of conventional machines. It is a two-stage amplifier, consisting of two separately excited direct-current generators that are driven at constant speed by an induction motor. Figure 112 shows one of these regulators, complete with its control devices, mounted as a packaged unit in an enclosure. One generator is direct coupled to the induction motor, and the other is belt-driven from it.

A simplified circuit of this regulator is shown in Fig. 113, where it acts to maintain the speed of a motor constant at some preset value. The motor takes its armature power from a direct-current adjustable-voltage generator, and its field is excited from constant-voltage lines. The shunt field of the adjustable-voltage generator receives its excitation from the regulator output. The sensing device is a tachometer

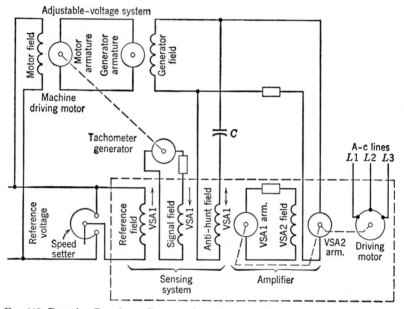

Fig. 113. Rotating Regulator Connected to Maintain Constant Speed on a Motor.

generator, which is driven by the controlled motor. The speed selector furnishes a reference taken from a reliable reference voltage source.

The amplifying generators are driven by the alternating-current motor, and, therefore, the principal power involved within the regulator comes from the alternating-current lines. The input stage is generator VSA1, and it is fitted with a number of shunt-field coils. These shunt-field coils, whose ampere turns combine algebraically to excite the machine, are the sensing system of the regulator. When used in this form they operate as a magnetic comparison system.

The speed setter determines the speed level by presetting the reference-field ampere turns. The sense of the reference field is to increase the regulator output. This strengthens the adjustable-voltage generator field, raises its armature voltage, and increases the speed of the controlled motor. The reference field operates in opposition to the signal field.

The signal field takes its signal from the tachometer generator. When operating normally, the ampere-turns of the signal and reference field just about balance, and any small difference is the error that is amplified through the regulator. The steady-state operating point is automatically attained when the net difference ampere turns just produce the required regulator output.

The voltage produced at the armature of the input unit, VSA1, as a result of the error ampere turns, is applied to the shunt field of the second stage generator, VSA2. The armature output of VSA2 furnishes the shunt-field excitation for the adjustable-voltage generator. The generator furnishes power for the controlled motor and thus completes the closed-loop regulating system.

The anti-hunt field in Fig. 113 is connected to feed transients from the regulator output, back into the input. The capacitor C prevents steady-state feedback. The sense of the anti-hunt field is always in opposition to the change taking place.

Rotating regulators have advantages that, to a considerable degree, determine where they are used in preference to other types. They can readily be built in large kilowatt ratings, are rugged, and are serviced much the same as any rotating electric machinery. This adapts them for use with large mill machinery, where rugged apparatus is wanted and where service techniques are similar to those of existing apparatus. A further advantage is the ability of the regulator output polarity to reverse. Designers make use of this feature in forcing the fields handled by regulators and particularly when they want to kill the fields rapidly.

Electronic Regulator. Electronic regulators employ vacuum and gaseous tubes to amplify error signals to the power levels required to control industry's machines. While these regulators have the disadvantage of using components having unpredictable life, when compared with other types, they have many advantages of superior performance.

The error signal, set up in the sensing system, is applied to a grid circuit of a high-vacuum tube in the input stage. The input tube characteristic requires very low signal power, which enables the regulator to operate from low-energy signals. The signal input can be from a high-impedance circuit. Stages of amplification are used as required to get the necessary overall gain for the application.

The output stage usually uses Thyratron tubes connected in single-phase or polyphase circuits, supplying direct current for motor-armature or shunt-field circuits. A wide range of output kilowatt ratings is available because of the wide selection of Thyratrons available and the various circuit connections that are used.

These regulators can have extremely low time constants because the electronic components are inherently fast. The low-energy grid circuits can be designed for high rates of response. When moderate rates of response are required, saturable-core reactors are used in phase-shift circuits to control the output Thyratrons. When extremely fast regulator action is required, other phase-shift circuits are used that eliminate the time constant of the saturable-core reactor.

Much material has been published on electronic regulators, giving theory and circuit details. This discussion is limited to a brief treatment of regulator types.

Figure 114 shows simplified circuit elements of an electronic speed regulator. In this system, the regulator output is the power supply for the armature of the controlled motor. The motor field is excited at constant voltage from a full-wave rectifier $3T$. The sensing device is a tachometer generator which is driven by the motor. The reference voltage supply is from rectifier $2T$. It is held relatively constant by the action of the voltage regulating tube VR.

The reference is established by the speed-setter potentiometer, which selects a portion of the reference voltage for comparison purposes. In the "voltage-comparison" sensing system, the tachometer signal voltage is compared with the reference, and the error voltage is applied to the grid of the input tube $1T$. The input tube shown is a duotriode. This tube has two identical load circuits and is connected across the regulated reference voltage. The output of the first stage is determined by the difference of conduction of the two halves of the duotriode. This difference establishes a voltage drop on the saturating winding of the saturable-core reactor SR through a blocking rectifier which makes the circuit unidirectional.

The alternating-current winding of SR is a variable impedance in one leg of a phase-shift bridge, supplied with power from a secondary of transformer $1PT$. This bridge controls the grid to anode-voltage phase relationship of the Thyratrons, $4T$ and $5T$, by phase shifting the primary of the grid transformer, $2PT$.

The saturating winding of SR, through the phase-shift system, can regulate the conduction of the Thyratrons, $4T$ and $5T$, and, thereby, the average voltage supplied to the motor armature.

The sense of the reference is to turn on the Thyratrons and increase the speed. The sense of the tachometer signal is to cut off the Thyratrons. Under steady-state operation, the error voltage is just sufficient to produce the proper armature voltage to produce a tachometer signal that is just right to sustain the error. The magnitude of the error is directly related to the system gain. In practice, the circuit of Fig. 114 might have one or more intermediate stages, between the input and output stages, to obtain increased regulator gain.

The anti-hunt system employed is a transient-voltage feedback from the motor armature circuit. This transient signal is fed, through

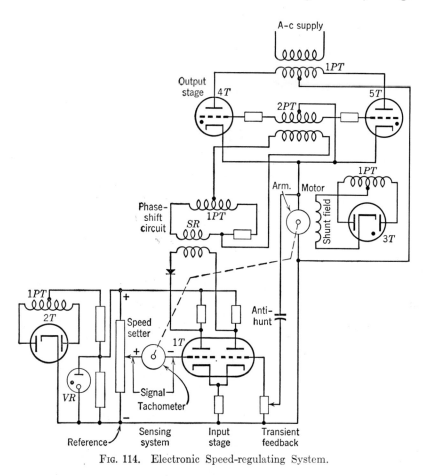

FIG. 114. Electronic Speed-regulating System.

capacitor C, to the second control grid of the input tube, as shown. The sense of the transient feedback is to send a signal through the regulator, opposing the change that produced the transient.

An electronic regulator built to the requirements of mill-type control, is shown in Fig. 115. This uses industrial-type components, with special care given to adequate electrical creepage and clearance distances. The upper panel mounts the three Thyratrons which operate

FIG. 115. Electronic Regulator Assembly, Constructed to Meet Heavy-duty
Mill Requirements.

in the three-phase power-supply circuit of the regulator. Directly below the Thyratron panel is the amplifier panel. The circuits of this panel can be disconnected by use of the plug connectors shown. The amplifier panel can then be removed for inspection and servicing. The operating conditions are indicated by the instruments. The remainder of the panel devices consist of a removable direct-current supply panel, constant-voltage transformer, anode transformer, and miscellaneous contactors and relays. The wiring, on the back of the panels, is formed and cleated down, much like industrial practice for magnetic devices.

Electronic regulators meet requirements for some applications that would be extremely difficult to meet with other types of regulators. They can operate from very weak signals. They can be built for high gain and fast rates of response, which, in combination, enable them to regulate to more precision than can be done with other types. They are flexible and lend themselves readily to unusual circuit requirements.

Magnetic-amplifier Regulator. Regulators which use saturable reactors for power amplification are generally called magnetic-amplifier regulators. The use of saturable reactors as power amplifiers is quite old. Because of some serious performance limitations, they were not widely used, except in applications such as theater dimmers.

With the development of improved core materials and improvements in selenium rectifiers, a new field of development and application of saturable reactors opened up. The core materials of nickel-iron alloys are put through special processing which produce low ampere-turn requirements for saturation. Low magnetizing-force requirements produce steep saturation curves and greater amplification. Selenium-rectifier development has stabilized the characteristics of the disks, increased the voltage ratings of the disks, and reduced the back current. These factors have combined to step up the performance of saturable reactors and to reduce their cost.

The real advancement in the use of saturable reactors as regulating system amplifiers was made possible by the discovery of the principle of self-saturation in reactors in 1936. About ten years later the idea of magnetic-amplifier regulators suddenly caught the fancy of development people, and steady progress began at once. The following paragraphs will discuss, briefly, the basic principles and applications of magnetic-amplifier regulators.

Saturable Reactor. A saturable reactor consists of a closed iron magnetic structure, on which are mounted one or more load windings and one or more control windings. The load windings act as an impedance in the alternating-current circuit to be controlled. The control windings are usually operated from direct current. By varying the current in the control windings, the degree of saturation of the core is varied, and the impedance of the load coils to the flow of alternating current is varied.

Maximum impedance and minimum load current are obtained when the control current is zero. For this condition, the core operates in the unsaturated region, and the load current is very nearly the saturating current of the reactor. If a direct voltage is applied to the control coils, the core will reach saturation for a portion of the alternating-current cycle and permit increased load current to flow. Maximum load current is obtained when the ampere turns due to the control windings are sufficient to keep the core saturated during the entire alternating-current cycle.

A saturable-reactor circuit and typical performance characteristics are shown in Fig. 116. The load coils L are on the outside legs of a three-legged core structure. The control coil C is mounted on the center leg. The load coils have equal ampere-turn effect and are so connected that the alternating-current flux, due to these coils, cancels out in the center leg and does not induce alternating voltages of fundamental frequency in the control coil. The load coils are connected in parallel and are in series with a full-wave rectifier across the alternating-current supply. The output of the rectifier supplies direct current to the load.

The simplest form is without coil FB and with the output of the rectifier connected to the load as indicated by the dotted connection. This arrangement produces the symmetrical V curve of output load amperes plotted against control ampere turns, as indicated by the dotted curve of Fig. 116. This curve brings out two significant disadvantages of the device. First, there is the relatively low gain or amplification, as indicated by the slope of the straight-line portion of the curve. Second, the device does not discriminate between positive and negative control, making it usually necessary to employ auxiliary means to avoid reversal of control.

The gain can be substantially increased by the use of positive feedback. A feedback coil, such as FB, is connected so as to carry all, or a portion of, the load current, and the polarity such that its ampere turns are cumulative with those of coil C. The performance is shown by the solid curve, the V curve being tipped over to a degree, determined by the percentage of the load current that is fed back. The high gain slope results when the feedback is positive and low gain on the opposite side when coils C and FB are in opposition.

The saturable-reactor circuit of Fig. 116 relies entirely on the ampere turns on the center leg to saturate the core. These ampere turns are additive with the load-coil ampere turns during the positive half cycle and differential with them during the negative half cycle of the alternating supply. This requires, then, that the ampere turns on the center leg must equal the total of the load-coil ampere turns, plus the ampere turns necessary to saturate the core. The requirement

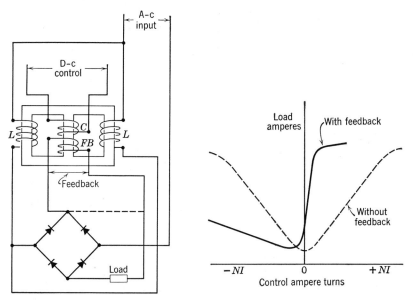

FIG. 116. Simple Saturable Reactor.

for large control coils adds to the physical size of the structure and, therefore, to the cost. The large control coils also have an unfavorable L/R ratio when considered in relation to the low time constants required of regulating equipment. The application of this type of device to regulating systems has been limited because of its low power gain, its slow rates of response, and its cost.

Self-saturable Reactor. The self-saturable reactor has, to a great extent, overcome the inherent disadvantages of the saturable reactor described above. Its name comes from the fact that the load coils, by the very nature of the connection of the circuit, provide 100 per cent feedback and assist in saturating the core. The control-coil ampere turns and watts can be relatively low.

A simple reactor circuit, along with performance graphs, is shown in Fig. 117 to explain the principle of self-saturation in saturable-core reactors. The load is supplied with power from the alternating-current lines through a winding on the reactor and a half-wave rectifier. The series connection of the reactor load coil and a rectifier, limiting the load coil to unidirectional current, is the basic difference between

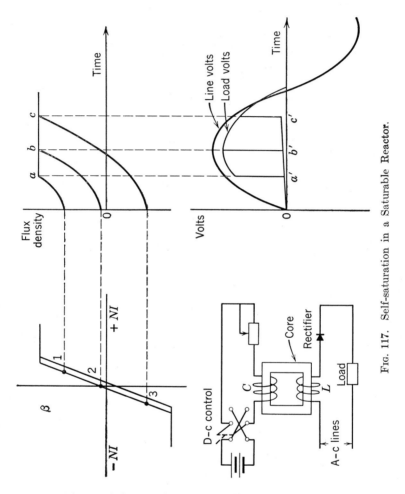

FIG. 117. Self-saturation in a Saturable Reactor.

self-saturation and the previous type. The control coil C is connected to a direct-current source in a manner enabling the magnitude and polarity of the control current to be varied.

The magnetization curve of the core material, plotted between ampere turns and flux density, is shown in Fig. 117. For simplicity of explanation, the curve selected has a very narrow hysteresis loop and a sharp break at saturation. While this is somewhat idealized, it is similar to that obtained with certain grain-oriented magnetic materials. The plots of time against flux density and time against volts further explain the action that takes place in the circuit.

Assume that at zero time the core is excited to point 1 by the application of positive ampere turns in the control coil. As the line voltage rises, it appears almost entirely as voltage drop across the reactor load coil. The load voltage is small, being only that drop in the load itself, due to the alternating-current exciting current. This continues as long as the core is unsaturated and is still capable of storing flux. At point a the core saturates—it can no longer store flux, and the load coil impedance drops sharply to a low value. This results in an abrupt rise of the voltage across the load at a^1, and for the remainder of the half cycle most of the line voltage is applied to the load.

If at the beginning of the half cycle the core is preconditioned to point 3 by the application of negative-control-coil ampere turns, core saturation occurs later in the half cycle at point c. The transfer of line voltage from the reactor load coil to the load occurs at c^1, and the rms load voltage is considerably less than it was when the transfer was at point a^1. In this example point b^1 produces about one-half of maximum load voltage and results from zero ampere turns from the control coil. Minimum load voltage is obtained by preconditioning the core far enough negative so it will not saturate in the positive direction at all. Maximum load voltage is obtained by the application of sufficient positive-control ampere turns to produce saturation at the start of the line-voltage half cycle. From the above it is seen that these reactors are turned on and off in much the same fashion as Thyratrons are phased on and off in electronic circuits.

Bridge-output Self-saturable Reactor. The principle of self-saturation can be utilized in circuits having either direct-current or alternating-current load output. Direct-current output circuits are usually used for industrial-control regulators because the regulator load circuit is usually a shunt field. A typical single-phase input connection is shown in Fig. 118. Along with it is a typical performance curve plotted between control-coil ampere turns and the load-circuit amperes.

In Fig. 118 it is noted that each load winding has a rectifier in series with it. These are so connected that the windings have unidirectional current through them and each conducts on alternate half cycles. Additional rectifiers complete the bridge circuit so that the load current is rectified full wave. The performance curve, for a definite value of applied voltage and a definite value of load resistance, is shown in typical form. By converting the scales to watts, the power gain is directly indicated, and the slope represents the amplification. Power gains of 15,000 or more in single stages are possible with the materials usually used for industrial control, but such gains are never actually used because they occur at prohibitively long time constants. The power gain is the ratio of the load watts to the control-coil watts. The units are usually desensitized to gains of 50 to 1000 in order to obtain high rates of response. Sometimes bias windings are added to the control leg of the reactor to shift the performance curve to the

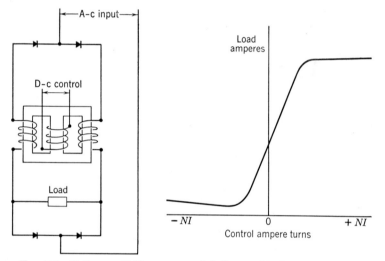

Fig. 118.   Full-wave Bridge-connected Self-saturable Reactor Circuit.

right or left, relative to zero-control ampere turns. This is usually done to permit unidirectional control power but may be to preselect the operating point on the curve. Maximum gain is usually near the central part of the curve.

Self-saturable Reactor Performance. The load-output performance curve of the self-saturable reactor shifts vertically with changes in the applied line voltage. Increasing the line voltage increases the output. The line-voltage fluctuation should be within the limits set by the manufacturer if proper performance is to be obtained.

The efficient use of self-saturable reactors requires matching the load resistance to the reactors. Figure 119 shows output amperes plotted against control ampere turns for two values of load resistance. If the unit is to be rated for continuous duty, the load resistance selected will limit the reactor temperature to the allowable rise. The necessity for load-circuit matching is not a serious drawback because the load circuits usually have extra resistance connected in them to reduce the time constants, and this resistance can be adjusted somewhat to get the desired condition.

The response time of the self-saturable reactor is usually expressed as the time required to obtain 63 per cent of an ultimate change in output. It is expressed in cycles or seconds. A response-time curve for a small reactor is shown in Fig. 119, where the response time is plotted against control-coil watts. The response time is predominately a function of the L/R ratio of the control-coil circuit, and this ratio can be made low economically, because the principle of self-saturation

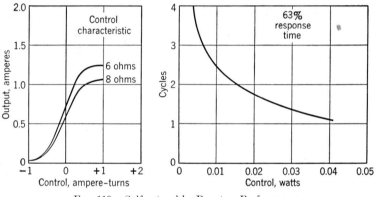

Fig. 119.   Self-saturable Reactor Performance.

requires very little control energy.   Time delay in the load windings is negligible because changes take place within the one-half cycle the winding is active.   In Fig. 119 a 4-cycle 63 per cent response is obtained with 0.004 watt of control.   In order to reduce the response time to 2 cycles, resistance is added in series with the control coil, sufficient to increase the control-circuit power to 0.016 watt.   Increasing the control watts fourfold reduces the response time one-half in this example.   Response times of $1\frac{1}{2}$ to 2 cycles are usually used for the different stages of industrial control regulators.

Multistage Magnetic-amplifier Regulator.   Saturable-core reactors, employing self-saturation circuits, can readily be cascaded to obtain the required overall gain.   Along with this gain, it is also necessary to design for some predetermined regulator time constant.   With increased system sensitivity, the rate of regulator response must also be increased, if system stability is to be realized.

The designer starts with known performance requirements and, from these, determines the type and amount of equipment needed to do the job.   The required accuracy is usually expressed in the per cent permissible deviation from the preset quantity.   The deviation, or error, must be related to the amount and nature of the disturbance which causes the error. For instance, a generator voltage regulator might be permitted a steady-state error of 1 per cent, when operating at rated voltage, for a load change from no load to full load. A further part of the specification might permit a 5 per cent transient change in voltage, with recovery to within the 1 per cent band within 10 cycles, upon sudden application or removal of full load.

In the discussion of constant-tension regulation, it was pointed out that the regulator changes the motor shunt-field flux to compensate for diameter changes of the roll being wound. In winding from empty mandrel to full roll, the regulator must swing the motor shunt-field voltage through its entire range, and this is independent of the linear speed of the strip. The permitted error must swing the regulator output as much as 10 to 1, for certain wide-speed-range winder motors. This illustrates the need to relate the error to the performance requirements of the application, to completely define accuracy.

The tension system in Fig. 120 uses a three-stage magnetic-amplifier regulator. The maximum roll-diameter change ratio is 3/1, and the adjustable-speed constant-horsepower-rated driving motor selected has a shunt-field-control speed range of 4/1. In compensating for changes in roll diameter, the regulator must vary the motor shunt field over a range of 250/50 volts, for the 4/1 speed range. Constant tension throughout the coil is obtained by regulating the motor armature current to a preselected constant value.

The three magnetic amplifiers are cascaded in the order of input, intermediate, and output stages. Only the essential control-coil circuits are shown for each stage. It is understood that each stage has load-coil windings and the associated rectifiers that combine into self-saturable reactor circuits, operating from some alternating-current input. The output of the first stage supplies the control power for coil 2C of the intermediate stage. The output of the intermediate stage supplies the control power for coil 3C of the output stage. The power from the output stage supplies the winder-motor shunt-field excitation.

The power amplification, in progression through the stages, is illustrated by the performance curves. In each case, these are plotted between control-coil ampere turns and output watts of the unit involved. On these curves is indicated the approximate excursion, or portion of curve used, necessary to produce the steady-state swing of 250/50 volts of the motor shunt field. The ratio of the output-watts excursion to the control-watts excursion is the power gain of the stage. The ratio of the output-stage output-watts excursion to the input-stage control-watts excursion is the regulator power gain.

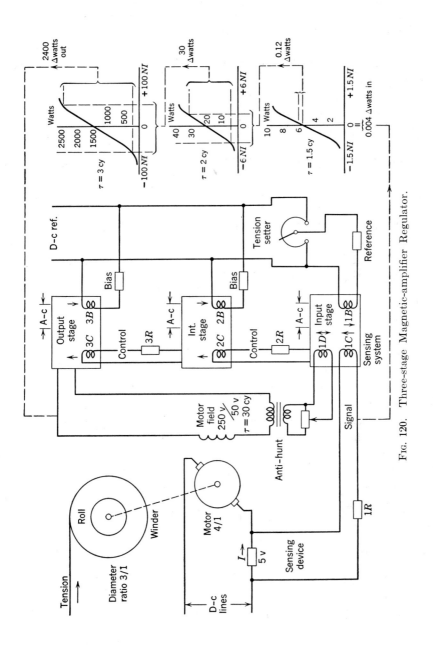

Fig. 120.   Three-stage Magnetic-amplifier Regulator.

The bias coils receive their power from the direct-current reference voltage lines. Bias coil 1B of the input stage is, in this case, the reference of a magnetic comparison system. It is connected to a potentiometer rheostat which is used to preselect the desired tension. Coils 2B and 3B, in the intermediate and output stages, apply a fixed bias. By means of this bias, the stage can be made to operate on the most desirable portion of its performance curve. The bias shifts the curve to the right or left with reference to the zero-control ampere-turn point. With proper adjustment, the need for reversal of the control-coil ampere turns, to control the device over its entire output range, is eliminated. The bias coils normally operate with appreciable resistance in series with them, to avoid time delays caused by their inductance.

It was pointed out previously that the power gain of a particular magnetic amplifier is dependent upon the rate of response needed. The response time is adjusted by adjusting the control watts. This adjustment is made with a resistance in the control-coil circuit. In Fig. 120 the response time selected for 63 per cent response of the intermediate stage is 2 cycles. A typical unit for this purpose might have a power gain of as much as 10,000, if operated without resistance in its control-coil circuit. However, at that high gain, the response time might be 50 cycles. The speed of response is increased by adding resistor 2R in series with coil 2C. When adjusted for 2 cycles response time, the actual power gain realized in the intermediate stage might be about 250. For a typical case, the resistance of 2R would be nine or ten times the resistance of coil 2C.

The sensing device is a resistor in the motor-armature circuit. This armature supply is usually an adjustable-voltage system which also supplies other motors involved in the process. At the maximum tension setting the armature current I produces a 5-volt signal. This signal voltage is proportionately less for lower tension settings. Series windings in the motor can be used in place of the dropping resistor, providing they produce a sufficiently high signal voltage.

The Fig. 120 circuit employs magnetic comparison in the sensing system. The tension-setter rheostat preselects the ampere turns of the reference coil 1B which act to reduce the stage output. The ampere turns of the control coil 1C are in opposition to the reference and act to increase the stage output. They automatically find an operating point where the resultant ampere turns of these two bucking coils produce sufficient output to adjust the motor field excitation to the roll-diameter requirement. The 1R resistor sets up a favorable ratio of inductance to resistance in the control-coil circuit, to obtain the needed speed of response of the input stage.

The bias coils of the intermediate and output stages are connected to reduce the stage output. The sense of the control coils is to increase the stage output.

The anti-hunt winding $1D$ in the input stage is connected to feed transient output changes back into the input stage. The anti-hunt transformer has its primary winding connected in series with the motor shunt field. Rapid changes in shunt-field current induce voltages in the secondary winding of the transformer. A portion of the induced voltage, as selected by a potentiometer rheostat, is fed into coil $1D$. The sense of coil $1D$ can be either to increase or to decrease the regulator output. It is always in the direction to oppose the change that is taking place in the motor field current.

The action of the regulator as the roll diameter increases has been described in the paragraphs under constant-tension control system.

Magnetic-amplifier Alternator Voltage Regulator. Alternators used as power supplies for high cycle hand tools and for continuous seam welding require regulators to maintain the terminal voltage under operating conditions of fluctuating load. These are usually 180- or 360-cycle machines, and they have inherent poor load regulation. The alternators used for welding must have fast response, to apply and remove the weld heat rapidly.

A magnetic-amplifier regulator for an alternator of this type is shown in Fig. 121. The alternator is driven at constant speed by a synchronous motor. The alternator output voltage is adjustable over an 8-to-1 voltage range, single phase, and 180 cycles. The accuracy requirement is to hold the preset voltage within plus or minus 1 per cent, with a change of load from no load to full load. A dynamic accuracy of 5 per cent is permitted with voltage recovery within 10 cycles.

The three regulator stages operate in cascade. In each stage the load circuits are omitted, and only the control-coil circuits are shown. The load circuits of the intermediate and output stages operate from a three-phase power circuit. It is understood that the load circuits consist of reactors and rectifiers, connected in the self-saturation manner. Each stage has three reactors and six rectifiers, arranged in three-phase bridge connection, rather than the single-phase bridge circuit previously described. However, the same basic theory applies to the three-phase amplifier stages as to single phase.

A three-phase rectifier is used to supply direct current for the bias coils of the intermediate and output stages. The output stage supplies

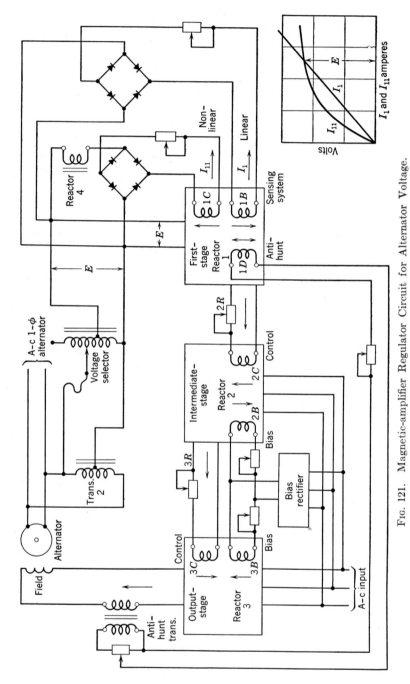

FIG. 121. Magnetic-amplifier Regulator Circuit for Alternator Voltage.

the field excitation for the alternator. At the time of starting, there is no alternator output and, therefore, no signal passing through the regulator. There must be field excitation in order to start generating. For that reason the bias sense in the output stage is in the direction to turn it full on and apply full forcing voltage on the field. The bias coil $2B$ in the intermediate stage is arranged to turn the intermediate stage off, so that it will not interfere with the field forcing for starting.

The output of the first stage connects to the $2C$ control coil of the intermediate stage through a suitable resistor $2R$ to obtain the rate of response required. The sense of $2C$ is to increase the output of the intermediate stage. The output of the intermediate stage connects to the $3C$ control coil of the output stage. The sense of $3C$ is in the direction to reduce the alternator field excitation.

The operating power for the first stage comes from the alternator output. Autotransformer 2 steps the alternator voltage down to the value required by the detector system. The detector system is designed to operate at voltage E, which is constant, regardless of the alternator voltage. The alternator voltage is preset by a variable autotransformer voltage selector which changes the ratio of transformation between the alternator output and the detector system voltage E. By increasing the voltage selector ratio, the alternator output voltage is increased.

The first stage has its load coil circuit supplied from the single-phase supply E. It has a magnetic-comparison sensing system, with coils $1B$ and $1C$ operating in opposition. The fixed reference is bias coil $1B$, supplied from voltage E, through a bridge rectifier and a circuit that is predominantly resistive in nature. The I_1 current relationship of this circuit, with voltage, is linear, as plotted in the lower right-hand corner of Fig. 121.

The signal in coil $1C$ also comes from voltage E through a bridge rectifier, but this circuit is made non-linear by the use of reactor 4. The $1C$ coil current I_{11} when plotted against the voltage, is non-linear and crosses the linear curve at the regulating voltage E. The system regulates at the voltage crossover point of the two curves. This makes a sensitive detector circuit, giving large corrections for small deviations from voltage E.

If the generator voltage becomes high, the detector voltage also increases slightly beyond E. Owing to the shape of the I_1 and I_{11} curves, I_{11} becomes relatively greater. Coil $1C$ ampere turns exceed those of coil $1B$, increasing the output of the first stage. This increases the ampere turns of coil $2C$ in the intermediate stage and increases the output of the intermediate stage. The increased control power from

Fig. 122.   Vickers Electric Division, 3.2-Kilowatt Magnetic-amplifier Regulator
Panel, with Three-phase Input.

FIG. 123. Complete Magnetic-amplifier Regulator Assembly for Mill Applications.

the intermediate stage strengthens coil 3C of the output stage. The sense of coil 3C causes the change to decrease the output of the final stage and weakens the alternator field. This restores the desired alternator voltage and also restores the detector voltage E.

An anti-hunt transformer, operating from the alternator field current, couples transient feedback into the first stage. This stabilizes the system by feeding back signals which are in opposition to the change taking place.

A regulator having circuit connections like Fig. 121 is shown in Fig. 122. This regulator can supply 3.5 kilowatts of field excitation continuously. It also has a 5-kilowatt intermittent rating for field forcing. The three large reactors and the large rectifier bank furnish the 3.5 kilowatts of direct-current power. Figure 123 shows the regulator mounted in a cubicle enclosure. The assembly includes a field-circuit contactor, other control devices, and instruments.

References

E. S. Smith, *Automatic Control Engineering,* McGraw-Hill Book Company, New York, 1944.

Automatic Regulation, Ahrendt and Taplin, P. O. Box 4673, Washington, D. C., 1947.

W. Richter, *Fundamentals of Industrial Electronic Circuits,* McGraw-Hill Book Company, New York, 1947.

Westinghouse Electric Corporation, *Industrial Electronics Reference Book,* Chapter 30, John Wiley & Sons, New York, 1948.

R. R. Batcher and W. Moulic, *The Electronic Control Handbook,* Cadwell-Clements, 1946.

W. J. Dornhoefer, "Self-saturation in Magnetic Amplifiers," *AIEE Technical Paper* 49-140, May, 1949.

J. H. Reyner, *The Magnetic Amplifier,* Stuart and Richards, London, 1950.

The Transductor Amplifier, Its Manner of Action and Comments on Its Use for Automatic Regulators, Lindhska Boktryckeriet, Orebro, Sweden, 1947.

Problems Based on an Automatic Regulating System

A. The constant-tension regulating system, shown in Fig. 108, has the following assigned data:

Maximum linear speed = S = 1000 feet per minute.

Tension = P = 330 pounds.

Adjustable-voltage lines, 235 direct volts.

Diameter of mandrel = 1 foot.

Diameter of full roll = 4 feet.

Gear ratio between armature and mandrel = 6/1.

Mechanical efficiency of winder = 80 per cent.

1. What horsepower is required to wind the strip?

2. What is the motor speed at the start of a roll?

3. What is the motor speed at a full roll?

4. What is the motor torque at the start of a roll?

5. What is the motor torque at a full roll?

6. What type of motor and what horsepower rating should be selected?

7. What speed range, by motor shunt-field control, is required of the motor to allow for automatic tension regulation at the roll-diameter extremes?

8. With 230 volts supplied to the motor armature, what armature current produces 330 pounds tension?

9. How many ohms are required in the sensing-device resistor to produce a signal of $e = 5$ volts, to operate the automatic tension regulator?

B. Assume a mechanical efficiency of 40 per cent for the mandrel winder of problem *A.* The regulator accuracy is the same in both cases.

1. What is the loss (friction and windage) horsepower?

2. What motor horsepower is required?

3. State the ratio of the per cent of the motor horsepower that produces useful tension in the high-efficiency drive to that in the low-efficiency drive.

4. The regulator holds the total horsepower to a constant value. Why then is it important that the variable losses be as low as possible?

C. The mandrel winder of problem *A* has a sensing-device resistor which produces a 5-volt signal for maximum tension. This signal must change 0.1 volt to swing the regulator from the empty mandrel to the full roll conditions.

1. What per cent error, from constant armature current, does this produce at the maximum tension setting?

2. When preset for one-fifth of maximum tension, the sensing device will produce a 1-volt signal. What is the per cent error in this case?

3. What conclusion can be made relative to defining the signal level when specifying the regulator accuracy?

D. A constant-speed application takes a regulating signal from a tachometer-generator sensing device. The regulator requires a signal change of 0.1 volt to produce the necessary corrections.

1. If the allowable error at maximum speed is 1 per cent, what voltage must the tachometer generator produce at the maximum speed?

2. What tachometer voltage is required at the maximum speed to reduce the allowable error to 0.5 per cent?

3. What conclusion can be made relative to the magnitude of the signal level where a choice exists?

11

THE DIRECT-CURRENT SERIES MOTOR

Series motors are those having the main field connected in series with the armature, and so carrying the load current. They may be provided with a relatively light shunt field also, to prevent excess speed under light loads; they are then called series-shunt motors. The relative strength of the two fields may be anything up to 50 per cent for each. Since the load current passes through the series field, the field strength will vary with the load, and the speed will decrease on heavy load and increase on light load.

Construction. The general construction of a series-wound motor is similar to that of a shunt-wound motor, except that the field windings

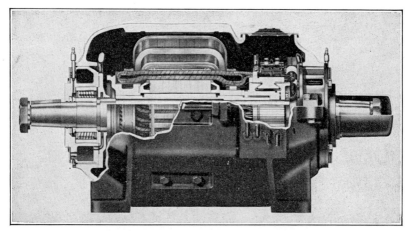

Fig. 124. Westinghouse Type-MC Series-wound Mill Motor.

are of heavy wire or strap, for connection in series with the armature. The vital dimensions have been standardized by the AISE. The frame is of heavy steel construction and may be split horizontally and hinged, so that the top half may be swung back for easy access to the armature and the bearings. Armatures are relatively long and of small diameter to reduce their inertia, which helps in quick starting, stopping, and reversal. In the motor shown in Fig. 124, the field coils are wound in a sealed steel box, into which the field pole fits, the bottom of the box being held between the pole and the motor frame. The commutator and brush construction is similar to that of a shunt motor. The motors are made in several types according to the degree of protection desired. Totally enclosed motors have a solid frame, without openings. Open motors have openings in the top and the bottom halves of the frame. These are covered with perforated metal or louvers. Protected self-ventilated motors have a solid top frame and openings in the bottom frame.

Motor Torque. The general equation for direct-current motor torque

$$\text{Torque} = \text{Armature current} \times \text{Field strength}$$

applies to the series motor. The field current and field strength change whenever the armature current changes. Since the field coils are

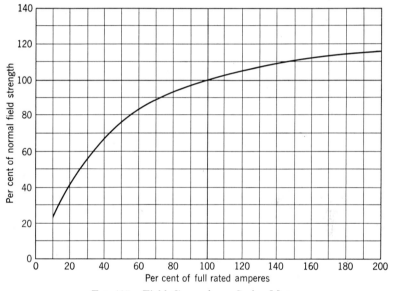

FIG. 125. Field Curve for a Series Motor.

wound on iron cores, which are subject to saturation, the field strength does not vary directly with the field current but follows a saturation curve, like that of Fig. 125. The design of motors is sufficiently standardized so that a typical curve will apply to most of them accurately enough for most controller calculations. The curve of Fig. 125, compiled from data on a number of motors and checked against many others, has been found satisfactory for general use.

If a shunt motor were started with an initial inrush current of 1.5 times its rated current, the starting torque would also be 1.5 times normal. With a series motor, if saturation were not present, the field strength would also be 1.5 times normal and the torque would be 2.25 times normal. The curve of Fig. 125 shows the actual field strength to be 1.11 times normal, and the torque would actually be 1.5 × 1.11 or 1.67 times normal. These figures illustrate one of the advantages of the series motor, as the high torque results in rapid starting and reversing.

Motor Speed. The general equation for speed also applies to the series motor.

$$S = \frac{E - I_a R_m}{F(E - I_n R_m)}$$

where S = speed in percentage of full-load rated speed.

E = line voltage in percentage of normal voltage.

I_a = armature current in percentage of full rated current.

R_m = resistance of the motor in percentage of E/I_n.

F = field strength in percentage of normal.

I_n = normal, or full load, current.

Since F will vary with the load, a series motor will not accelerate to a constant stable speed like a shunt motor, but will accelerate to a speed determined by the load. With light loads and corresponding low currents the speed may be excessively high, even runaway. The motor must not be applied to drives where the load may at any time fall below a safe value, unless some arrangement is made in the control to prevent a runaway. The inherent characteristic of running slowly under heavy load and fast under light load is exactly what is desired for many applications, particularly cranes and hoists.

Acceleration of Series Motors. Series motors are commonly accelerated by means of series resistance, just as shunt motors are, but the starting curves are different owing to the different field characteristics. Figure 126 shows the starting of a series motor using a resistance calculated to give 150 per cent of current for the inrush peaks. The accelerating curves are plotted against torque. The current-torque curve shows that, for 150 per cent current, the torque is approximately 167 per cent. The motor first accelerates along the curve ab, and at b the first resistance step is cut out. This gives the second current inrush c, and the motor accelerates along the curve cd until the second step is cut out. These curves do not pass through 100 per cent speed at zero current, as in a shunt motor, but show that the speed keeps on increasing as the load decreases. In plotting the curves, the resistance

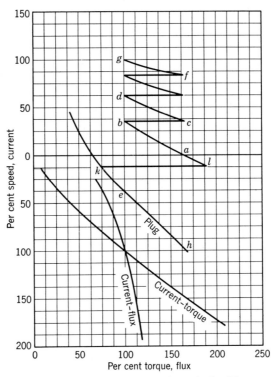

FIG. 126. Acceleration Curves for a Series Motor.

of the motor and leads has been assumed as 11 per cent. The equation
for any one of the curves is

$$\text{Per cent speed} = \frac{1 - RI}{\text{Flux}\,(1 - 0.11)}$$

where I is the current in percentage of full-load current.
R is the resistance in circuit expressed in percentage of

$$\frac{\text{Line voltage}}{\text{Full-load current}}$$

The value of the steps of resistance may be obtained by determining
the distance between the curves on the line bg, just as with the shunt
motor.

Probably the best method of graphical solution is first to plot the
speed-current curve of the motor alone and then assume a value for

the resistance in the last step of the controller. Applying this value in the above equation, plot the curve for that step. In the same manner, assume values for the other steps and plot those curves. From the point where each curve crosses the full-load line, draw a straight line vertically until it intersects the next curve. If equal peaks are not obtained, select new values for the resistance and try again. If the curves are very nearly correct, it will be possible to draw them in closely enough freehand, following the shape of the nearest calculated curve.

This is, admittedly, a cut-and-try method; it is easier to calculate the resistance values by the non-graphical method and then plot the curves if desired. The speed-torque curve is generally of more interest than the speed-current curve. The curve of the motor alone can always be obtained from the motor manufacturer, and such curves usually give the losses at any load. The motor resistance and the voltage drop across the motor at full load can be calculated from the losses. Average values are $0.23E/I$ for motors up to 10 horsepower, $0.14E/I$ for motors up to 50 horsepower, and 0.11 per cent for the larger motors. If no speed-torque curve for a motor is available, one can be plotted from the average flux curve of Fig. 125. Table 17 gives the values of inrush current and resistor taper for series motors. The accelerating steps do not include the plugging step.

TABLE 17
RESISTOR DESIGN FOR SERIES MOTORS

Accelerating Steps	Accelerating Peak in per cent of Full Load	Plugging Peak in per cent of Full Load	Motor Resistance, per cent E/I
1	185	150	23
2	159	150	14
3	147	150	11
4	133	150	10
5	133	150	8

The total resistance for plugging is obtained by dividing the plugging voltage by the plugging inrush current and subtracting the motor resistance.

$$R_t = \frac{E \times 1.8}{I_p} - R_m$$

The total resistance for accelerating is

$$R_{acc} = \frac{E}{I_{acc}} - R_m$$

To be exact, the value of E in these two equations should be multiplied by a factor to cover the increase in voltage caused by the increase of the field strength above normal, which will depend on the values of I_p and I_{acc}. If these current values were 150 per cent of normal, the factor would be about 1.11, and the increase in the resistance values would just about equal the value of R_m. The general practice is to neglect both the increase in field strength and R_m, since they practically balance each other.

The resistance of the plugging step above is

$$R_p = R_t - R_{\text{acc}}$$

The accelerating resistance may be divided as shown by Table 18.

TABLE 18

Resistor Taper for Series Motors

Per Cent of Total Accelerating Resistance

No. Steps	Step 1	Step 2	Step 3	Step 4	Step 5
1	100	..	..	....	..
2	66	34	..	....	..
3	43	33	24	....	..
4	32.5	26	23	18.5	..
5	24	22	20	18	16

Figure 126 is a typical speed-torque curve plotted from these values. The equations are

$$S = \frac{E - RI_a}{\text{Flux} \ (E - R_m I_n)}, \ T = \text{Flux} \times I_a$$

where S = speed in percentage of full-load speed.

T = torque in percentage of full-load torque.

E = line voltage = 100 per cent.

R = total resistance including the motor in percentage of E/I_n.

I_a = current in percentage of full-load current I_n.

R_m = resistance of the motor in percentage of E/I_n.

Flux = field strength from field curve.

Reversing and Plugging. The series motor may be reversed by reversing either the armature or the series field, but not both. The usual practice is to reverse the armature. Series motors are often plugged by connecting the armature for reversed direction while the motor is running in the forward direction. This is done to get a quick stop or, more frequently, a quick reversal. When the motor is plugged, the countervoltage of the armature is added to the line voltage, and it is necessary to provide an additional step of resistance in the controller to limit the inrush current to a safe value. The practice of plugging series motors is so general that it is customary either to provide a plugging resistance step or, when it is known that plugging is not desired, to arrange the control so that the operator cannot plug. It is assumed that he will try to do so.

Figure 126 includes a curve which shows the plugging of a series motor. Additional resistance, measured by the line eb, has been added to limit the current inrush to 150 per cent. When the motor is plugged, it decelerates along the line hk to the point k, at which point the plugging step of resistance is short-circuited and the motor continues to decelerate along the curve la to a. At this point it has come to rest, and from there on it accelerates in the opposite direction. It is possible to delay short-circuiting of the plugging resistance until the current has dropped to the point k, because it is certain that the motor will continue to decelerate to zero speed, and then reverse. The curve shows that at zero speed the current is below point k.

Dynamic Braking. Dynamic braking may be obtained with a series motor, as shown in Fig. 127, but the connections become a little compli-

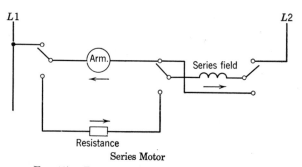

Fig. 127. Dynamic Braking of a Series Motor.

cated. If the motor were simply disconnected from the line and shunted by a step of resistance, no braking would be obtained, because the current would flow through the field in the wrong direction, and the field would be demagnetized. Assuming that, with the motor running, the current is flowing from $L1$ to $L2$, the countervoltage of the armature is in the opposing direction as shown by the arrow. Current is flowing in the field from $L1$ to $L2$. When the motor is disconnected from the line and connected for braking, it will be evident that the field must be connected in the reverse direction in order that the current will flow through it in the same direction as it was flowing with the motor on the line.

Sometimes, for dynamic braking, the series field is connected directly across the line in series with a resistance. It thus becomes temporarily a shunt field. This method is wasteful of energy since a high percentage of full-load current must be supplied to the field.

Since dynamic braking is present only when the motor is turning, a mechanical brake of some sort is required to hold the load after stopping it. Such brakes are usually released electrically and applied mechanically by springs. When they are used with series motors, the usual practice is to equip the brake with a series coil and connect it in series with the motor. This arrangement insures that the brake will release only when current is flowing through the motor and motor torque is available to hold or move the load.

Speeds below Normal. The speed of a series motor may be reduced below normal by means of series resistance, and also by armature shunt resistance, and the results are the same as with a shunt motor, except that in calculating the speeds the current in the series field must always be considered.

Series Motor. Armature Shunt. The method followed in designing an armature shunt resistance for a series motor differs from that for

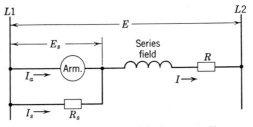

FIG. 128. Series Motor with Armature Shunt.

a shunt motor, in that the effect of the series field must be considered. The field current will be the sum of the currents through the armature and the shunt, so that, to obtain normal full-load torque, the armature current will be less than the full-load value. The torque desired at the reduced speed will be known, but neither the armature current nor the field current can be readily determined. Direct calculation for the shunt resistance becomes very involved, if not impossible. The simpler method is to assume a value for the field strength and calculate the speed obtained at the desired torque. If we refer to Fig. 128, and use all values in percentage of normal:

E = line voltage—known.

R = series resistance plus field resistance—known.

R_m = armature resistance—known.

T = torque required—known.

F = field strength—assumed.

I_f = the current in the series field. This is determined by the assumed value of field strength.

I_a = the current in the armature = T/F.

I_s = the current in the shunt = $I_f - I_a$.

E_s = the voltage across the armature (and the shunt) = $E - I_f R$.

E_a = the countervoltage of the motor = $E_s - I_a R_m$.

$$S = \text{the speed} = \frac{E_a}{F(E - I_a R_m)}.$$

The value of F which will give the desired speed having, by a few trials, been determined, the shunt resistance is

$$R_s = \frac{E_s}{I_s}$$

Speeds above Normal. It is possible to increase the speed of a series motor above normal by shunting the series field and so reducing the current through it, but the method is not very practical because of the low resistance of the field and so is infrequently used.

Overhauling Loads. It may seem something of a paradox that the series motor, which will run away if too lightly loaded, should be the motor most universally used on cranes to handle overhauling loads. One reason has been mentioned, the fact that its speed characteristics are exactly those desired for hoisting loads. The high torque available for rapid acceleration is also desirable. Still another reason for its popularity is the fact that the heavy windings of the series fields are much less liable to damage in service than the fine wire windings of the shunt motor.

The series motor can readily be made to handle overhauling loads safely by suitable arrangement of the control. If a series motor were connected for dynamic braking, as shown in Fig. 127, and were then driven by an overhauling load, the motor would generate current, dissipating energy in the resistance, and act as a brake on the load. Almost any desired speed could be obtained by varying the resistance. The speed would, however, vary considerably for different loads, and a light load could not be driven down. To overcome these objections, a circuit like Fig. 145 is used. Here the motor armature and field are connected in parallel, each with resistance in series, and the motor characteristics are like those of a shunt machine. The armature circuit resistance is used to prevent excessive starting inrushes, and is cut out in several steps as the motor accelerates. The minimum resistance in the field circuit must be high enough to limit the field current to about normal, and additional resistance is then cut in in several steps to weaken the field and increase the motor speed. On the hoisting side of the controller the circuits are the same as for a straight non-reversing control. A controller of this kind is called a dynamic-lowering hoist controller, and is described in detail in Chapter 13.

Motor Protection. Controllers for series motors usually include magnetic overload relays, which have a time-delay action at ordinary overloads but trip instantaneously if the motor stalls. It is not necessary to guard against loss of the series field, as the heavy construction makes this unlikely, and the circuit is such that opening of the field could hardly happen without the armature being disconnected also. Controllers for series-shunt motors often include a relay to protect against loss of the shunt field. Ordinarily no other protection is provided for a series motor.

Manually Operated Controllers. Manually operated face-plate controllers are used to some extent with small series motors, both for starting and for speed regulation. Their construction is the same as that of similar starters for shunt motors.

Multiple-switch starters are seldom, if ever, used for series motors, because the starter is inherently one which takes time to operate, while the motor is particularly adaptable to machines which must be started frequently and rapidly.

Drum Controllers. Drum controllers are widely used for the control of series motors, particularly on street-railway cars and on cranes. Their general construction is the same as that of the drums used for controlling shunt motors.

The reversing and non-reversing drums used for crane trolley and bridge motions are arranged for 50 per cent speed reduction by resistance in the armature circuit. If greater speed reduction is desired, an armature shunt is used, and 90 per cent reduction may be obtained in this way. The drum ratings are the same as for shunt motors.

Dynamic lowering drum controllers are for use with hoists. They are employed with series motors, and the circuits are so arranged that, when the drum cylinder is moved in the hoist direction, the motor is brought up to speed gradually by reducing the resistance in the circuit in the usual manner. The drum is arranged so that, when the cylinder is moved to the "lower" position, the motor, when overhauled by the load, acts as a generator and forces current through a resistor. If the speed increases the voltage on the terminals of the motor also increases, forcing more current through the resistor. The speed is thus automatically kept at a safe value with the controller on any given point, but by moving the controller to another point the speed can be changed by increasing or decreasing the value of the resistance through which the generated current must flow.

Figure 129 shows in an elementary manner how the above effects are secured. It will be noted that in the off position a resistance is

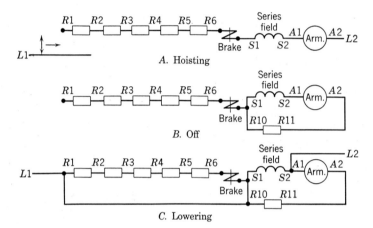

Fig. 129. Connections for a Dynamic-lowering Drum Controller.

connected around the armature and field of the motor. The residual magnetism causes the motor to build up as a series generator, and current is forced through the resistance until the inertia of the motor and the falling load is overcome.

In the lowering direction, the series field of the motor is connected across the line in series with a resistor, and another resistor is connected across the armature. This gives the effect of a shunt-wound motor, since the strength of the field is independent of the armature current. An inspection of Fig. 129 will show that, if the load is not heavy enough to overhaul the motor, current will flow from the line through the armature and fields of the motor in such a direction as to drive the load downward. These drums also are rated the same as those for shunt motors.

Dinkey Controller. The controller shown in Fig. 130 is a face-plate type built to stand hard service and rough treatment. This type of controller is named for its inventor, Mr. A. C. Dinkey, and was developed particularly for steel-mill operations. It represents the earliest form of controller which successfully withstood the abuses of that service.

The controller is built in two types, one for plain reversing and the other for dynamic lowering. Several sizes are available, for motors up to 100 horsepower. The contacts are arranged in four quadrants, the armature-reversing contacts being grouped around the center of the slate and the accelerating con-
tacts around the periphery. The contacts are mounted on lugs, to which the connecting wires are attached. They are easily removable, and when worn on one side they may be reversed. The moving contacts are mounted on a double-ended arm of simple construction, which can be removed by taking out one bolt. The same attention to accessibility and ease of repair has been given to the resistor, which is mounted in a frame at the rear of the panel. The connections are grouped at the top, and by removing the connecting wires the resistor sections may be lifted out for repair. The very considerable success of this controller has led to its continued use in many mills to the present day. Its principal disadvantages are its size, weight, and cost, which are greater

Fig. 130. Dinkey Controller.

than those of a drum controller, and the fact that the arcing contacts are exposed.

Magnetic Controllers. Magnetic controllers for series motors are generally used on cranes, coal and ore bridges, and for auxiliary machinery in the processing of steel and other metals. They are made in several types as follows:

Non-reversing, plain starting duty.
Non-reversing, starting and regulating duty.
Non-reversing, starting and regulating duty, with dynamic braking.
Reversing, plugging.
Reversing, with dynamic braking.
Reversing, dynamic lowering. These are described in detail in a separate chapter.

TABLE 19

NEMA Ratings for Steel-mill Auxiliary Controllers

8-hour Contactor Rating, amperes	Contactor Mill Rating, amperes	For Continuous Duty		For Intermittent Duty	
		Hp Rating, 230 V	Minimum Number of Accelerating Contactors	Hp Rating, 230 V	Minimum Number of Accelerating Contactors
100	133	25	2	35	2
150	200	40	2	55	2
300	400	75	2	110	2
600	800	150	3	225	2 or 3
900	1200	225	3	330	3
1350	1800	350	4	500	4
2500	3350	600	5	1000	5

The number of accelerating contactors does not include the plugging contactor.

TABLE 20

NEMA Ratings for Crane Controllers

8-hour Contactor Rating, amperes	Contactor Crane Rating, amperes	Hp Rating, 230 V	Minimum Number of Accelerating Contactors exclusive of Plugging Contactor
100	133	35	3
150	200	55	3
300	400	110	3
600	800	225	4
900	1200	330	5
1350	1800	500	6

A typical controller of the reversing, dynamic-braking type would include the devices listed below, mounted on slate or impregnated-asbestos panel board. The panel would be mounted on an angle-iron supporting frame and might be either open or enclosed in a steel protecting case.

1 double-pole single-throw main disconnect knife switch.
1 double-pole single-throw control circuit knife switch.
2 fuses for the control circuit.
2 magnetic overload relays.
1 set of reversing contactors, mechanically interlocked.
1 negative line, or main, contactor.
1 set of accelerating contactors.
1 spring-closed dynamic-braking contactor.
1 undervoltage relay.
1 set of accelerating devices (series or time relays).
1 plugging contactor.

For separate installation there would be a master controller, a set of resistor material, and possibly limit switches, or other accessory devices. The main or motor circuits of these controllers are much alike, but the control circuits vary widely with the application, depending on the functions required. Figure 131 is typical of the control schemes used for mill auxiliary machines. It is for a motor driving a

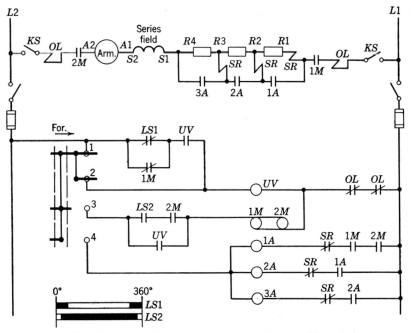

Fig. 131. Single-cycle Controller for a Steel Mill Auxiliary Drive.

machine through an eccentric, each operation of the motor causing the wheel of the drive to make one revolution and moving the eccentric rod forward and back. Such a machine might be used to push steel billets into a furnace. In the off position of the master the relay *UV* closes. When the master is moved to the forward position, contactors *1M* and *2M* are energized through a contact of *UV*. The motor starts and accelerates to full speed under the control of the series relays. The limit switch contacts *LS1* and *LS2* are those of a rotating cam-type switch (see Fig. 31), geared to the driven wheel. As soon as the wheel rotates a small amount, contact *LS2* closes. Shortly afterward contact *LS1* opens, de-energizing *UV*, which opens. The motor continues to run until *LS2* opens, and then it stops. Just before this happens, contact *LS1* recloses, but, when the motor stops, it cannot restart until the operator returns the master to the off position and recloses UV. The machine then makes one complete cycle for each operation of the master. In case of trouble the operator can stop the motor at any point in the cycle. The normally closed interlock contacts on $1M$ permit him to reset UV if he makes an emergency stop at a point in the cycle where $LS1$ is open.

Crane-protective Panels. When drum controllers are used for one or more of the motors of a crane, it is usual practice to obtain low voltage and overload protection by means of a crane-protective panel, mounting the apparatus listed below.

1 double-pole isolating knife switch, with provision for padlocking in the open position.

2 single-pole (or one double-pole) contactors arranged to open both sides of the line.

1 set of automatic-reset overload relays, one in the positive circuit to each motor, and one in the common return to the other side of the line.

2 pilot lights with fuses.

2 control-circuit fuses.

TABLE 21

RATINGS FOR CONTACTORS USED ON CRANE-PROTECTIVE PANELS

8-hour Rating, amperes	Total horsepower of All Motors at 230 V	Horsepower of Largest Individual Motor at 230 V
100	55	35
150	80	55
300	160	110
600	320	225
900	480	330
1350	725	500

For motors of other voltage ratings, the 8-hour rating of the main-line contactors should not be less than 50 per cent of the combined ½-hour or 1-hour rating of the motors, nor less than 75 per cent of the ½-hour or 1-hour rating of the largest individual motor.

Sometimes magnetic controllers are also connected behind a crane-protective panel, and the disconnect knife switch, overload relays, and undervoltage relay are then omitted from the individual controllers. With that arrangement the main-line contactor should not be of smaller rating than that of the largest contactor on any of the individual controllers.

The line contactors of the crane-protective panel are operated by a two-button momentary-contact pushbutton station, marked RESET and STOP. The circuit is arranged so that the contactors cannot be held closed under overload.

Dynamic Braking for Crane Bridges. The method of obtaining dynamic braking with a series motor has been described, but, when it is desired to obtain such braking on a crane bridge, the problem is complicated by the fact that the braking must be effective in both directions of travel and also when power fails. It should preferably be graduated, so that enough braking effort is available at low speeds, but undue shock is avoided when the braking is applied at high speed.

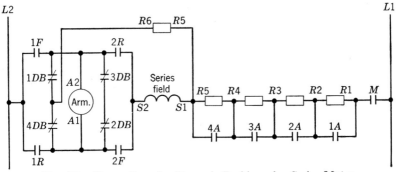

Fig. 132. Connections for Dynamic Braking of a Series Motor.

Figure 132 shows a method used with a single motor. In addition to the regular equipment of a reversing controller, there are four spring-closed dynamic-braking contactors, 1DB, 2DB, 3DB, and 4DB. These are mounted in a row on the control panel and are free to open at any time when their coils are energized. They are all open when the motor is running. A camshaft, extending across the four contactors, is turned to either of two positions by a pair of electromagnets. One of the magnets is energized when the forward-direction contactors are energized, and the camshaft is turned so that contactors 1DB and 2DB are locked open by the cams. Then, when the motor is stopping, only contactors 3DB and 4DB can close. When the motor is running in the forward direction, current flows through the armature from A2 to A1, and through the series field from S2 to S1. The motor counter-voltage is in the direction from A1 to A2. When the motor is stopped, or if voltage fails, 3DB and 4DB close, and current flows from A1 to A2, through 3DB, from S2 to S1, through the braking resistor, through 4DB back to A1. The field is energized in the same direction as when running, and braking is secured.

When the motor is reversed, the camshaft is rotated to the opposite position, and contactors $3DB$ and $4DB$ are locked open, while $1DB$ and $2DB$ are free to close. Current flows through the armature from $A1$ to $A2$, and through the field from $S2$ to $S1$. The countervoltage is in the direction from $A2$ to $A1$. Now, when the motor is stopped, $1DB$ and $2DB$ close, and current flows from $A2$ through the armature to $A1$, through $2DB$, through the series field from $S2$ to $S1$, through the braking resistor, through $1DB$, back to $A2$. Again the field current is flowing in the right direction to obtain braking.

This arrangement is used on single-motor cranes and on other machines where a quick stop is essential even though power fails. The position of the camshaft, and the locking out of the proper contactors, are not affected by power failure.

For crane bridges driven by two motors the arrangement shown in Figs. 133 and 134 will meet all the requirements of good braking. This method was developed and patented by Herman Wilson and Charles Ritchie, two electrical engineers in one of the steel mills, and is known as the Wilson-Ritchie method of braking. The armature of one motor is handled by the reversing contactors in the conventional way, but the field of the other motor is reversed. Four spring-closed, magnetically released contactors are used for the braking circuit. These are standard contactors without any additional mechanism. All of them are open when the motor is running and closed during braking.

Referring to Fig. 133, which shows the basic scheme, and assuming that the bridge is moving forward, current is flowing from $L2$ to $L1$, through armature 1 in the direction from $A2$ to $A1$, and through armature 2 in the direction from $A12$ to $A11$. Current flows through field 1 from $S2$ to $S1$, and through field 2 from $S12$ to $S11$. In stopping, all direction contactors open, and all braking contactors close. The countervoltage of armature 1 causes current to flow through the armature from $A1$ to $A2$, and through field 2 from $S12$ to $S11$. Similarly, the countervoltage of armature 2 causes current to flow from $A11$ to $A12$, and through field 1 from $S2$ to $S1$. Both fields are therefore energized in the right direction, and each provides a braking field for the armature of the other motor. It is evident that this must be so for either direction of travel, since current always flows in the same direction through armature 1 and field 2, which form one braking circuit, and since armature 2 and field 1 are always reversed together. The controller of Fig. 133 therefore gives a simple and positive braking method, either for normal stopping or when power fails.

Since the speed of a crane bridge varies widely, being low on short runs and high on long runs, the available countervoltage, and corre-

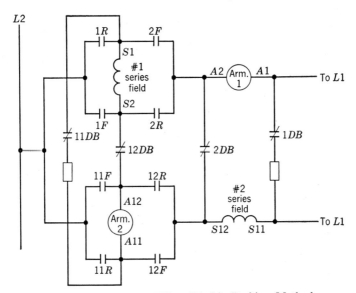

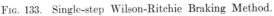

FIG. 133.   Single-step Wilson-Ritchie Braking Method.

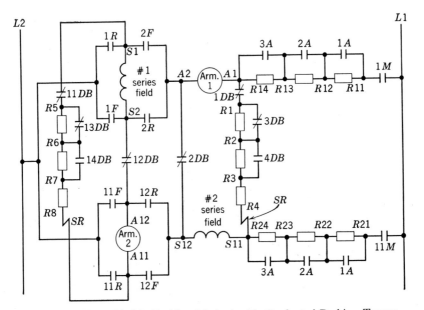

FIG. 134.   Wilson-Ritchie Braking Method with Graduated Braking Torque.

sponding braking effect, will also vary widely. It is usually desirable to provide several steps of braking resistance if the braking is to be used for normal or service stopping. Figure 134 shows the usual arrangement, with three steps. The contactors which short-circuit these steps are controlled either from the operating master or from a separate master or foot switch having three positions. For stopping from high speed, point 1 is used, on which contactors 3DB, 4DB, 13DB, and 14DB are open and all braking resistance is in circuit. This resistance will allow approximately 125 per cent of normal current to flow. On the second point, contactors 3DB and 13DB are closed, and the remaining resistance will allow approximately the same current if the motor is at normal speed. On the third point, contactors 4DB and 14DB close, and the remaining resistor is designed to allow sufficient current for good braking from half speed. Series relays are connected in the braking circuits, controlling 4DB and 14DB, so that, if an attempt is made to close these contactors at too high a speed, the relays will operate to prevent it. On power failure the circuit is the same as it is on the second, or normal speed, braking position. If power failed with the bridge at high speed, the braking would be more severe than might be satisfactory for service stopping but not too severe for an emergency condition.

The Wilson-Ritchie scheme has been successfully applied to a number of cranes. Some interesting tests were made at one installation, where there were three cranes on one runway, each equipped with this control. It was therefore possible to operate the center crane in either direction, or to allow it to drift, or to remain at rest for some time, and then in each case push it with one of the other cranes. It was found that braking always occurred, even after the crane had been allowed to stand at rest for some time. There was always sufficient residual magnetism in the fields to start a current flow, and the braking effect, once started, built up rapidly. With this in mind, the scheme has been applied to large coal and ore bridges, which are liable to be moved on their tracks by a strong wind. If that happened, dynamic braking would apply to limit the speed. To the best of the author's knowledge, no other control scheme will accomplish this result.

Application of Series Motors. Series motors are applicable to drives requiring high starting torque, fast reversing, and a motor as sturdy in construction as is available. These characteristics make the series motor ideal for such applications in steel mills, as roll tables, screwdowns, furnace pushers, manipulators, and many others. The motor is ideal for cranes, hoists, coal- and ore-handling bucket hoists, and cargo winches, because of its inherent characteristic of running fast with light loads and slowly with heavy loads. Its ready adaptability to dynamic braking and dynamic lowering is a further advantage on this service. Its speed and torque characteristics make it ideal for street-railway cars and other motor-driven vehicles.

Series-shunt motors are applied to drives when it is desired to limit the speed with light load. Crane bridges and trolleys may use series-shunt motors for that reason. Car dumpers, which may require a high starting and accelerating torque, may have some portion of their cycle in which the load is very light, or even overhauling, and some shunt field is desirable to limit the speed there.

References

D. R. Shoults, *Electric Motors in Industry,* John Wiley & Sons, 1942.
Symposium, "Equipment for Mill-crane Bridge Drives," *Iron and Steel Engineer,* November, 1940.
A. A. Merrill, "Adjusting Crane Control by Speed-torque Curves," *Steel,* August, September, 1943.
A. A. Merrill, "Speed-torque Curves—How They Picture Crane Performance," *Steel,* July, 1933.
E. J. Posselt, "Plugging Methods for Mill and Crane Motors," *Iron and Steel Engineer,* July, 1947.

Problems

Note. Use field curve Fig. 125 in calculations.

1. Write an equation for the torque of a series motor.

2. Write an equation for the speed of a series motor.

3. A series motor is driving a load which causes it to take 110 per cent of rated full-load current. Approximately how much current would an equivalent shunt motor require to supply the same torque?

4. The torque required to drive a certain machine is 5000 pound-feet. The inrush current when starting the driving motor is limited to 175 per cent of normal full-load current. What is the starting torque if a shunt motor is used? What is the starting torque if a series motor is used?

5. The resistance of the armature and field of a series motor is $0.11E/I$. If the full-load speed of the motor is 1000 rpm, what is the speed at half load?

6. A motor is provided with both series and shunt fields, so proportioned that at full load the series field provides 80 per cent of the field strength. If the resistance of the armature and series field is $0.11E/I$, what will be the speed at half load?

7. Plot the speed-torque curves for acceleration of a series motor with three steps of resistance, using the data given in Table 17.

8. If the resistance of a motor armature and field is $0.11E/I$, what is the motor countervoltage when running at full load?

9. What is the total voltage if the motor is plugged?

10. If this is a 100-horsepower 230-volt 375-ampere motor, what will be the ohmic value of a resistor which will limit the starting current to 150 per cent of normal when the motor is plugged?

11. A motor is provided with both series and shunt fields, so proportioned that the series field provides 70 per cent of the field strength. What will be the speed if the shunt field circuit is opened?

12. A 20-horsepower 230-volt 80-ampere motor has an armature and field resistance of $0.14E/I$ and is provided with a dynamic-braking resistor of 1.8 ohms. What initial braking torque will be obtained?

13. A 30-horsepower 230-volt 110-ampere motor is used with a series resistor of 1.3 ohms. Calculate the value of an armature shunt resistance which will produce a speed of 30 per cent of full-load speed, with a torque of 50 per cent of full rated torque. Assume armature resistance of $0.10E/I$, and field resistance of $0.04E/I$.

14. A 40-horsepower 230-volt 146-ampere motor is used with a series resistor of 1.0 ohms, and an armature shunt resistor of 2.0 ohms. What will be the speed of this motor in per cent of normal speed when the armature current is 50 amperes, if the resistance of the armature and the field are neglected?

15. What per cent of full rated torque will the motor be delivering?

16. Draw an elementary diagram of a single-cycle controller like that of Fig. 131, except arranged for reversing in emergency. The reversing operation may be continuous and not under the control of the limit switch.

17. Draw an elementary diagram for the control circuits of Fig. 132, using a master controller having five speed points in each direction, and omitting any method of delaying the accelerating contactors.

18. Draw an elementary diagram for a controller for a 50-horsepower 230-volt 190-ampere series motor, the controller to have the following characteristics:

> Reversing.
> Three steps of accelerating resistance.
> Inductive-timed acceleration like Fig. 52.
> Armature shunt on the first point in each direction.
> Field shunt on the last point forward only.
> Master controller with 5 speed points in each direction.
> Low-voltage protection and overload protection.

19. Calculate the ohms required in each step of the accelerating resistance, using the data of Tables 17 and 18.

20. Calculate the ohms required in the armature shunt step to give a speed of 50 per cent of full-load speed, when the motor is running at zero load.

21. Calculate the ohms required in the field-shunting resistor to give a speed of 115 per cent of full-load speed, when the motor is running at 100 per cent load.

22. A small series motor is started by a controller having a single step of resistance, the accelerating contactor being set to close at 100 per cent of rated current. If the controller is changed to use a five-step resistor, with the same contactor setting, how much will the average accelerating torque be reduced? Use data of Table 17.

23. A 75-horsepower 230-volt 280-ampere series motor has a resistance of 11 per cent of E/I. Using the data of Tables 17 and 18, calculate the ohms in each step of a five-step resistor which will give the following performance:

Current on first point when plugging, 100 per cent of rated current.
Current on second point when plugging, 150 per cent of rated current.
Current on third point starting from rest—see table.

24. A motor is provided with both series and shunt fields, the shunt field providing 30 per cent of the field strength. The motor is belted to the machine which it drives. What speed will the motor reach if the belt breaks?

25. A mill has a series-shunt motor rated 100 horsepower, 230 volts, and 375 amperes. It has a shunt field which provides 50 per cent of the field strength. How many ohms must be used in series with the motor to obtain 50 per cent speed at full rated load?

12

TWO-MOTOR DRIVES

It frequently happens that two motors, instead of one motor of twice the size, may be used to definite advantage for a drive. The motors are usually connected mechanically, so that any change in speed or direction of rotation of one is accompanied by a corresponding change in the other. The mechanical connection may be accomplished by direct coupling, or by gearing, or it may be through track and wheels in a car or a crane bridge.

Space conditions will sometimes influence the choice of two motors, as it may be easier to find room for two small motors than for one large one. If the single motor were of an odd size it might be advantageous to select two smaller ones in order to make them duplicates of other machines in the plant, and so eliminate the necessity of carrying a new line of repair parts. Where emergency operation of a machine is essential, as in hot-metal-handling equipment, it is advantageous to have two motors. In the event of motor burnout the damaged machine may be dismantled, and the equipment operated temporarily by one motor. Some two-motor drives have been installed with the idea of obtaining more rapid acceleration and reversal, because the moment of inertia of two small motors is less than that of one large one. There is some difference of opinion as to whether this condition actually obtains in practice, but undoubtedly many two-motor drives have been installed for that reason.

When using two motors mechanically connected together, the principal difficulties are to obtain equal division of the load when starting and when running, to avoid circulating currents when plugging, to commutate highly inductive currents when the motors are in series.

Division of Running Load. Motors which are supposedly exact duplicates may vary enough in their characteristics to cause serious unbalancing of the load; this is particularly true of shunt motors. Slight imperfections in manufacture, unequal heating of the field coils, differences in the length of leads, or any one of a number of other causes may result in unbalancing the load. The effect is most marked in shunt motors because of their flat speed-current characteristic.

The speed of a shunt motor changes very little over a wide range of load current, and, conversely, if the motor is forced, by mechanical connection, to run at a speed only slightly different from its natural speed, wide variation in current will result. With a series motor the speed changes more rapidly with changes in load, and consequently a slightly incorrect speed will not cause a very great unbalancing of load. The unbalancing obtained with compound motors will be somewhere between that of the shunt and the series motors, depending upon the percentage of compounding.

Calculations based on some typical motor curves show that, when two shunt motors having a difference of 5 per cent in full-load speed are mechanically coupled, one may take twice as much current as the other. When series motors having the same speed difference are coupled, the load of one might be approximately 15 per cent higher than that of the other. It will be evident that the control equipment is not the factor which causes unbalancing of the running load. However, the blame is often laid to the control equipment, and control engineers are called upon to correct the trouble. For that reason a brief description of a method of balancing, applicable to shunt or compound motors in parallel, is given here.

Balancing Shunt Motors.

1. Set the motor brushes at neutral.

2. Check the speed at full field. If the speed is different, increase the speed of the slow motor by taking out shims of the main field poles. If there are no shims on the main field poles, or if all have been taken out, the speed of the fast motor should be decreased by adding shims to the main field poles. The thickness of the shims should be not more than $\frac{1}{32}$ inch.

3. Check the speed of the motors with weak field maximum speed, at no load. If necessary, disconnect the motors to obtain no load. The brushes are to remain on neutral. If this speed differs more than 1 per cent, adjust the field resistor to make the speed the same.

4. Check the speed at full load with weakened field. If the speed differs, shift the brushes of the fast motor in the direction of rotation. The brushes should not be shifted more than one bar at the maximum. If this is not sufficient, return the brush to neutral and increase the air gap on the interpoles of the fast motor. First take out the shims of the two adjacent poles. If this does not suffice, shift the brushes, not more than one bar, in the direction of rotation on the fast motor. If still more adjustment is required, return the brush to neutral and take out shims of the other two interpoles on the fast motor, and shift brushes, if necessary. If the removal of the shims from the interpoles

slows down the motor from which they are removed to such an extent that it becomes slower than the other motor, the other motor then becomes the fast motor, and the brushes on it should be shifted, not more than one bar, in the direction of rotation. The shims removed at any one time should be not more than $\frac{1}{32}$ inch thick.

5. If the motors do not parallel and equalize the load on the intermediate steps, adjust the field resistor.

Notes. The fast motor is the one that takes the greater load; and vice versa, the slow motor is the one that takes the lesser load.

The motors should be adjusted so that difference in current taken by them is not more than 5 per cent of full-load current. This may mean that on light loads one of the motors may take more than twice as much current as the other, in extreme instances. This is considered satisfactory because the load on either of the motors will be well within its rating.

Starting Motors in Parallel. Shunt motors, or slightly compounded motors, may be started as shown in Fig. 135*A*, using a common starting resistor and one set of accelerating contactors. A common set of reversing contactors may be used for shunt motors, as shown in Fig. 135*B*. With compound motors two sets of reverse contactors will be required, in order that the series fields may receive current in the same direction and that the current of each armature may pass through its own series field. If a single set of reversing contactors were used, the series fields would have to be connected in parallel, outside of the reversing contactors. The current would then divide through the fields in inverse ratio to their resistances. Since the resistance of a series field is very low, it is difficult to balance two of them exactly and to maintain this balance whether the motors are hot or cold. If the series field is only a small percentage of the shunt field strength this objection may not be very serious, but two sets of direction contactors make a better arrangement, and with heavily compounded motors or series motors they become a necessity. The connections shown in Fig. 135*C*, therefore, are satisfactory for starting series motors or for reversing them if plugging is not required.

Since each motor develops full horsepower, and since the armature current of both passes through the starting resistor, it is evident that the resistor, and the control contactors, must be designed on the basis of the total horsepower of both motors. If one motor is cut out of service, the starting currents will remain the same and the second motor will receive double its normal starting peaks. This may be satisfactory in emergency, but where such a condition is likely to be of frequent occurrence it is customary to provide some arrangement for

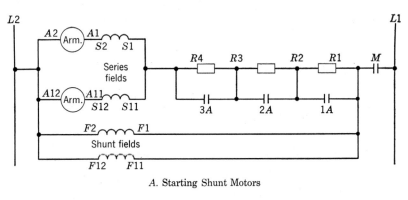

A. Starting Shunt Motors

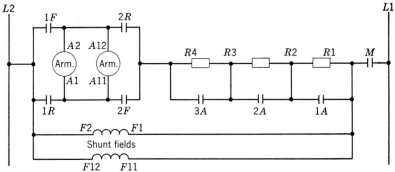

B. Reversing Shunt Motors

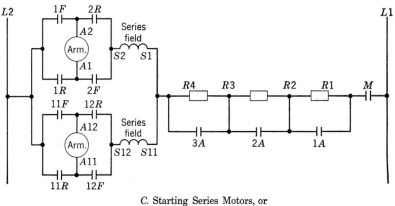

C. Starting Series Motors, or
Reversing without Plugging

Fig. 135. Starting Motors in Parallel.

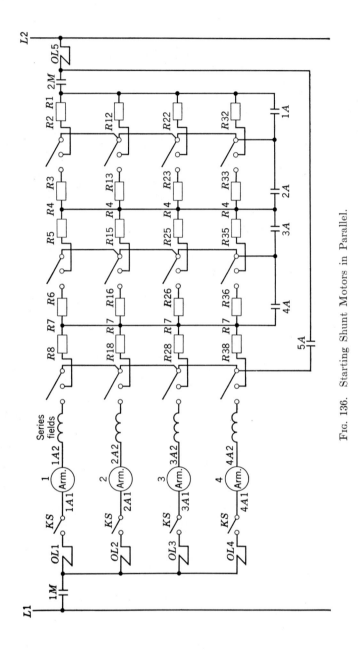

Fig. 136. Starting Shunt Motors in Parallel.

changing the resistance when one motor is cut out. Figure 136 shows an arrangement for starting a number of motors together. In this case it was frequently desired to start different combinations of motors. Each motor was provided with its own resistor, which could be paralleled with any other resistor by closing a four-pole knife switch. The knife switches used had two clips for each blade, as this was necessary to break up the circuit properly. When starting any combination of motors, the knife switches for those motors were closed, thus providing the correct resistance for the combination and, at the same time, permitting the use of a single common set of accelerating contactors. One pole of each knife switch disconnected the motor, so that it was impossible to set up an incorrect resistor combination.

The connections shown in Figs. 135 and 136 are also satisfactory for speed regulation by armature resistor. With speed regulation by field resistor it is customary to provide separate rheostats in each motor field. However, for certain types of drives—cloth calender trains, for example—a single rheostat is used to control all the fields in parallel. Correction is then applied by a small vernier rheostat in each field, except that of the leading motor.

Plugging Motors in Parallel. When series motors in parallel are to be plugged, none of the control schemes discussed so far will be satisfactory. The series fields cannot be simply connected in parallel, as each machine must feed its own field to insure proper division of starting and running current. The connections shown in Fig. 135C will cause serious trouble. There is certain to be some slight difference in the resistance of the two series fields. As long as the motors are running forward, they will tend to balance the load, as any increase in load on one motor will cause an increase of current through the corresponding series field, and that motor will tend to slow down, allowing the other motor to take a greater share of the load. However, when the motors are plugged the conditions are different. The counter-voltage of the armatures, which has been opposing the line voltage, is then added to the line voltage. Since there is certain to be some difference in the field characteristics, there is also certain to be some difference in the countervoltage developed by the two armatures. The armatures and fields form a closed loop of very low resistance, and any difference in countervoltage will force current around the loop. Because of the low resistance of the loop, a small voltage will cause a considerable current flow. Even if the initial current flow is very small the result is disastrous, because the circulating current strengthens the field of the motor whose voltage is already high and

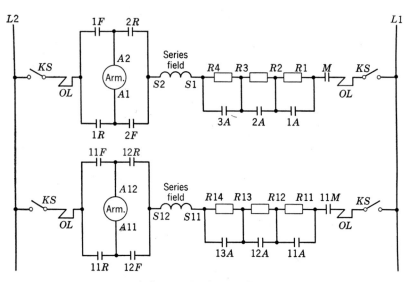

A. Separate Accelerating Contactors

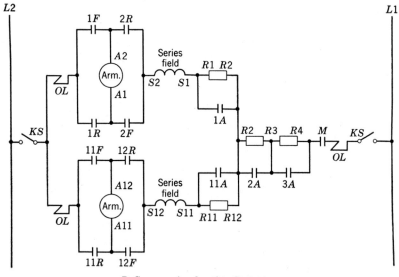

B. Common Accelerating Contactors

FIG. 137. Plugging Series Motors in Parallel.

weakens the field of the motor whose voltage is low. Consequently, the voltage of the strong motor increases still more, while that of the weak motor decreases further. The result is an increasingly greater difference in voltage and heavier circulating current, and the effect builds up until the weak motor is not generating any voltage. It then acts as a short circuit across the other motor.

In order to avoid the effect just described, it is necessary to insert resistance into the motor loop during the plugging period. One method of doing this is to have entirely separate plugging and accelerating contactors for each motor, as shown in Fig. 137A. This is really having two separate controllers operated from one master. No circulating currents can occur, and the scheme is highly satisfactory for starting, reversing, and plugging. Since each motor has its own contactors and its own resistor, it is a very simple matter to cut out one motor in case of trouble. In order to insure smooth acceleration by closing the corresponding accelerators of each motor at the same time, double-pole accelerators may be used, or single-pole contactors may be mechanically tied together in pairs. Both methods have certain advantages. With double-pole contactors, the number of coils will be smaller and the control circuit simpler. The controller with single-pole contactors will be somewhat more flexible, and the contactors will duplicate those for single-motor controllers.

Another method of arranging a plugging controller is shown in Fig. 137B. Here there are separate plugging contactors and resistance in the loop circuit, to limit the circulating currents, but the rest of the accelerating contactors are common to the two motors. The only advantage of this arrangement is lower cost, and this is somewhat offset by the fact that the common contactors must have capacity for the current of the two motors. If it happened that the motor size was such that the same size of contactor was required for either one or two motors, then this arrangement would result in a worth while saving, but, where the common contactors must be larger, very little saving results.

Series Motors in Series. When series motors are connected in series, the armatures are in series inside the reversing contactors and the fields are in series outside the reversing contactors. The purpose of this arrangement is to limit the speed of the motors to one-half of its normal value. For some drives the acceleration appears to be more rapid if the motors are required to reach only half speed, and also there is less tendency to reach undesirable speeds on light loads. The current flowing through the circuit is limited to that of one motor;

and, since the voltage across each motor is half line voltage, it follows that the total horsepower of the drive is that of one motor. The contactors are selected and the resistance designed on that basis, with the exception that the severity of the arcing must be taken into account. The inductance of the two series fields in series is greater than that of a single field, and this causes the arcing to be more severe when the circuit is opened by the contactors. It is therefore advisable not to use contactors to the limit of their rating, but to allow some margin of capacity. The life of the arcing contacts will be increased by so doing. In plugging, the countervoltage of two motors in series will rise higher than that of a single motor and, coupled with the increased inductance of the fields, will cause severe arcing. The ohmic value of the plugging resistance should be high enough to compensate for the higher countervoltage. The usual practice is to have approximately 50 per cent more ohms than in a single motor.

Frequently a standard single-motor controller may be satisfactory to handle two motors in series, but the capacity of the contactors should be considered and the plugging resistance increased.

Series Motors—Dynamic Lowering. Two series motors are often used to drive the hoist motion of a large crane or of a bucket hoist. The characteristics of the series motors are such as to insure proper division of the load during hoisting. If one motor should attempt to take more load than the other, its field strength would be increased and it would tend to slow down. The other motor would tend to speed up until the load was equalized. During dynamic lowering, however, the opposite takes place, and, if one of the motors takes the greater part of the load, it tends to slow down and increase the unbalancing still more.

A satisfactory means of insuring a balance during lowering is a control scheme similar to that shown in Fig. 138, in which the series fields of the motors are cross-connected during lowering. In the hoisting direction, contactors $1P$, $2P$, $11P$, $12P$ are closed, and each motor armature is in series with its own field. The connections are then the same as they would be with two separate controllers. In the lowering direction contactors $1KO$, $11KO$, $1D$, and $11D$ are closed. The armature of motor 1 is now connected in a dynamic-braking loop circuit including the field of motor 2, and the armature of 2 is similarly connected to the field of 1. Any tendency of one motor to take more current will increase the field strength of the other motor and so equalize the load again.

This control scheme has been used on many bucket hoists and on some large cranes, and it insures proper division of the load. However, there are other considerations which often outweigh this one when

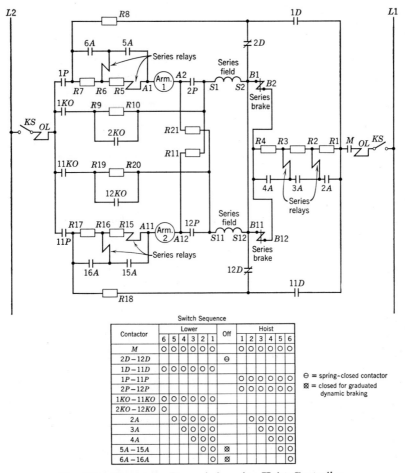

FIG. 138. Two-motor Dynamic-lowering Hoist Controller.

determining crane hoist control. Most of the cranes large enough to require a two-motor hoist are ladle cranes, and here it is essential to be able to move the hoist with one motor in the event of trouble. The cross-connected scheme does not lend itself readily to single-motor operation; consequently the majority of ladle-crane controllers consist simply of two entirely separate controllers operated from a single master and provided with knife switches to cut out either motor in case of trouble. With such controllers it is possible to secure fairly satisfactory division of load by carefully balancing the motors on each step of the control during lowering, and it is necessary to accept some unbalancing in order to secure the flexibility of the separate control scheme.

Motors Not Mechanically Coupled. Some machines require two or more motors which are not mechanically tied together, or which have a somewhat flexible mechanical tie. In such installations the problem is not one of division of load but often one of speed synchronization or position synchronization. For example, a machine for making paper consists of a number of separate sections, each driven by its own motor, and the only tie between the sections is the piece of paper under process. The paper is, of course, too weak to hold the sections to the same speed, and so some sort of accurate speed synchronization is necessary. The same is true of a multistand continuous steel rolling mill. Most of the speed-synchronizing methods are quite complicated and usually peculiar to one particular process. They are really a part of the problem of applying automatic control to a definite manufacturing process. Some are described in Chapter 10.

The bridge motion of an ore or coal bridge is a good example of position synchronization. The cross-member of such a bridge is mounted on large king pins, so that the ends of the bridge may move out of line with each other without doing any harm. It is of advantage to be able to move one end of the bridge without moving the other, for such purposes as loading or moving freight cars. A large bridge may permit a misalignment of 40 feet before the danger point is reached. The control generally consists of separate drum- or magnetic-type controllers for motors on each end of the bridge. A skew limit switch is used to prevent misalignment beyond the danger point. This switch is mounted at the top of one of the bridge legs and is operated by a cam on the cross-member of the bridge. As the end of the bridge moves, the cross-member turns on the king pin, and when the danger point is reached the cam trips the skew limit switch, stopping further motion in that direction. Generally a second contact of the limit switch is used to slow down before final stop occurs. If the bridge is moving with both motors energized, and one side gets too far ahead, the skew switch will operate and slow down the leading motor. If further misalignment occurs, the leading motor will be stopped.

Series-parallel Control. Two motors mechanically connected may be controlled by the series-parallel method. With this arrangement the motors are first connected to the line in series and with resistance in circuit. The resistance is then gradually cut out until the motors are across the line in series. The next step is to re-insert the resistance and connect the motors in parallel. Then the resistance ·is again cut out step by step until the motors are across the line in parallel. With the motors in series across the line, half speed is obtained; with the motors in parallel, full speed. Since the half speed is obtained without power loss in the resistance, the scheme is of advantage where half speed is frequently required. A further power saving is obtained where the accelerating period is long, as the motors may be accelerated in series with half of the current that would be required if they were in parallel. The series-parallel control also gives a smooth, even acceleration.

The principal application of this type of control is to moving cars. In operating city trolley cars, for instance, a considerable power saving is effected by having two running speeds which are obtained without losses in resistors. A relatively long acceleration period is required, and a smooth acceleration is desirable. Similar requirements are found in controlling electric locomotives, interurban cars, larry cars in steel mills and coke plants, and ore bridges.

The most important feature of a series-parallel control scheme is the method of transition from series to parallel. It is desirable that the transition be rapid, smooth, and without loss of speed or torque. In order to obtain these results, additional control material is required so that the series-parallel controller is relatively complicated and expensive. Three types of transition are common. They are known as open-circuit transition, shunt transition, and bridging transition.

Open-circuit Transition. This method is illustrated in Fig. 139. The motors are first connected in series with resistance in circuit. The resistance is then cut out until the motors are across the line in series and running at half speed. At the transition point the motor circuit is opened and the motors are momentarily disconnected. They are then reconnected in parallel and with the resistance back in circuit. The resistance is then cut out until the motors are across the line in parallel and at full speed. This method is simple and involves the minimum complication of the controller, but the opening of the circuit is undesirable, as it causes a loss of speed and torque during the change-over period. The arcing which occurs when the circuit is opened shortens the life of the controller contacts. For these reasons the open-circuit method is limited to small motors.

Shunt Transition. The shunt-transition method shown in Fig. 140 provides a simple means of avoiding an open circuit during the change from series to parallel. The motors are brought up to half speed in

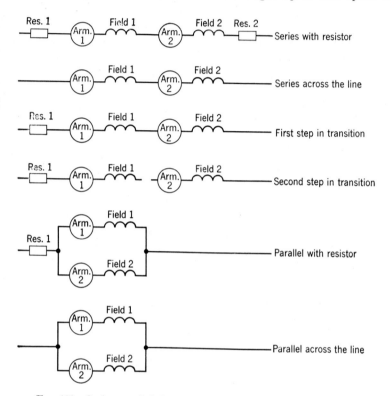

FIG. 139. Series-parallel Controller with Open-circuit Transition.

the same manner as for open-circuit transition. At the transition point resistance is introduced into the circuit, and then one of the motors is short-circuited. The resistance compensates for the counter-voltage which the short-circuited motor has been developing and prevents an excessive inrush of current. The short-circuited motor is now disconnected and reconnected in parallel with the other motor, after which the resistance is cut out of circuit until the motors are across the line in parallel and at full speed. With this method the circuit is never broken, and at least one motor is always producing driving torque. The total torque, however, is reduced during the transition. The most serious objections to the method are that the short-circuited motor receives a heavy overload for a short period, and that the sudden application of this overload and the sudden change in torque produce severe shocks to the driven machinery.

Bridging Transition. The bridging method is shown in Fig. 141. With this arrangement the motors are brought up to half speed in series

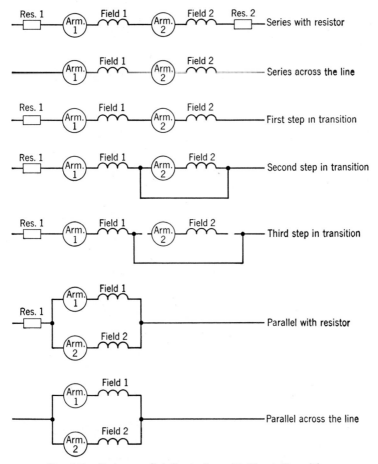

Fig. 140. Series-parallel Controller with Shunt Transition.

in the usual manner. Resistance is then connected in parallel with each motor, so that the circuit is equivalent to that of a Wheatstone bridge. If the resistances are of equal value, no current will flow in the bridging circuit. When this circuit is opened, the motors are connected in parallel. The resistance is then cut out until the motors are up to full speed. By adjusting the resistances to suitable values, the torque may be kept up during the transition or may even be increased. Increasing the current through the resistors will increase the motor torque when the bridge is opened.

The bridging method gives a smooth, even acceleration without loss of speed or torque and without shock to the driven machine. It is,

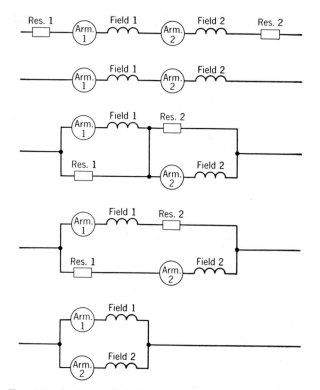

FIG. 141.   Series-parallel Controller with Bridging Transition.

therefore, the most extensively used method, although it requires a more complicated and expensive controller.

Types of Series-parallel Controllers. Series-parallel controllers may be either of the drum type or of the magnetic-contactor type. Since their greatest field of application is to cars, where space is usually limited, drums are widely used. However, the advantages of magnetic control in general apply to series-parallel control also, and, where space conditions will permit, magnetic control is desirable.

Figure 142 illustrates the connections of a magnetic-contactor controller; it includes a sequence table, showing the contactors which are

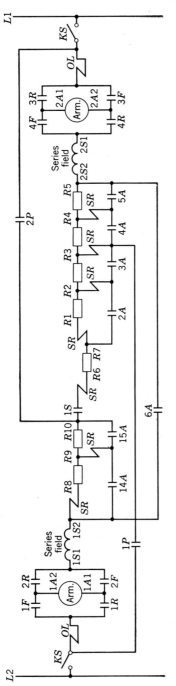

Sequence Table													
Contactor	Forward						Off	Reverse					
	6	5	4	3	2	1		1	2	3	4	5	6
1F – 2F – 3F – 4F	O	O	O	O	O	O							
1R – 2R – 3R – 4R								O	O	O	O	O	O
1S				O	O	O		O	O	O			
1P – 2P	O	O										O	O
2A		O										O	
3A			O	O						O	O		
4A			O	O	O					O	O	O	
14A	O	O	O					O	O	O			
5A	O	O						O	O				
15A	O							O	O				
6A	O							O					

Fig. 142. Connections for a Series-parallel Magnetic Controller.

closed on each point of the master controller. On the first point forward, the direction contactors 1*F*, 2*F*, 3*F*, and 4*F* are closed, and the series contactor is 1*S*. The motors are then connected in series with all the resistance in circuit. On the second point, contactors 2*A* and 3*A* are closed, and a portion of the resistance is short-circuited. On the next point contactors 4*A*, 14*A*, 5*A*, and 15*A* are closed, short-circuiting all the resistance except the step *R*6–*R*7. This step is cut out on the fourth point, by closing contacts 6*A*, and the motors are then across the line, in series, and at half speed.

The transition starts on the fourth point and is completed on the fifth point. As soon as contactor 6*A* closes, it energizes a relay which opens the circuit to the series contactor 1*S* and to the resistance contactors 2*A*, 3*A*, 4*A*, 5*A*, 14*A*, and 15*A*. This does not affect the operation in any way, as the circuit is still complete through 6*A*, but it does prepare the resistance circuit for the next step in the transition. When the master is moved to the fifth point, the parallel contactors 1*P* and 2*P* are closed, thus setting up the bridging circuit. Two relays are also energized at this time. One of these is used to connect the coils of contactors 4*A* and 14*A* together, and also the coils of 5*A* and 15*A*. This is done to insure equal acceleration of the motors in parallel, by cutting out the resistance steps in each motor circuit at exactly the same time. The second relay opens the circuit to 6*A*, thus opening the bridge and connecting the motors in parallel, with resistance in each motor circuit. On the sixth point the resistance contactors 4*A* and 14*A* are closed and then 5*A* and 15*A*, and the motors are in parallel across the line at full speed.

The operation in the reverse direction is the same, except that the direction contactors 1*R*, 2*R*, 3*R*, and 4*R* are closed instead of the forward-direction contactors.

In the controller just described, six speeds in each direction are obtained. This is the maximum number generally employed, but the same controller could give a number of additional speeds if desired. It would be necessary only to change the master so that each resistance contactor would be energized on a separate point. The maximum number of speeds in each direction would be as follows:

Speed	Series	Speed	Series	Speed	Parallel
1	1*S*	5	14*A*		
2	2*A*	6	5*A*	9	1*P*–2*P*
3	3*A*	7	15*A*	10	4*A*–14*A*
4	4*A*	8	6*A*	11	5*A*–15*A*

The resistance contactors are under the control of series relays, and they are so interlocked as to insure their closing in the proper sequence. The circuits are also arranged so that the master may be moved rapidly to the full-speed point, and the contactors will still go through the proper sequence to start the motors in series, effect the transition, and bring them up to speed in parallel.

The resistance steps $R3$–$R4$–$R5$ and $R8$–$R9$–$R10$ are the accelerating resistance, and should limit the current inrush to 150 per cent. The total of these four steps is then $E \div 1.50 = 0.66E/I$. The steps $R1$–$R2$–$R3$ are plugging steps and should limit the current to 150 per cent when the controller is plugged. If plugged from parallel to series, the countervoltage of both motors must be added to the line voltage. If we assume the countervoltage of each motor to be 80 per cent,

$$E + 0.8E + 0.8E = 2.6E$$

$$\text{Total resistance} = \frac{2.6E}{1.5I}$$

$$= 1.72E/I$$

$$R1\text{–}R2\text{–}R3 = 1.72E/I - 0.66E/I$$

$$= 1.06E/I$$

The step $R6$–$R7$ is of low resistance and is used to prevent a short circuit if an arc should hang on contactor $1S$ until contactors $1P$ and $2P$ closed. When the plug steps and the accelerating steps are tapered in the usual manner, the following table is obtained:

Step	Ohms in per cent of E/I	Step	Ohms in per cent of E/I
R1–R2	64	R8–R9	22
R2–R3	42	R9–R10	11
R3–R4	22	R6–R7	10
R4–R5	11		

Simplified Series Parallel. It is not always necessary to have full series-parallel control. Sometimes a controller giving series operation or parallel operation, but without transition, will meet the requirements of the drive. The controller can then be considerably simplified. A controller of this type might be used in connection with a screwdown on a rolling mill. The characteristics of the service require a slow speed at full torque in the lowering direction, and a high speed in the up direction. This can be obtained by connecting the motors in parallel when hoisting, and in series when lowering, and the ratio of speeds would be 2 to 1. If the controller were further simplified by connecting the series fields permanently in series and the armatures

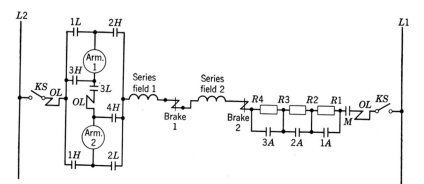

Fig. 143. Connections for a Simplified Series-parallel Controller.

in series parallel, the hoisting speed would be 155 per cent of the lowering speed, which might be sufficient to meet the requirements of the installation. Figure 143 shows the connections.

References

C. B. Hathaway, "Parallel Operation of Commutating-pole Motors and Generators," *Electric Journal*, June, 1922.

C. T. Pearce, "Operation of D-c Motors in Parallel and Series with Different Types of Loads," *Electric Journal*, 1928, Vol. 25, p. 581.

E. J. Posselt, "Starting Currents and Distribution of Loads in Bridge-drive Motors," *Iron and Steel Engineer Yearbook*, 1944, p. 398.

J. D. Leitch, "Dynamic Braking of Two D-c Series Motors," *Transactions AIEE*, 1947, Vol. 66, p. 787.

Problems

1. Three 100-horsepower 230-volt 350-ampere 480-rpm series motors are connected in series to drive a machine. Using the equations of the series motor, calculate the speed of the combination.

2. Calculate the total horsepower which will be delivered by the three motors of problem 1.

3. Draw an elementary diagram for the main and control circuits of a nonreversing controller for the motors of problem 1, including the following:

Main and control knife switches.
2 overload relays.
2 line contactors.

3 accelerating contactors.
Current limit acceleration.
Low-voltage relay.
Four-speed master.

4. Draw an elementary diagram for the main and control circuits of a reversing controller for the motors of problem 1, including the following:

Main and control knife switches.
2 overload relays.
1 line contactor.
4 reversing contactors.
3 accelerating contactors.
Inductive-timed acceleration.
Low-voltage relay.
Four-speed master.

5. Calculate the ohmic value of a starting resistor for the motors of problem 1, to give an initial starting current of 150 per cent of rated current, and assuming the resistance of each motor as 11 per cent of E/I.

6. Calculate the ohmic value of a series speed-regulating resistor for the motors of problem 1, to give 50 per cent speed at full load.

7. Calculate the wattage to be dissipated by the resistor of problem 6. How does this compare with the wattage to be dissipated by a similar resistor for a single 100-horsepower motor?

8. Draw an elementary diagram for the control circuits of the arrangement shown in Fig. 135C, using a four-speed master controller, and condenser-timed acceleration.

9. Calculate the ohmic value and wattage capacity of a speed-regulating resistor for a controller like Fig. 135C, for two 35-horsepower 230-volt 140-ampere motors. The speed is to be reduced to 50 per cent of rated speed, when running at 75 per cent of rated load.

10. Draw an elementary diagram for the control circuits of Fig. 137B, using a four-speed master controller and inductive timing without a separate inductor.

11. Calculate the ohmic value of each step of a plugging resistor for two 25-horsepower 230-volt 100-ampere motors, using a controller like Fig. 137B and the data of Tables 17 and 18.

12. Two 50-horsepower 230-volt 200-ampere series motors are used to drive a crane trolley, using a controller like Fig. 137B except having two steps of resistor for plugging, and three steps of resistor for accelerating. Draw the elementary diagram of the main circuits only.

13. If the plugging inrush current is to be 70 per cent of rated current on the first point, and 150 per cent on the second point, calculate the ohms in all steps of the resistor, using the data of Tables 17 and 18.

14. Draw an elementary diagram of the main circuits only, of a reversing, plugging controller for four series motors, connected two in series, and the two pairs in parallel.

15. Two 50-horsepower 230-volt 200-ampere series motors are connected in a series-parallel arrangement like Fig. 142. If the resistance of each motor is 11 per cent of E/I, calculate the ohmic values of the resistor steps of the controller.

16. Using the data of problem 15, calculate the speed which will be obtained on each point of the controller, when the motors are fully loaded.

17. Draw an elementary diagram of the control circuits of the controller shown in Fig. 143, using a reversing master arranged to give the maximum number of speeds for hoisting and lowering. Omit any means of delaying the accelerating contactors.

13

DYNAMIC LOWERING HOIST CONTROLLERS

Characteristics Required. Dynamic lowering control is used in connection with series motors, or compound motors having a predominating series field, to operate crane hoists, winches, or other drives where the load may be overhauling. The requirements for hoisting are that it should be possible to take up a slack cable without undue jerking, and to accelerate and hoist both light and heavy loads smoothly, with a choice of several speeds. The requirements for lowering are that it should be possible to lower both light and heavy loads safely, with a choice of several speeds, and to lower an empty hook at a high speed, although the load under that condition would not be overhauling.

General Principles. The connections for the hoisting direction are the same as those of a full reverse controller; that is, the armature and the series field are connected in series. If this connection were used in the lowering direction, the motor would not retard an overhauling load but would soon reach a runaway speed. By connecting the armature and the field in parallel, with resistance in each circuit, characteristics approximating those of a shunt motor are obtained. With a light load the motor drives the hook down, taking a relatively heavy current from the line. As the load is increased the current taken from the line becomes less, as less torque is required to drive the load. When the load is heavy enough to overcome the friction of the drive, it begins to overhaul the motor, which then acts as a generator and retards the load. The speed is varied by changing the amount of resistance in the braking loop or in the series field circuit.

Dynamic lowering controllers, as built by different control manufacturers, vary somewhat in detail, but the underlying principles are the same and the control schemes similar. Both current-limit acceleration and time-limit acceleration are used, with the trend decidedly toward time limit. The controller described below is of the inductive time limit type. Several manufacturers have almost identical control schemes, with the exception of the method of acceleration. Since the purpose here is to describe the dynamic lowering principles, one control will serve as well as another. For a description of the inductive method of acceleration, see Chapter 6.

299

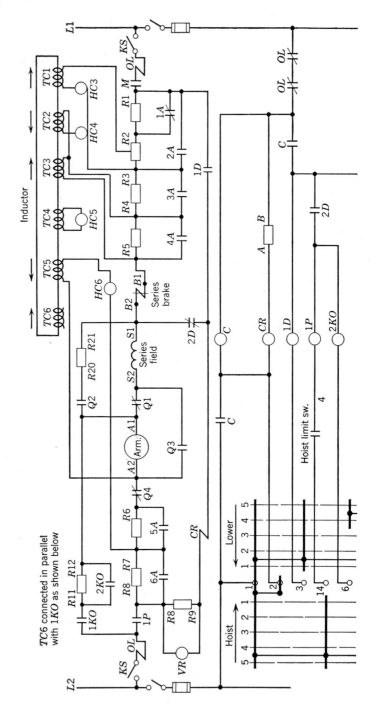

Reference to the line diagram, Fig. 144, and to the step-by-step line diagram, Fig. 145, will show the circuits obtained, and the method by which they are obtained, on the various hoisting and lowering points. Figure 146 shows the speed-torque curves of the hoist.

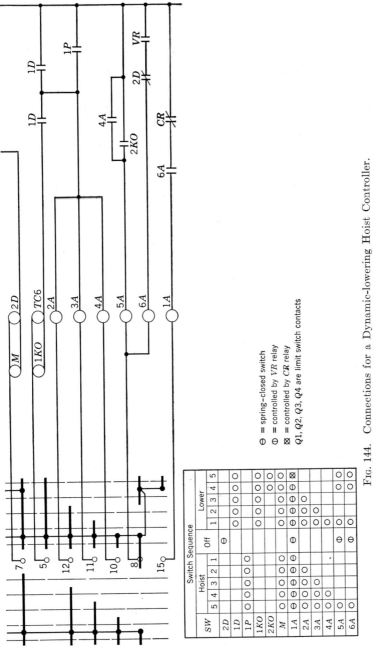

Fig. 144. Connections for a Dynamic-lowering Hoist Controller.

Off Position. In the off position the motor is disconnected from the line, and the armature and field are short-circuited through resistances R6, R7, R8, and R9, and through the contacts of the spring-closed contactor 2D. This gives a dynamic-braking connection which prevents dropping the load if the electromechanical brake should fail. The brake is de-energized and set in the off position.

Hoisting. Moving the master to the first point hoisting energizes the coils of contactors M, $2D$, and $1P$. Since the coil of $1P$ is interlocked behind $2D$, the braking loop around the armature is opened before power is applied to the motor. The closing of contactors $1P$ and

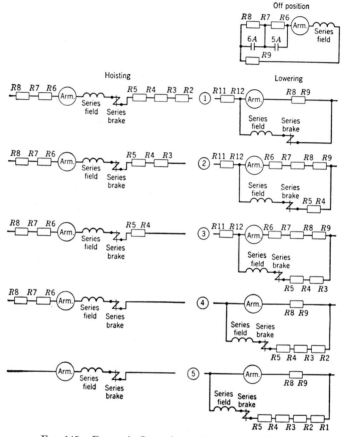

Fig. 145. Dynamic Lowering. Step-by-step Circuits.

M connects the motor to the line through the starting resistance steps $R2$ to $R5$, and $R6$ to $R8$. Since the motor armature and field are in series, the motor starts and operates as a series motor, exerting approximately 40 per cent torque on this first point. The motor current also flows through the series brake coil, releasing the brake. It will be noted that resistance step $R1$–$R2$ is short-circuited and is not used in hoisting.

On the second point hoisting, the contactor $2A$ is energized, short-circuiting resistor step $R2$–$R3$ and increasing the current to approxi-

mately 100 per cent and the torque to approximately 100 per cent, if
the motor has not started on the first point. The first point is, therefore, a slack cable point, and the second point is the slowest hoisting
speed.   Since the current obtained when 2A is closed is not excessive,
no time delay is introduced in the closing of this contactor.

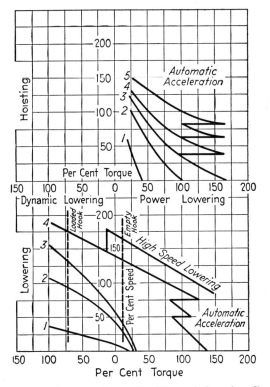

Fig. 146.   Speed-torque Curves for Dynamic-lowering Control.

On the third point of the master, contactor 3A is closed, short-
circuiting resistor step R3–R4, which gives an increased hoisting speed.
On this point the current is approximately 150 per cent and the torque
approximately 165 per cent.   On the fourth point the contactor 4A is
closed, and on the fifth point the contactors 5A and 6A.   Each of
these points gives additional hoisting torque and speed.   On the last
point the resistor is entirely short-circuited and the motor is connected
directly to the line.

Accelerating Time.   If the operator moves the master directly to
the last point, the contactor 2A will close at once, since there is no
time delay in connection with it.   The contactors 3A, 4A, 5A, and 6A

will close in a definite time, under control of the inductive time-limit acceleration. This time is usually adjusted to be approximately $2\frac{1}{2}$ seconds, of which slightly more than 1 second is obtained on the contactor $3A$ and the rest on contactors $4A$, $5A$, and $6A$.

In order to obtain time delay on the resistor contactors, it is necessary to energize their holdout coils before the closing coils are energized. Consequently, in hoisting, contactor M is closed first, and then contactor $1P$. This applies power to the motor and causes current to flow through the starting resistor, which in turn energizes the holdout coils of the accelerators. The closing coils are connected behind interlocks on the contactor $1P$, so that they are not energized until the contactor is closed and after the holdout coils have been energized.

Lowering. In the lowering direction the motor is connected to operate somewhat as a shunt motor; that is, the field is in parallel with the armature. On the first point the contactors $1KO$, $1D$, $2D$, M, and all the accelerating contactors are energized. Current flows from line $L2$ through the resistor $R11$–$R12$, to the junction of the armature and the series field. Here it divides, a portion flowing through the series field and the series brake to the line $L1$, and the rest flowing through the armature and resistance $R7$–$R8$ to line $L1$. The brake will release, but the starting torque obtained is low, and if there is no load on the hook the motor may not have sufficient torque on this point to start the empty hook down.

On the second point the contactors $4A$, $5A$, and $6A$ are de-energized and opened, inserting resistance step $R6$–$R7$, step $R7$–$R8$ in series with the armature, and step $R4$–$R5$ in series with the field. This does not increase the starting torque, but it does increase the lowering speed.

On the third point contactor $3A$ is opened, inserting resistance step $R3$–$R4$ in series with the field. This weakens the field and increases the speed on all loads. The starting torque with light hook is low on all these points.

On the fourth point the resistance $R11$–$R12$ is cut out by the closing of contactor $2KO$. Contactors $5A$ and $6A$ are reclosed, short-circuiting resistance steps $R6$–$R7$ and $R7$–$R8$ in the armature circuit. At the same time contactor $2A$ is opened, inserting resistance step $R2$–$R3$ in the field circuit. This gives the highest lowering speed for heavy loads, and it also gives a high starting torque for starting to drive down a light load.

The fifth point is used to lower light loads at high speed. On this point the spring-closed contactor $1A$ is energized and opened, inserting resistance step $R1$–$R2$ into the circuit, to weaken the field further.

Resistance step $R1$–$R2$ is designed to give the desired lowering speed with a light load, but if a heavy load were lowered on this point the speed would be excessive and probably unsafe. The controller is arranged to prevent an unsafe speed automatically. This is the function of the compound current relay CR, which has a shunt coil connected across the line and a series coil connected in the armature circuit during lowering. As long as the motor is driving the load, or as long as the load is only slightly overhauling, current flows through the series coil from $L2$ to $L1$, and under this condition the series coil is arranged to oppose the shunt coil. The relay, therefore, does not open its contacts, and contactor $1A$ is permitted to remain open, allowing the motor to run at high speed. However, as soon as the load begins to overhaul, the current in the series coil of the relay reverses, and the two coils become accumulative. The relay then opens its contacts and de-energizes contactor $1A$, cutting out the high-speed resistance and preventing the motor from operating on an excessive speed.

The use of a spring-closed, magnetically opened contactor for $1A$ insures that, in the event of voltage failure, the contactor will close. This will also happen if the contactor coil should burn out. In either of these conditions, the equipment will be safe, as the contactor will close and hold the motor speed to a safe value. The arrangement is quite flexible since the light-load lowering speed is directly governed by the value of resistance $R1$–$R2$, and the full-load lowering speed is governed by the maximum value of $R2$–$R3$. Consequently these resistances can be independently adjusted for obtaining the light-load and the full-load speeds desired, and both speeds may be made any desirable safe value. The curves, Fig. 146, show a light-load lowering speed of 170 per cent of full-load hoisting speed, and a full-load lowering speed of 175 per cent of full-load hoisting speed, but these speeds are often made as high as 200 per cent.

If the operator moves the master handle rapidly to the last point lowering, or if the motor does not start until that point is reached, automatic starting is obtained through the timing of contactors $5A$ and $6A$. The time on these contactors for acceleration on the last point lowering is approximately 1.2 seconds. Because of this automatic acceleration on the last point lowering, ample torque is obtained without excessive current peaks.

Since the slowest lowering speed is obtained with the resistor contactors closed, it is desirable that they close immediately, without any time delay, when the master is moved to the first point lowering. This is accomplished by energizing the closing coils on this point before power has been applied to the motor. It will be noted that the closing coils are energized through an interlock on the $1D$ contactor, and that the contactor $1KO$ is also energized by this same interlock. It is necessary that $1KO$ be closed before power is applied to the motor and before the holdout coils of the resistor contactors are energized. Consequently the closing coils are energized first, and the contactors closed immediately on the first point lowering.

Decelerating Time. If the master has been moved over to the last or next to the last point in the lowering direction and is then moved back towards the off position to slow down, time for decelerating is obtained on the resistor contactors. It is desired that this time be less than the time of acceleration in the hoisting direction. The motor requires less time for decelerating than for accelerating, and the shorter this time can safely be made, the more accurately the load may be checked and stopped. In order to accomplish a change in timing, the inductor coil $TC6$ is used. It is connected in parallel with the coil of contactor $1KO$ and is energized in the lowering direction only. It serves to saturate the inductor somewhat; consequently the flux changes obtained when the other inductor coils are cut out are less effective than they would be without coil $TC6$. Similarly, the voltages induced in the holding-out coils are less, and the time obtained on the contactors is less, than it is in the hoisting direction. By thus automatically causing a difference in the time of acceleration in the hoisting direction and of deceleration in the lowering direction, the efficiency of the hoist is improved and accurate spotting of the load in lowering is easily accomplished.

If it is desired to change the rate of automatic deceleration in slowing down, adjustment should be made on contactor $3A$, since the time obtained on this contactor is important in the decelerating period but not so important in the hoisting direction.

Stopping. In returning the master to the off position, from the lowering direction, automatic graduated dynamic braking is obtained. The spring-closed contactor $2D$ is de-energized, and closes, so that the armature and series field are short-circuited through resistors $R6–R7$, $R7–R8$, and $R8–R9$. This applies a strong but not excessive dynamic braking current which checks the motor. The contactors $5A$ and $6A$ then close in order, in a definite time, short-circuiting resistor steps $R6–R7$ and $R7–R8$, respectively, and so decreasing the value of the dynamic braking resistor and maintaining a strong dynamic braking current as the motor comes to a stop. By this means stopping is mainly accomplished by the motor, which saves wear on the brake. Because the braking is automatically graduated with time-limit control, the current peaks are kept down to a value that may be safely commutated by the motor.

When the motor has come to rest, the contactors $5A$ and $6A$ are de-energized by means of relay VR, and the load is then held by the brake. The function of the relay is simply to provide for the disconnecting of all circuits in the off position after the graduated dynamic braking has been accomplished.

It will be noted that this controller gives high speeds for lowering light or heavy loads, and also very slow speeds for careful handling of heavy loads. The intermediate points of the master give intermediate speeds for hoisting or lowering any type of load.

Power-limit Switch. It is considered good practice to use a limit switch to stop the hoist motor in case of overtravel in the hoisting direction, and to use a switch which will open the motor circuit directly, rather than a pilot switch which would open the contactor coils. The contacts marked Q in Fig. 144 represent such a switch.

The switching mechanism is a double-pole, double-throw, cam-operated, quick-make and quick-break device. It is reset to the normal position by a weight. The crane hoist cable runs through a slot in the weight, and when the crane hook is raised too high the hook block will strike the weight and lift it, tripping the switch.

As long as the hoist is in a safe position, contacts $Q1$ and $Q4$ are closed and contacts $Q2$ and $Q3$ are open. When the hoist overtravels and the switch is tripped, contacts $Q1$ and $Q4$ open to cut off power. At the same time contacts $Q2$ and $Q3$ close to set up a dynamic braking circuit and stop the motor quickly. When the limit switch is tripped the motor cannot be energized in the hoisting direction but can still be energized in the lowering direction, which permits moving out of the danger zone. The limit switch will reset when the hoist has reached a safe position.

Voltage Relay. The diagram also shows the connections for the low-voltage protection relay which is supplied as standard on all types of controllers. Relay C is energized in the off position of the master by segment 2. When closed the relay provides a feed for itself through one of its two contacts. The other contact provides a circuit for the coils of line contactors $1D$, M, $1P$, and $2D$. When the master is moved to any running position, the relay coil is energized only through its own contact. If the relay opens, on account of voltage failure or the tripping of an overload relay, all contactors are opened and the equipment stopped. To restart, it is necessary to return the master to the off position and energize the relay again.

Calculation of Horsepower. The horsepower required to operate a crane hoist may be calculated as outlined below, and it is advisable to check the actual requirements against the rating of the motor actually used. If the hoist is overmotored, which is not uncommon practice, it may be necessary to increase the ohmic value of the resistor steps which determine the full-load lowering speed, as a design based on full rated horsepower may not permit fast enough lowering speeds.

The following information is generally obtainable from the crane builder.

W = the rated load in pounds.
S = calculated full-load hoisting speed in feet per minute.
G = the gear reduction between the motor and the winding drum.
D = the pitch diameter of the winding drum in feet.
R = the rope reduction between drum and hook.
Eff = the estimated overall efficiency of the hoist.
The make and type of hoist motor.
The ½-hour rating of the motor.
The rpm at rated load.

The horsepower required for hoisting can be calculated from the equation

$$\text{Horsepower} = \frac{W \times S}{33{,}000 \times \text{Efficiency}}$$

It often happens that S is not definitely known, and then the horsepower is calculated from the torque required. The torque in pound-feet at the motor shaft is

$$T = \frac{W \times D}{2 \times G \times R \times \text{Efficiency}}$$

When the torque is known, the motor speed can be determined from the torque-speed curve. The horsepower can usually be obtained from the motor curve or can be calculated from the motor speed and torque

$$\text{Horsepower} = \frac{T \times RPM \times 2\pi}{33{,}000}$$

Resistor Design. The resistor must be designed to meet both hoisting and lowering conditions. Step $R2$–$R3$ is designed to give low torque for slack cable take-up. Steps $R4$–$R5$, $R6$–$R7$, and $R7$–$R8$, in series, limit the accelerating current in hoisting. Considered with the motor resistance, they should limit the accelerating current peaks to approximately 150 per cent of full-load motor current. Step $R3$–$R4$

is designed to give a suitable lowering speed when it is in circuit and an intermediate low torque point in hoisting. Step $R2$–$R3$ determines the full-load lowering speed; step $R1$–$R2$, the light-load lowering speed.

Resistance $R11$–$R12$ determines the starting, or kickoff, current in the lowering direction. For satisfactory operation this current should be approximately 125 per cent of full load, so that the resistance step should be approximately $0.8E/I$.

The resistance of the dynamic step $R8$–$R9$ is $0.25E/I$. A number of conditions affect the value of this step. In lowering, the step is in series with the motor armature; and, with a light load, the ratio of armature current to field current is dependent on the value of the resistance. An equal distribution of the current will give the maximum torque. It is also important that sufficient current flow through the field circuit to insure that the series brake will operate. About 40 per cent of full-load current is required to lift the brake. In the last position lowering, steps $R6$–$R7$, $R7$–$R8$, and $R8$–$R9$ are in series with the armature, and, if the operator moves the master lever so fast that the brake does not lift until the last point is reached, these resistances determine the inrush. Steps $R6$–$R7$ and $R7$–$R8$ are cut out as the motor accelerates, and $R8$–$R9$ should be high enough to limit the current to a safe value.

When the master is moved to the off position, these three steps establish a loop around the armature and field, serving to limit the initial braking current to a safe value. In stopping, contactors $5A$ and $6A$ are closed, with time delay, to give graduated dynamic braking.

In the last position lowering step $R8$–$R9$ is in series with the armature, across the line, and the countervoltage of the armature is dependent on the voltage drop across the resistance. With an empty hook the voltage drop will reduce the speed of the motor, but with an overhauling load it will add to the armature voltage and increase the motor speed. It is desirable to have the empty hook speed relatively high; therefore from this standpoint the resistance step should be as low as possible. The value used is a compromise which best meets all the conditions desired. The complete resistor stepping is as follows:

Step	Ohms in Percentage of E/I	Step	Ohms in Percentage of E/I
$R1$–$R2$	105	$R6$–$R7$	19
$R2$–$R3$	85	$R7$–$R8$	14
$R3$–$R4$	40	$R8$–$R9$	25
$R4$–$R5$	25	$R11$–$R12$	80

Calculation of Speed-torque Curves. The designer of a dynamic-lowering controller is interested in the speeds which are obtained in each point of the controller, in the lowering direction, and under varying load conditions. Sometimes these speeds are definitely specified by the purchaser or fixed by the requirements of the installation; in any event they must be within the limits of safety and good practice. A speed-torque curve, plotted for each point of the controller, will give the desired information. A method of calculating and plotting such curves follows:

All dynamic-lowering circuits when connected for lowering take the form shown in Fig. 145, in which the armature circuit and the series field circuit are connected in parallel. Either the armature or the field or both may have a resistance in series. The resistance in the line is generally in circuit on the slow speeds and cut out on high speeds. It will be understood that this circuit is typical. In an actual controller, any of these resistances may consist of two or more steps, but the circuit obtained on any given point in the lowering direction can always be reduced to a simple circuit similar to that shown. With this arrangement, and with a light load, the motor will drive the load down, exerting a torque in the lowering direction. With an overhauling load the motor will be driven as a generator and will exert a retarding torque. The countervoltage of the motor will depend upon the speed and the field strength. The torque will depend upon the field strength and the current in the armature. The circuit may be solved by Kirchhoff's laws, as follows:

$$\text{Armature resistance} = 0.08E/I \text{ (assumed)}$$

$$\text{Field resistance} = 0.03E/I \text{ (assumed)}$$

$$\text{Resistance in line circuit} = 0.80E/I \text{ (assumed)}$$

$$\text{Resistance in field circuit} = 0.26E/I \text{ (assumed)}$$

$$\text{Resistance in armature circuit} = 0.57E/I \text{ (assumed)}$$

E = line voltage = 1.0.
E_a = countervoltage of armature as compared to line voltage.
I_a = current in armature as compared to full-load current.
I_f = current in field as compared to full-load current.
I_l = current in the line as compared to full-load current.
I_n = full-load current = 1.0.
S = speed as compared to rated or full-load speed.
T = torque as compared to rated or full-load torque.
F = field strength or flux as compared to full field strength.

Then, R_a = total resistance in the armature circuit = $0.65E/I$
  R_f = total resistance in the field circuit   = $0.29E/I$
  R_l = total resistance in the line circuit   = $0.80E/I$

The equation for speed is

$$S = \frac{E - I_a R}{F(E - I_m R_m)} = \frac{E_a}{F \times 0.89}$$

The equation for torque is

$$T = F \times I_a$$

By Kirchhoff's laws,

$$I_l = I_a + I_f \tag{1}$$

$$I_f R_f + I_l R_l = E - 1.0 \tag{2}$$

$$I_f R_f - I_a R_a = E_a \tag{3}$$

$$S = \frac{E_a}{0.89F} \tag{4}$$

$$T = F \times I_a \tag{5}$$

To calculate points on the speed-torque curve, assume values for I_f. To approximate the range of such assumed values, two points are readily calculated. These are zero speed, and zero torque.

At zero speed, $E_a = 0$

From equation 1, $I_l = \dfrac{E}{R_l + \dfrac{R_a \times R_f}{R_a + R_f}} = \dfrac{1.0}{0.80 + 0.20} = 1.0$

From equation 2, $I_f = \dfrac{E - I_l R_l}{R_f} = \dfrac{1.0 - 0.80}{0.29} = 0.69$

At zero torque, $I_a = 0$

From equation 1, $I_f = I_l = \dfrac{E}{R_l + R_f} = \dfrac{1.0}{1.09} = 0.917$

Now, having some idea of what the values of I_f will be, assume other values and prepare a table as shown below. The field strength is read from the curve of Fig. 125, and the other values are calculated from the equations indicated in the table headings.

I_f	$I_f R_f$	$I_l R_l$ [1]	I_l	I_a [2]	$I_a R_a$	E_a [3]	F	S [4]	T [5]
0.69	0.20	0.80	1.00	+0.31	+0.20	0.00	0.883	0.00	+0.274
0.917	0.266	0.734	0.917	0.00	0.00	0.266	0.973	0.307	0.00
1.20	0.348	0.652	0.815	−0.385	−0.25	0.598	1.052	0.638	−0.405
1.50	0.435	0.565	0.707	−0.793	−0.515	0.950	1.11	0.962	−0.88

The speed-torque curve may now be plotted. Figure 147 shows the curve obtained in this example. If all of the line resistance is cut out, the field strength will be constant, and the curve will become a straight line. Decreasing the resistance in the armature circuit will make the curve more flat; that is, the speed will not vary so much with changes in load. Decreasing the resistance in the field circuit will decrease the speed in all loads. When estimating the resistance of the motor armature and series field, it may be assumed that about 70 per cent

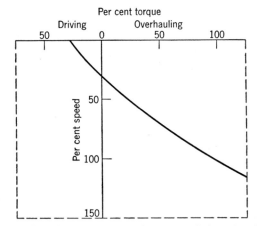

Fig. 147. Speed-torque Curve of a Dynamic-lowering Hoist.

of the motor resistance is in the armature, and 30 per cent in the field. If the circuit includes a series brake, it will be in the field circuit, and the brake resistance should be included in the value of the resistance of that circuit. Since the resistance of a series brake coil is very low, it will not make much difference in the calculations. An average value is $0.01E/I$.

Calculation of Speed-torque Curves—Alternate Method. It is possible to calculate the data for speed-torque curves directly in rpm and pound-feet. It is necessary to know the resistance of the motor armature and series field. If these values are not known, the motor resistance can be calculated from the motor efficiency curve, and it may be assumed that 70 per cent of the motor resistance is in the armature and 30 per cent in the field. A speed-torque curve of the motor is also necessary.

From the equations for the speed and torque of a series motor, and with constants added so that the equations are correct for actual values (not percentages),

$$KF = \frac{T}{I_a} \qquad\qquad [6]$$

$$K_1F = \frac{E - I_aR_m}{S(E - I_nR_m)} \qquad\qquad [7]$$

F = field strength in any desired units.
T = torque in pound-feet.
I_a = armature current in amperes.
E = line voltage in volts.
R_m = motor resistance in ohms.
S = speed in rpm.
I_f = motor field current in amperes.
I_m = motor current in amperes.
I_n = motor full-load current in amperes.
K, K_1, K_2 = constants.

Since $E - I_nR_m$ is also a constant, and since $E - I_aR_m$ is the counter-voltage, equation 7 may be written,

$$K_2F = \frac{E_a}{S} \qquad\qquad [8]$$

It will be evident that, with a series motor operating normally,

$$I_f = I_a$$

The first step in the calculation is to assume a set of values for I_f (which will also be those of I_m and I_a), and from the motor curve read the corresponding values of T and S.

With T and I_a known, KF can be calculated from equation 6. Since E, I_a, and R_m are known, the countervoltage E_a can be determined. Then, with S known, K_2F can be calculated. A table listing these values would be headed as follows:

$$I_f \qquad T \qquad KF \qquad I_aR_m \qquad E_a \qquad S \qquad K_2F$$

It is now possible to plot curves for T/I_a and E_a/S, against I_f, and to use these curves for the calculation of the dynamic-lowering circuit.

The lowering circuit consists of three branches. One branch consists of the motor armature and a resistor in series with it. The current in this branch is I_a, and its total resistance (armature and external resistor) is R_a. A second branch consists of the motor field and a resistor in series with it. The current in this branch is I_f, and the total resistance (field and external resistor) is R_f. These two branches are

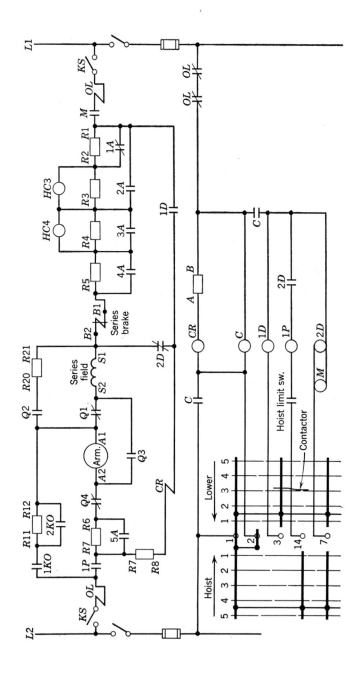

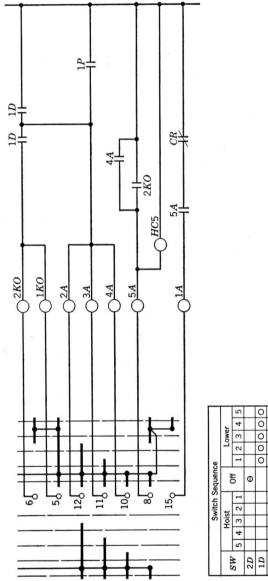

FIG. 148. Connections for Simplified Dynamic-lowering Hoist Controller.

⊖ = spring-closed switch
⊠ = controlled by CR relay
Q1, Q2, Q3, Q4 are limit switch contacts

SW	Switch Sequence										
	Hoist					Off	Lower				
	5	4	3	2	1		1	2	3	4	5
2D						⊖					
1D			O	O	O		O	O	O	O	O
1P	O	O	O	O							
1KO	O	O	O	O	O		O	O	O	O	O
2KO	⊖	O	O	O	O	⊖	O	O	O	O	⊠
M	O	O	O	O	O		O	⊖	⊖	⊖	⊖
1A	⊖	⊖	⊖	⊖	O		⊖	⊖	O	O	O
2A	O	O	O	O			O	O	O		
3A	O	O	O				O	O			
4A	O	O					O				
5A	O						O				

connected in parallel. In series with the combination is the third branch which is a resistor R_l. The current in this branch is I_l.

The next step is to set up a table with headings as follows:

$$I_f \qquad I_fR_f \qquad I_lR_l \qquad I_l \qquad I_a \qquad I_aR_a \qquad E_a \qquad \frac{E_a}{S} \qquad S \qquad \frac{T}{I_a} \qquad T$$

Then assume values of I_f, and calculate the other values.

$$I_f = \text{assumed.}$$

$$R_f = \text{known.}$$

$$R_l = \text{known.}$$

The voltage across $R_l = E - I_fR_f$. Call this E_1.

$$I_l = \frac{E_1}{R_l}$$

$$I_a = I_l - I_f$$

$$R_a = \text{known}$$

$$E_a = I_fR_f - I_aR_a$$

$$\frac{E_a}{S} = \text{read from curve}$$

$$S = \frac{E_a}{E_a/S}$$

$$\frac{T}{I_a} = \text{read from curve}$$

$$T = I_a \times \frac{T}{I_a}$$

The speed-torque curve may now be plotted from the values of S and T.

The method described works equally well for series and for series-shunt motors. It will be evident that if the same values of I_f are used in preparing the preliminary table and the final table it is not necessary to plot the curves of I_f vs. T/I_a and I_f vs. E_a/S.

Accuracy of the Method. There will be slight errors in the results of these calculations because the calculations are based on the motor curve which is correct for normal series motor operation and the same current in armature and field. Under the conditions of dynamic lowering, the motor and field currents are not the same, and the motor is sometimes acting as a generator. Cross-magnetizing armature reaction will affect the field strength, tending toward demagnetization. Currents flowing in armature coils which are being commutated also affect the field strength. The net effect of these factors is to decrease the field strength when the armature current is high. In general, if the field current is higher than 50 per cent of normal, and if the armature current under this condition is not more than 100 per cent of normal, the curves will be quite accurate. If the field current is higher than 50 per cent, the armature current may be correspondingly higher without affecting the accuracy of the curves.

Adjustments. As an aid to the understanding of the controller described, the results which may be obtained by adjusting the various resistance steps are given below in tabular form.

HOISTING

Step	Effect of Increasing Ohmic Value	Effect of Decreasing Ohmic Value
R1–R2	Not used in hoisting	Not used in hoisting
R2–R3 Slack cable step	Speed and torque on the first point will be reduced. Current taken from the line on the first point will be reduced. If the ohms are made too high, the brake will be slow in releasing.	Speed, torque, and current from the line will be increased on the first point.
R3–R4 Slack cable step	Speed and torque on the second point will be reduced.	Speed and torque on the second point will be increased.
R4–R5 R6–R7 R7–R8	These steps are designed for equal current peaks of approximately 150 per cent of normal full-load current. Adjustment for hoisting should not be necessary. Increasing the ohms of any step will decrease the speed and torque on that point and will also decrease the current peak at that point. The peak occurring when the step is cut out will be increased. If these steps are out of adjustment enough to cause very unequal peaks during acceleration, the operation will be jerky and there will be strains on the ropes and gears.	Decreasing the ohms on any point will increase the speed and torque on that point. It will increase the current peak on that point and decrease the peak occurring when the step is cut out of circuit.

Hoisting

Step	Effect of Increasing Ohmic Value	Effect of Decreasing Ohmic Value
R8–R9 Dynamic	Not used in hoisting.	
R11–R12 Kickoff	Not used in hoisting.	

Lowering

Step	Increasing Ohmic Value	Decreasing Ohmic Value
R1–R2	Light-load lowering speed will be increased. Full-load lowering speed will not be affected.	Light-load lowering speed will be decreased. Full-load lowering speed will not be affected.
R2–R3	Increasing the ohmic value will increase the speed on the fourth point and full-load speed on the fifth point.	Speed on the fourth point will be decreased, and on the fifth point with full load.
R3 R4 R4–R5	Speed on the third point will be increased.	Speed on the third point will be decreased.
R6–R7 R7–R8	Speed on the second point with overhauling load will be increased. Starting torque on the second point will be decreased. In the off position, the first and second steps of dynamic braking will be less effective.	Speed on the second point with overhauling load will be decreased. Starting torque on the second point will be increased. In the off position, the first and second steps of dynamic braking will be stronger.
R8–R9	All three steps of the graduated, off position, dynamic braking will be decreased in effect.	All three steps of the graduated off position, dynamic braking will be increased in effect.
	The torque for starting and lowering will be decreased. The torque on all points lowering on power will be decreased.	The torque for starting and lowering will be increased. The torque on all points lowering on power will be increased.
	Light hook lowering speed will be decreased.	Light hook lowering speed will be increased.
	Full-load lowering speed will be increased.	Full-load lowering speed will be decreased.
	If made too high, the proper ratio of full-load and light-load speeds will not be maintained, and the crane may not operate at its best efficiency.	If made too low, the brake may be slow in releasing. Also the accelerating inrush on the last point may be too high. Also sparking of the commutator may

Step	Increasing Ohmic Value	Decreasing Ohmic Value
		occur during dynamic braking in the off position.
R11–R12	Speed and torque will be decreased on the first four points. Current taken from the line on starting will be decreased.	Speed and torque will be increased on the first four points. Current taken from the line on starting will be increased.

Simplified Controller. The controller which has been described is suitable for use with any of the common sizes of crane hoist motors, but a somewhat simplified arrangement is generally satisfactory for the smaller sizes, up to 55 horsepower. A single step of dynamic-braking resistance is used, and a lesser number of accelerating steps. A diagram of the simplified controller is shown in Fig. 148. The speed-torque curves obtained with this controller are similar to those of Fig. 146, and the operating speeds may be just as high as with the first controller described.

References

D. L. Pettit, "Dynamic-lowering D-c Hoist Control," *Transactions AIEE*, 1948, Vol. 67, p. 1576.

Problems

1. Using the following values, calculate and plot a speed-torque curve similar to Fig. 147, for a dynamic-lowering hoist controller:

Armature resistance	$= 0.08E/I$
Field resistance	$= 0.03E/I$
Resistance in line circuit	$= 0.80E/I$
Resistance in field circuit	$= 1.50E/I$
Resistance in armature circuit	$= 0.25E/I$

2. Calculate and plot a similar curve for the same circuit, but with the line-circuit resistance reduced to zero.

3. A bucket hoist has the following duty cycles:

Closing the bucket	6 seconds at 40 hp
Hoisting	10 seconds at 80 hp
Opening the bucket	3 seconds at 30 hp
Lowering	10 seconds at 45 hp
Resting	16 seconds at 0 hp

If the rate of cooling of the motor at standstill is one-third of the rate when running, what is the rms horsepower required of the motor?

4. Assuming that it requires 150 per cent of full-load current to supply the desired initial starting torque, how many ohms will be required in the accelerating resistor of a controller for the hoist of problem 3? The power is supplied at 230 volts.

5. The bucket of a bucket hoist weighs 5000 pounds, and the load in it weighs 10,000 pounds. The hoisting speed is 150 feet per minute, and the efficiency of the hoist is 80 per cent. What is the horsepower for which the controller must be designed?

6. A hoist has the following characteristics:

Weight of bucket	2000 pounds
Weight of load	6000 pounds
Diameter of winding drum	2 feet
Efficiency of the hoist	80 per cent
Gear reduction	5 to 1
Rope reduction	2 to 1

What is the torque on the motor shaft when hoisting full load?

7. What is the torque on the motor shaft when lowering the empty bucket?

8. Draw a step-by-step elementary diagram similar to Fig. 145, for the hoist controller of Fig. 148.

9. A 50-horsepower 230-volt 200-ampere hoist motor has a controller with the circuits of Fig. 145. If the controller is in the off position, but with the brake released, and if the load is lowering at a speed which causes 100 amperes to flow in the motor armature, what is the lowering speed, in per cent of full-load hoisting speed? The resistor values are:

	Per Cent of E/I
$R6$–$R7$	19
$R7$–$R8$	14
$R8$–$R9$	25
Armature	8
Field	3
Field curve	Fig. 125

10. What is the torque at the motor shaft, in per cent of full-rated torque?

11. What will be the lowering speed after contactors $5A$ and $6A$ are closed?

12. A small crane is to be equipped with a controller like that of Fig. 148, except that it is to be simplified by the omission of $1A$, $4A$, the limit stop contacts $Q1$–$Q4$ inclusive, and relay CR. The master is to have three speeds in each direction. Make an elementary diagram for the controller.

14

ALTERNATING-CURRENT CONTACTORS AND RELAYS

Alternating-current Magnets. The principal difference between alternating-current contactors and direct-current contactors is in the design of the operating magnet. With the direct-current contactor, any heating of the iron frame arises from copper loss in the coil. With the alternating-current contactor, heating of the frame comes from iron loss in the frame itself. The resistance of the coil is relatively low, and the copper loss is small. In order to reduce the iron losses, alternating-current-contactor magnets are made of thin laminations bolted together. The laminations must be bolted tightly together to prevent humming when the contactor is operated, but care must be exercised in locating the holding bolts, since they are solid and will be subject to heating. The bolts must be located at points of low flux density.

With a direct-current contactor, the current in the coil and consequently the flux available for closing the contactor are dependent upon the line voltage and the coil resistance. In the alternating-current contactor, the current is dependent upon these factors and in addition upon the reluctance of the circuit, the frequency of the supply, and the number of turns in the coil. Alternating-current contactors are quite sensitive to slight changes in voltage and frequency and are likely to overheat if the voltage is higher or the frequency lower than normal. On the other hand, if the voltage is lower than it should be or the frequency higher, the contactor may not have sufficient closing pull and will become noisy because it will start to open each time the voltage passes through zero.

Two types of alternating-current magnets have been in general use. One type is similar to the direct-current magnet in that the coil is mounted upon a core which extends clear through it, and the armature is a straight piece which seats against the end of the core. A more efficient type is the so-called hammer-head magnet in which the armature projects inside the coil. The hammer-head magnet has a higher initial closing pull but a lower sealing pull as compared to the first type of magnet described.

One design of alternating-current contactor has the magnet in the center of the two contacts. A more flexible arrangement is to have the magnet at the side of the contacts. This arrangement allows the same magnet to be used for contactors of one, two, three, or four poles by simply changing the length of the contact shaft. It also permits the use of a simple square shaft on which the contacts are mounted and which is easily insulated.

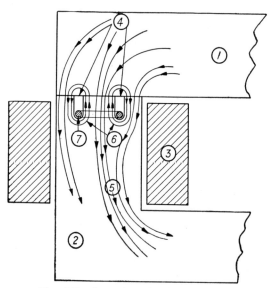

FIG. 149. Operation of a Shading Coil.

Alternating-current contactors are shown on the controllers of Figs. 172, 176, and 218.

Shading Coils. With alternating current the pull of the contactor closing coil reverses in direction at each cycle, and each time that this reversal occurs the flux passes through zero and the contactor tends to open. Some means must be provided to overcome this tendency, or else the contactor will be extremely noisy and probably will soon hammer itself to pieces as a result of the vibration.

The tendency to open with each reversal of flux is overcome by mounting a small auxiliary coil in a slot in the contactor face. This is called a shading coil. It may be a single loop of wire or strap, or it may be several turns of wire. At any rate, it is short-circuited and depends for its action upon the flux induced in it by the main flux. With reference to Fig. 149, 1 represents the moving armature of the contactor and 2 the stationary frame; 3 is the main operating coil of the contactor. The shading coil 7, embedded in the slot 4, is shown as a single short-circuited loop of wire. The main flux 5 passes partly through the shading coil and partly outside of it. This induces alternating current in the shading coil. The resistance and reactance of the shading coil itself are in such proportions that the induced current is out of phase with the main flux by approximately 120 degrees. Therefore, whenever the main flux is approaching or passing through the zero point there is an auxiliary flux from the shading coil which is holding the contactor tightly closed, and when the auxiliary flux is at the zero point the main flux has again built up to a safe value.

Shading-coil design is largely a matter of cut and try. Different coils are usually mounted in a contactor frame, and the pull is measured by means of a scale. Curves are plotted of pull in ounces against cross-section of the shading coil. However, the coil which gives a maximum pull cannot always be selected, because the question of wattage loss in the coil also enters into the problem. Somewhere in the neighborhood of one-third of the iron loss in the contactor frame is due to the shading coil. The loss caused by the shading coil increases with the cross-section of the coil; it can be measured by measuring the wattage taken by the closing coil of the contactor. The final design must then be a compromise between wattage and pull. Shading coils are sometimes punched out of a solid piece, so that there will not need to be any joints in the coil. If a joint is unavoidable, it is usually welded to insure a low resistance and also to insure a joint which will not loosen under the vibration caused by the alternating current.

With well-designed shading coils, alternating-current contactors can be made to operate very quietly. A broken shading coil will make its presence known, as the contactor will immediately become extremely noisy. Such a condition should be remedied at once, as the contactor will be subject to overheating and will soon cease to operate properly.

If the surface of the armature and the magnet frame becomes dirty or rusty, the contactor will not seal properly and will become noisy. These surfaces are usually fitted very accurately by the manufacturer and are then greased to prevent rust until such time as the contactor is put into operation. The layer of grease or Vaseline should be removed when the contactor is about to be used, as the operation of the contactor will tend to keep the magnet surface clean.

Alternating-current Coils. Direct-current contactor coils have a large number of turns and a high ohmic resistance. The current through them is limited by the resistance. In alternating-current coils, the current through the coil is limited by the impedance of the circuit, and the reactance has a greater effect than the resistance. Consequently, the resistance of an alternating-current contactor coil is low, and the number of turns is relatively small. It is possible, therefore, to use heavier wire for these coils, which is fortunate for several reasons. With a relatively small number of turns there is a higher voltage drop per turn. Also, the alternating-current coils are subject to continuous vibration caused by the reversal of the flux. A short-circuited turn in a direct-current coil does not do any particular damage, merely reducing the resistance of the coil a very slight amount. An alternating-current coil, however, will be ruined by a short-circuited turn. The short-circuited turn acts as the secondary winding of a transformer, the primary of which is the winding of the rest of the coil. A heavy current is induced in the short-circuited turn, which will overheat and burn out.

For the above reasons, insulation is of greater importance in alternating- than in direct-current coils. It is customary to use a double-insulated wire and to impregnate the coils thoroughly with a binding compound. On the other hand, the outer covering of the coils is not quite so important as it is with direct current, because high voltages due to self-inductance will not be present, and furthermore the danger from electrolysis is not so great.

Inrush Currents. With a direct-current magnet, the current in the coil is the same whether the contactor is opened or closed. However, with an alternating-current magnet, the current in the coil is largely determined by the reactance of the circuit, which is lower when the contactor is open, because of the air gap in the magnetic circuit. Therefore, there will be a high inrush of current through the coil when the contactor is first connected to the supply line. The inrush may be five to twenty times as high as the current which will flow through the coil when the contactor has closed. This fact must be taken into account when alternating-current contactors and relays are used, and care must be taken that the pilot device which handles the coil circuit has ample capacity to pass the inrush current. Since the current through the coil is automatically reduced as soon as the contactor has closed, it becomes unnecessary to insert protecting resistance as is done with direct-current coils.

The fact that the inrush current is so much higher than the sealed current makes it undesirable to tie alternating-current contactors together mechanically, since, if anything happens to prevent one contactor from closing, the coil of the other will be burned out.

Furthermore, when two alternating-current contactors are tied together mechanically, there is a good possibility of their chattering and being noisy unless the mechanical link is very carefully designed and applied.

Remote Control. When controlling an alternating-current contactor from any considerable distance, the inrush current to the coil must be taken into account, since this current will cause a relatively high voltage drop in the control line between the contactor and the push-button station. If the voltage drop is too high, the contactor coil will not have sufficient voltage to enable the contactor to close. In such an installation the maximum allowable resistance of the control circuit should be calculated, and the size of wire for the control circuit should be so selected that the resistance will be below that value.

The maximum allowable resistance of the control wire for a given installation may be calculated as follows:

It is first necessary to measure the ohmic resistance of the coil of the contactor and the inrush current which occurs when the contactor is open. This may be done by holding the contactor open by hand until the value of the current is read. With reference to Fig. 150, the line OA is laid out so that

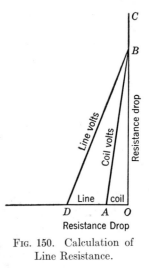

FIG. 150. Calculation of Line Resistance.

its length represents the resistance drop of the coil on inrush current; that is, it is a voltage equal to the ohmic resistance of the coil, multiplied by the inrush current. The line OC is drawn at a right angle to OA. From A the line AB is drawn to intersect the line OC. The length of AB should be such that it represents 90 per cent of line voltage. This is on the assumption that the minimum voltage across the coil on inrush should be 90 per cent of normal line voltage, in order to secure proper operation. Line AB then represents the voltage across the coil, and OB represents the reactance drop in the coil. From the point B the line BD is drawn to intersect the base line. The length of the line BD is selected to represent full line voltage, or, in other words, this length is 1.11 times the length of AB. The line AD then represents the additional resistance drop which may be included in the line in order to obtain 90 per cent of normal voltage across the coil on inrush. Dividing the value of AD by the value of the inrush current will then give the ohms allowable in the line, and from a wire table the proper size of wire can be selected.

If the line has already been constructed and is of too high a resistance, or if it is necessary to use a size of wire which will give a line of too high a resistance, the solution of the problem is to choose a small relay which will have a lower value of inrush current. The relay in turn will control the coil of the contactor which is to be operated.

Oil-immersed Contactors.   It is sometimes necessary to use contactors which have their live parts immersed in oil. Such a contactor

FIG. 151. Oil-immersed Contactor. Oil Tank Removed.

is shown in Fig. 151. The magnet which closes the contactor is similar to the magnet used for an air-break contactor, and it is mounted outside of the oil tank. The armature of the magnet operates a rod which extends down into the oil tank and connects to a shaft on which the contacts of the switch are mounted. The tank is arranged to be easily removable, so that the contactor parts and the oil may be inspected frequently.

Sometimes the entire contactor, including the magnet structure and the coil, is immersed in oil.

Control-voltage Transformer. There is a considerable hazard in using voltages higher than 230 volts for control circuits. Although pushbuttons and other pilot devices are usually designed with spacings suitable for 600 volts, faults, breakages, careless wiring, etc., may subject the operator to a shock which could be serious with higher voltages. Lower control voltages also reduce the risk of insulation breakdown and grounding in the control wiring and the pilot devices. So it is common practice to use a control-voltage transformer to provide 110 volts, or some other suitable low voltage, for the control circuits.

Transformers designed for general-purpose use are usually not suitable for control work, because they are designed for relatively constant loads. When a contactor is energized, the initial current may be 15 or 20 times the current required after the contactor closes. The transformer must be able to supply the required high inrush current without dropping its voltage more than 5 per cent. Since the transformer voltage-regulation curve will vary with the power factor of the load, the selection of the proper transformer involves an analysis of the entire control circuit.

To determine the size of transformer which is necessary for any given installation, the maximum possible inrush current obtained at any one time should be calculated. The current and power factor of each contactor coil, both when first energized and when closed, are determined. Then the various combinations of closed contactors, and contactors just energized are compiled, and the total current and its power factor under the worst condition are calculated. With this information, and a set of curves for the available transformers, a suitable transformer can be selected, it being kept in mind that the voltage must not drop below 95 per cent of normal rated voltage, with rated controller voltage on the primary winding.

The transformer will also be required to carry the sealed current of the maximum number of contactors which are closed when the equipment is running; consequently it should have a kilovolt-ampere capacity equal to this continuous current multiplied by the line voltage. For some installations this continuous capacity will be the determining factor, but for most installations it will be the inrush condition which

determines the size of transformer required.   The transformer must
meet both conditions.

Consideration must also be given to the open-circuit secondary
voltage, which should not be much higher than the secondary voltage
at rated load.   The reason for this requirement is that at times only
one small relay or contactor of a controller may be energized, and if
the voltage is too high a damaged coil may result.

Control Relays.   Alternating-current control relays, that is, purely
shunt relays, are similar to alternating-current contactors, except that

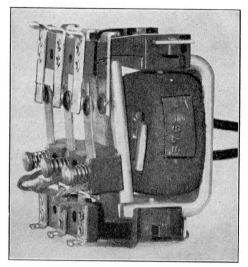

Fɪɢ. 152.   Small Control Relay.

they are smaller and have lighter contacts.   They are arranged with
various combinations of normally open and normally closed contacts,
to suit the convenience of the control designer.   They may be equipped
with magnetic blowouts and with mechanical interlocks, just as the
larger contactors are equipped.   Figure 152 shows a small three-pole
double-throw shunt relay, having a rating of 15 amperes on the normally open contacts and 10 amperes on the normally closed contacts.
Designed especially for small size, it is 2.75 inches high, 1.75 inches
wide, and 2.2 inches deep.

Accelerating Relays.   Figure 153 shows an alternating-current series
accelerating relay.   The relay has three coils, which are connected in
the secondary circuit of a slip-ring motor.   The relay is used for the
purpose of causing a contactor to short-circuit a step of resistance at
the proper time.   The three coils are used so that there will be a

balanced three-phase pull on the armature of the relay at all times. This insures that the relay will operate positively, and open and close at a definite value of current. The contacts of the relay are normally closed. When the motor is connected to the line, there will be an inrush of current in the secondary winding which will cause the relay to open its contacts. After the motor has accelerated to a predetermined speed, the current will have fallen to approximately the normal full-load

Fig. 153. Alternating-current Series Relay.

running current of the motor. The relay will be adjusted to close its contacts at that point and short-circuit the starting resistance. The opening point of the relay is determined by the adjusting tension spring, which opposes the pull of the coils. The closing point of the relay is set by moving in and out three metal plugs, which are shown in the armature member. These plugs consist of an outer shell of steel, which may be moved in and out to determine the magnetic gap when the relay is de-energized. Inside this shell there is a brass screw, which may be independently moved in and out to determine the magnetic gap when the relay is energized. The amount of the gap when the relay is de-energized has an effect on the point at which the relay armature will be attracted to the core, and the amount of the gap when the relay is energized determines the point at which the relay armature will move away from the core. One adjustment, therefore, affects the closing point of the relay, and the other adjustment the opening point.

Relays of this type may also be used as jamming relays, when they are set to open and insert a step of resistance in the secondary winding of a slip-ring motor if the motor becomes overloaded beyond a certain amount. Jamming relays are used in connection with installations of machinery which is subject to frequent high peaks of load. Such an installation will be provided with a heavy flywheel. When the load starts to build up, the jamming relay will operate, cutting resistance into the secondary circuit of the motor. The motor will then slow down, and the energy necessary to carry through the period of peak load will be taken from the flywheel. When the peak load is passed and the current has again dropped off to normal, the jam relay will allow the resistance to be cut out and the motor will bring the flywheel back to full speed. In this way high peaks caused by a heavy intermittent load may be reduced.

Magnetic Overload Relays. Magnetic overload relays for alternating current are similar to those for direct current, except that the plunger is usually slotted or laminated to prevent heating, and the dashpots are arranged for longer timing. Single-coil relays of this type are available, but, since the majority of alternating-current work is three-phase, double-coil relays like that shown in Fig. 154 are more generally used. These relays have two coils, each operating its own plunger and each connected in one phase of the motor circuit. There is only one set of normally closed contacts, and either plunger will open this set of contacts when an overload occurs. The tripping point is adjusted by moving weights in and out on levers attached to the plunger. The weights oppose the movement of the plunger.

Relays of this type may be arranged to be reset by hand or to reset automatically when the overload is removed. It is not practicable to arrange them with shunt coils to hold the plunger tripped when it has once operated, as is done with direct current, because there will be a transformer action between the series and the shunt coil which will prevent proper operation of the relay.

Although magnetic overload relays are still used for the protection of alternating-current motors, they have been largely replaced by the thermal type, especially on controllers for small motors.

Phase Failure Relays. Phase failure relays are used to prevent the starting of an alternating-current motor if one of the phases has been reversed, and also to prevent its starting if one phase has been disconnected by the blowing of a fuse or by some other means.

Attempting to operate the motor with one phase open will result in overheating and damage. Operating with one phase reversed will reverse the motor and cause it to run in a direction opposite to that which is anticipated. Such a reversal of direction might cause serious damage and danger to life, especially in hoists and elevators.

FIG. 154. Duplex Overload Relay.

The phase failure relay shown in Fig. 155 is in reality a small induction motor, the armature of which has a limited angular movement just sufficient to operate a sensitive pilot switch. The armature is a disk, to which the contact mechanism is coupled, and which is biased to the open contact position by a spring. The relay has four series coils, two of which are connected in one motor phase, the other two being connected in a second motor phase. The combined effect of these coils is to produce a torque which turns the disk, overcoming the spring, and causes the contacts to close. If one phase is open, there will be no torque. If one phase is reversed, the torque will rotate the disk in the opposite direction and will open the contacts. A shunt coil at the top of the relay operates a holding brake, which prevents the relay from tripping when the motor is disconnected from the line under normal operating conditions.

Whether or not a phase failure relay will protect a running motor on the failure of one phase depends on the load of the motor. If the motor is heavily loaded, and running single phase, the terminal voltage will be unbalanced sufficiently to cause the relay to open. However,

if the motor is running slightly loaded, it will continue to maintain a polyphase voltage across its terminals even when running single phase. The relay is ordinarily connected close to the motor, and, therefore, an open circuit in one phase will nearly always occur between the relay and the power supply. This leaves the relay connected to the motor, and it will be maintained in a closed position by the polyphase voltage of the motor. It would be highly desirable to shut the motor down in case a phase opened for any reason while the motor was running. However, since the conditions at the relay are the same whether the phase is open or not, the matter presents some difficulty, and so far as the writer knows no phase failure relay has yet been developed which will shut down a slightly loaded motor upon failure of one phase.

Fig. 155. Westinghouse Type-SRN Single-phase, Phase-reversal Relay.

Voltage Relays. Relays to open and close on a definite voltage are sometimes required. Such relays must necessarily be very light. The magnetic gap must be kept small so that the inrush current will not be very much greater than the sealed current. If this is not done, the relay coil will be likely to burn out, since the voltage may rise almost to the value for which the relay is set, and then remain there for some time. The relay would not be able to close, and the coil would probably burn out owing to the duration of the inrush current. The dropping-out point also presents some difficulty, as the relay is likely to become very noisy if the voltage has been reduced almost to the point for which the relay is set to open. It is possible to design relays for this purpose if the magnet gap is kept small and the contact pressure very light. However, a relay of the induction-motor type, as, for instance, the phase failure relay, is more suitable for definite voltage settings.

Thermal Overload Relay. Until the thermal type of overload relay was developed, no very satisfactory device was available for the protection of an alternating-current motor. Magnetic overload relays, fuses, and circuit breakers either fail to protect the motor sufficiently or else they trip too soon, causing an unnecessary delay.

Most alternating-current motors are rated on the basis of 40 C ambient temperature, and the final safe temperature will be approximately 95 C. The time required for a motor to reach an unsafe temperature will depend upon the amount that it is overloaded. Since the heating varies as the square of the current, the time required to reach the final temperature of 95 C under different amounts of overload varies inversely as the square of the current.

An ideal overload relay would have a tripping curve of the same shape, and following just below the motor curve. The thermal type of overload relay has a tripping characteristic more nearly approaching the ideal than that of any other type of overload relay. It has the further advantage that, since its tripping is dependent upon heating, the relay automatically compensates for differences in room temperature. On a cool day a motor will carry a greater load without danger than it will on a hot day, and the thermal relay will also require a higher current to trip it.

When a squirrel-cage motor is connected directly to the line to start, it draws a starting current which is commonly six to eight times its normal running current. Fuses used to protect such a motor must not blow out on the high inrush current, and in order to meet this requirement it is necessary to select fuses of approximately three times motor rating. No protection, therefore, is afforded to the motor on any overload below 300 per cent. Forty-degree-rated motors will carry 15 per cent overload continuously without danger, but any overload above this value will burn out the motor if the overload persists long enough. Fuses, therefore, do not furnish adequate protection. They are necessary to take care of short circuits or very heavy overloads. Under these conditions the fuse should blow out before the thermal relay trips, as otherwise the contactor operated by the relay will be required to open short-circuit current and may be damaged in doing so.

These characteristics are illustrated by the curves of Fig. 156, which show that the thermal relay will adequately protect the wiring, and that the fuse will blow first on a heavy short-circuit current. The curves also show that the thermal relay will allow the motor ample time to accelerate. The heating curve of the motor itself is considerably above the curve of the thermal relay for the short period of time covered by the curve, but at slightly longer time the curves come more closely together, until they practically coincide at a time of 1 hour. In other words, if the particular type of relay for which these curves

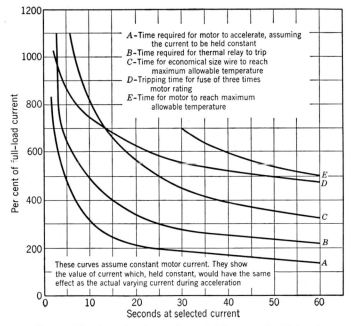

F.G. 156.   Curves Showing the Protection of Motor and Wiring by Thermal Overload Relay and by Fuses.

were made was set to open the circuit on an overload of 15 per cent, it would do this in approximately 1 hour's time, and on any higher overload would trip in a shorter time. Under any overload above 15 per cent, the tripping time would be shorter than the time required for the motor to reach a dangerous temperature.

Many different chemical and physical properties have been utilized in the design of thermal relays, as, for instance, the extension of a rod, the bending of a bimetallic strip under heat, the change of a liquid to a gas, and the change of a solid to a liquid. The type of relay depending upon the change of a liquid to a gas has commonly employed mercury. The relay depending upon a change of a solid to a liquid uses a slow-melting fusible metallic alloy. Of all types, the bimetallic strip relay and the fusible alloy relay have been the most successful.

Bimetallic Relays. The bimetallic relay (Fig. 157) has two heaters in series with the circuit to be protected, and above these heaters are two strips of bimetallic material which act as latches for the contact members. When the relay is closed, the contacts are held together by the latches. Bending of the bimetallic strips, under the heating of overload current, will release the latches and allow the contacts to

FIG. 157. General Electric Two-pole Temperature Overload Relay, with Detachable Heater and Thermal Unit.

open. Adjustment is usually made by varying the distance that the bimetallic strip must move before the relay will trip.

The bimetallic relay has a number of different forms. The requisite design details are: protection for the bimetallic strip to avoid accidental bending, avoidance of friction, a method of adjustment, and ample current capacity in the heaters.

One type of bimetallic relay made by the General Electric Company has the bimetal strip wound in a helix, and instead of a heater element it uses a coil connected in series with the motor. The bimetal helix is in the center of the coil, and is heated by induction. When heated by an overload current it unwinds slightly and causes the relay contacts to open.

Fusible Alloy Relays. The thermal element of the fusible alloy relay shown in Fig. 158 consists of a small tube, in the bottom of which are a quantity of a special low-melting alloy and a shaft which extends into the tube. The tube is fixed to the base of the relay. So long as the alloy is unmelted the shaft is prevented from turning. A gear wheel of insulating material is mounted on the outer end of the shaft. A heater coil, of Nichrome wire or strip, is mounted in a cover of molded insulating material; it is so arranged that when the cover is in place the heater surrounds the tube containing the fusible alloy. Adjustment is made by sliding the covers up or down, which changes the location of the heater with respect to the tube. There are two of these thermal elements. When the contacts of the relay are closed, they are held in place by latches operating in the teeth of the two

Fig. 158. Fusible-alloy Type of Thermal Overload Relay.

gear wheels. The contacts are biased to the open position by means of a spring. When an overload occurs the heater becomes warm enough to melt the fusible alloy in the tube. When the alloy melts, the shaft and gears are free to turn, and under the pressure of the contact spring they do turn and release the latches. This allows the contacts to open with a quick break. Turning of either of the shafts will release the contacts. To reset the device, the contacts are simply pushed back into place until the latches catch. A short time must be allowed for the alloy to cool and harden. Fusible alloy relays in different forms are made by several manufacturers. This type of relay is quite accurate in its tripping point. The success of the relay is dependent to a considerable degree upon the fusible alloy used. Eutectic alloys have the most desirable characteristics, since they have sharp melting and freezing points and do not have a range of temperature in which the metal is mushy. Also eutectic alloys, not being liable to segregation, maintain their characteristics over long periods of service.

Rating of Thermal Heater Coils. The ampere rating of a heater coil for a thermal overload relay is determined by testing it for the minimum current which will cause the relay to trip open, the heater being installed in an overload relay, and the relay being in a 40 C ambient temperature. This current having been determined from the average of a number of tests on duplicate heaters, the value is multiplied by 1.05 and the product becomes the heater rating. The 5 per cent is added to make allowance for variation in the wire of the coil and for variations in the manufacturing process, and to insure that the heater will always trip at its rating. In designing a line of heater coils, a ratio between sizes of 10 to 15 per cent is used. Assuming that the coils are 10 per cent apart, the motor rating of a heater may be determined by dividing the heater rating by 1.25 to get the minimum motor rating, and then multiplying the minimum rating by 1.10 to get the maximum motor rating. For example, assume a heater rated 0.238 ampere. The minimum motor current for which this heater should be used is 0.238 divided by 1.25, or 0.190 ampere. The maximum motor current is 0.190 multiplied by 1.10, or 0.209 ampere. Since the heater will trip on any current at or above its rating, a motor having a normal current of 0.209 ampere will be protected on any overload of 114 per cent or higher, and a motor having a full-load current of 0.190 ampere will be protected on any overload of 125 per cent or higher. Motors designed in accordance with NEMA standards have a 15 per cent service factor, which means that they can run continuously at 115 per cent of full load without injury. They are, therefore, suitably protected by a heater designed on the above basis. If too small a heater is used, the overload relay will trip out on overloads which the motor could safely carry, and unnecessary shutdowns might occur.

Effect of Ambient Temperature. It is customary to test and rate thermal overload heaters on the basis of 40 C ambient temperature, because that is the basis of rating the motor and represents about the worst service conditions. However, it is the usual practice to publish time-current characteristic curves on the basis of 25 C ambient temperature, because anyone making a test in the field is likely to be making it in about that temperature. Any curve may be changed from one ambient basis to another by the following equation:

$$\frac{I_a}{I_b} = \sqrt{\frac{T - a}{T - b}}$$

where I_a = amperes to trip in a given time at the lower ambient.

I_b = amperes to trip in the same time at the higher ambient.

a = the lower ambient in degrees centigrade.

b = the higher ambient in degrees centigrade.

T = the melting point of the alloy of the relay in degrees centigrade.

The value of T for Cutler-Hammer relays numbers 306, 307, and 489, is 98 C.

Derating Curves. When thermal relays are used as a part of an enclosed controller, it may be necessary to derate the heaters, because free ventilation is not available and the ambient temperature inside the enclosure may be relatively high. This is particularly true of small enclosures and accounts for the fact that the same heater may have several different ratings according to its application to a particular controller. The amount of derating necessary can be determined only by test.

Slow-trip Heaters. The current-time characteristics of thermal overload relays are designed to satisfy normal conditions. Many machines require an abnormally long time to come up to full speed, and, since the current of a squirrel-cage motor remains high until the motor is well up to speed, a standard heater coil would trip out during acceleration. For such applications slow-trip heaters are used. Some of these are specially built to have a greater mass of metal than a standard heater, so that more heat may be absorbed, and the relay element take longer to reach its tripping temperature. This does not change the rated ultimate tripping value but only lengthens the tripping time, to permit the motor to accelerate. Another way to accomplish the desired result is to connect the heaters through small saturated-core current transformers. These are designed to limit the secondary current, which flows through the heater, to about three times normal current, regardless of the amount of the primary or motor current. The heater is then not subject to a high current during the long accelerating period and so will not trip prematurely.

Use of Alternating-current Contactors on Direct-current Circuits. It sometimes happens that it is desirable to use an alternating-current contactor to commutate direct current, or to energize the coil of an alternating-current contactor by direct current. In the first case, no modification of the contactor is necessary, unless the conditions are unusual. However, if the magnet is to be energized from a direct-current source, it will be necessary to guard against sticking on residual magnetism. This may be done by placing a strip or washer of non-magnetic material either on the armature or on the frame so that there will be a gap in the magnetic circuit when the contactor is closed.

In designing a coil to operate on direct current, the inrush obtained on some standard alternating-current coil may be measured, and, since the turns in the coil will be known, the ampere-turns necessary to close the contactor may be calculated. A coil may then be designed to give the same ampere-turns when used on the direct-current supply. In general, it will be found that the wattage taken by the direct-current coil will be higher than that normally required by a direct-current magnet of a corresponding size. It may be quite difficult, if not impossible, to design a direct-current coil which will be good for continuous duty. It may be possible to design one which can be protected for continuous duty by the insertion of a resistor after the contactor has closed. However, even by this means it may be found difficult to get a coil which is satisfactory for more than part-time service.

Use of Direct-current Contactors on Alternating-current Circuits. Since the frame of a contactor must be laminated when an alternating-current coil is to be used, it is generally not practicable to operate a direct-current contactor on alternating current. However, it is often desirable to use a direct-current control circuit, and to commutate alternating current on the contacts. This can be done if precautions are taken to prevent heating of the blowout structure. In general the heating may be reduced to a safe value by cutting slots lengthwise in the blowout core and also in the pole pieces at the sides of the blowout. Sometimes a core of copper or brass is substituted for the steel core.

Standard Ratings. The following standard ratings are taken from NEMA Industrial Control Standards.

The 8-hour open rating for a-c contactors shall be 15, 25, 50, 100, 150, 300, 600, 900, 1350, and 2500 amperes.

The ampere ratings of contactors employed on standard enclosed across-the-line magnetic starters for induction motors shall be 90 per cent of their standard 8-hour ratings.

This reduction in current rating is made because the enclosure of the contactor reduces the amount of ventilating air.

Intermittent ratings for cranes and hoists are given in Table 22.

When used for motor secondary control, the ampere rating of a three-pole contactor, with its poles connected in delta, is 1.5 times its standard crane rating.

TABLE 22

Intermittent Ratings of A-c Contactors

Standard 8-hour Rating, amperes	Amperes	Crane Rating	
		Contactors in Motor Primary	
		Horsepower at 220 Volts	Horsepower at 440 and 550 Volts
50	50	15	25
100	133	40	75
150	200	60	125
300	400	150	300
600	800	300	...
900	1200	450	900
1350	1300	600	1200

Table 23 gives the ratings of high-voltage alternating-current contactors.

TABLE 23

High-voltage A-c Contactor Ratings

8-Hour Rating amperes	Maximum Horsepower 2200–2300 Volts		
	For Synchronous Motors		
	100 Per Cent Power Factor	80 Per Cent Power Factor	For Induction Motors
100	450	350	350
200	900	700	700
400	1750	1500	1500

8-Hour Rating amperes	Maximum Horsepower 4000–4600 Volts		
	For Synchronous Motors		
	100 Per Cent Power Factor	80 Per Cent Power Factor	For Induction Motors
100	....	....	....
200	1500	1250	1250
400	3000	2500	2500

Interrupting and Short-time Ratings. In addition to its regular duties of starting and stopping a motor, and occasionally opening the circuit under overload, a contactor may be called upon to open a line short circuit or to withstand such a short circuit long enough to permit a circuit breaker to operate or a fuse to blow and relieve the condition. The magnitude of a short circuit is determined by a number of factors, among them the capacity of the generating system feeding the lines,

REFERENCES 341

the impedance of the lines, and the point where the short circuit occurs. A contactor is designed to handle currents within its capacity, and to do this many thousands, even millions, of times. A circuit breaker is designed to open very high currents, far beyond the capacity of a contactor, but normally it has to do this only a few times in its life. Mechanically, then, a circuit breaker cannot approach the operating life of a contactor. The usual practice is to install a circuit breaker or fuses for short-circuit protection, a contactor for operation of the motor, and an overload relay for motor protection. If a short circuit occurs, the contactor should have enough thermal capacity to carry the short circuit for the short interval before the breaker opens.

Standard alternating-current air-break and oil-immersed contactors have the capacity to interrupt 10 times their normal motor rating. Note that this is their horsepower rating, not their ampere rating. They have a 1-second thermal capacity of 15 times the current corresponding to their horsepower rating.

For those installations where the available short-circuit current may be very high, controllers specially designed for the purpose are used. These controllers are built in two types. In one type the contacts of the controller are used both for starting the motor and for interrupting a short circuit. If these contacts are those of a magnetic contactor, the contactor will not be the same one that is used to open operating overloads only. The other type of high-interrupting capacity controller uses the contacts of the controller for starting the motor, and fuses for interrupting a short circuit. In this type of controller the contactor need interrupt only operating overloads, and be able to carry the short-circuit current long enough to permit the fuse to open it. The fuses used are of the current-limiting type, having a temperature-resistance characteristic which to some degree limits the amount of current that can pass through them. High-interrupting-capacity controllers without fuses are built to interrupt short circuits of 25,000 and 50,000 kva. High-interrupting-capacity controllers using current-limiting fuses are built to interrupt short circuits of 150,000 and 250,000 kva.

References

L. A. Doggett and F. S. Veith, "Design of Shading Coils for Alternating-current Electromagnets," *Pennsylvania State College Engineering Experimental Station Bulletin* 52, July, 1940.
H. C. Roters, *Electromagnetic Devices,* John Wiley & Sons.
C. W. Kuhn, "A-c Motor Protection," *Electrical Engineering,* May, 1937.
G. A. Moffett, "Thermal Overload Protection for A-c Induction Motors," *Electrical Manufacturing,* July, 1943.

Problems

1. An alternating-current contactor which is used on a 220-volt circuit has a coil with a resistance of 1.35 ohms. The impedance of the coil, with the contactor open, is 10.6 ohms. It is desired that the line voltage drop be no more than 10 per cent of rated voltage. If the wire between the contactor and the push-button is no. 14, having a resistance of 2.525 ohms per 1000 feet, how far may the pushbutton be located from the contactor?

2. When the contactor of problem 1 is operated on 440 volts, the coil resistance is 5.3 ohms, and its impedance with the contactor open is 40.5 ohms. Calculate the maximum allowable resistance of the line between the contactor and the pushbutton, when the line voltage drop is limited to 10 per cent of rated voltage.

3. If the impedance of the 440-volt contactor coil when the contactor is closed is 655 ohms, what is the current in the coil under the conditions of problem 2?

4. A contactor used on a 110-volt circuit has a coil with a resistance of 0.35 ohm and an impedance of 2.9 ohms when the contactor is open. The coil is energized from a 550-volt circuit, through a 550/110-volt transformer having an effective impedance of 0.13 ohm. What is the voltage on the coil?

5. The melting point of the alloy in a thermal overload relay is 98 C. If the relay trips at 52 amperes in an ambient temperature of 20 C, at what current will it trip in an ambient temperature of 60 C?

6. The melting point of the alloy of another thermal overload relay is 231 C. If this relay trips at 52 amperes in an ambient temperature of 20 C, at what current will it trip in an ambient temperature of 60 C?

7. If a thermal overload relay is found to trip at 50 amperes in an ambient temperature of 25 C, and at 40 amperes in an ambient temperature of 50 C, at what current will it trip in an ambient temperature of 10 C?

8. A direct-current contactor and an alternating-current contactor are mounted side by side, and their coils are energized continuously at rated voltage for 1 hour. The temperature rise of both coils is the same. The next day a second test is made, the coils being energized intermittently. At the end of an hour the temperature rise of both coils is again found to be the same. Have the contactors been operated the same number of times? If not, which has operated the greater number of times? Explain the answer.

9. A 110-volt 60-cycle coil for an alternating-current contactor has 230 turns of wire. Approximately how many turns will be required in a coil to operate on 440 volts, 25 cycles?

10. A number of tests of a certain thermal overload heater-coil design show that the average tripping current is 15.2 amperes. What is the heater rating? If it is desired to allow a motor to run at 15 per cent overload, but to protect it on any overload of more than 25 per cent, what is the range of motor full-load currents for which this heater is suitable?

15

AUTOMATIC ACCELERATING METHODS
FOR ALTERNATING-CURRENT MOTORS

The problem of finding a suitable means of obtaining automatic acceleration for an alternating-current motor arises principally in connection with the slip-ring motor. Most of the squirrel-cage motors are connected directly to the supply lines. When primary-resistance starting, autotransformer starting, or part-winding starting is used, there is ordinarily only one step of acceleration, which is controlled by a timing relay. This is also true of controllers for synchronous motors. It is only the slip-ring motor controller which is likely to have two or more steps of acceleration.

The most commonly used methods of controlling the acceleration of slip-ring motors are:

1. Timing relays operated by the contactors of the controller.
2. Timing relays operated by their own magnets.
3. Inductive time-limit acceleration.
4. Condenser-timed acceleration.
5. Series relays.
6. Frequency relays.

Timing Relays. Figure 159 shows the connections for a controller having three contactors which commutate resistors connected in the rotor circuit of a slip-ring motor. When the start button is pressed, the contactor M closes, connecting the stator to the supply lines. A timing relay is mechanically connected to contactor M so that, when M closes, the action of the timing relay is started. After the predetermined time delay, the contacts of the timing relay close, energizing the coil of acceleration contactor $1A$. A second timing relay is operated by the closing of $1A$, and the contacts of this relay close to energize the coil of accelerating contactor $2A$. In a similar manner, any desired number of accelerating contactors may be controlled to close in sequence, and with any desired time delay between them. Figure 160 shows one of the timing relays.

Magnetically Operated Timing Relays. Sometimes mechanical operation of a timing relay by a contactor is undesirable. The contactor may not have the ability to operate the relay and still operate itself properly, or the contactor may have to operate several extra electric interlocks, and so be unable to operate a timing relay also. It then becomes necessary to equip the timing relay with a magnet of its own. The connections for an arrangement of this kind are shown in Fig. 161. Interlocks on the line contactor M provide a circuit to energize the

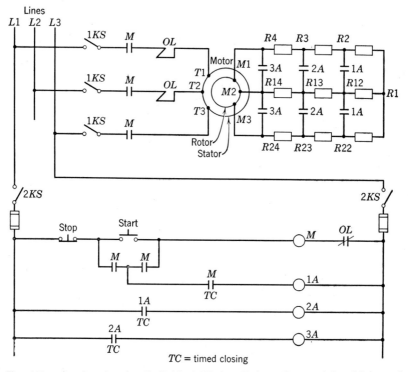

Fig. 159.   Acceleration by Individual Timing Relays Operated by Main and Accelerating Contactors.

coil of timing relay $1TR$, which, after a time delay, closes its contacts and provides a circuit to energize the coil of accelerating contactor $1A$. When $1A$ closes, its electric interlock sets up the circuit for the coil of timing relay $2TR$, and, after time delay, for the coil of accelerating contactor $2A$. The sequence may be continued for any desired number of accelerating contactors. This arrangement is a little more costly than the method of mechanically operating the timing relays.

Inductive Time-limit Acceleration.   The advantages of inductive time-limit acceleration are explained in Chapter 6, and these advantages apply to alternating-current controllers also. Of course, direct current is necessary for the operating of the inductive-delay mechanism.

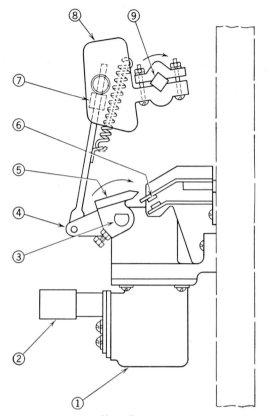

Normally open,
timed closing,
instantaneous opening

Item	Description of Part
1	Dashpot
2	Check valve for adjusting timing
3	Relay shaft
4	Operating arm on relay
5	Cam which operates relay contacts
6	Relay contacts
7	Connector lever adjusting nut
8	Lever mounted on shaft
9	Contactor shaft

FIG. 160. Mechanically Operated Timing Relay.

If the accelerating contactors themselves are of the inductive-delay type, having one coil to close them and another coil to hold them open during the timing period, then the closing coil must also be operated by direct current. If the closing coil were operated by alternating

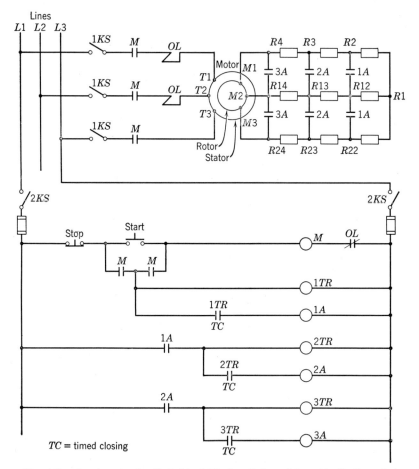

FIG. 161. Acceleration by Individual Timing Relays, Magnetically Operated.

current, a very high current would flow through it while the contactor was prevented from closing, and the coil would probably burn out. The accelerating contactors therefore have direct-current magnets and coils, but have the contacts and arc-extinguishing blowout magnets arranged to handle alternating current. The direct current which is required is obtained by the use of a rectifier. Figure 162 shows a controller of this type. Although the electric circuit appears a little complicated, actually the controller has a minimum of moving parts, and not many electric interlock contacts, so that it is well suited for use in places where there may be heavy accumulations of dirt, as, for example, on cranes in steel mills.

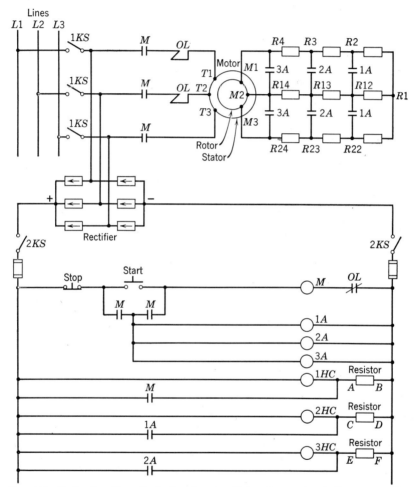

FIG. 162. Inductive Time-limit Acceleration Using Rotor-circuit Contactors Operated from a Rectifier.

When the line contactor M is closed, its electric interlock provides a circuit to energize the closing coils of all of the accelerating contactors, but they are prevented from closing because their holding-out coils are also energized. These holding coils are connected directly to the direct-current supply so that they are energized before the starting button is pressed. This insures that they are at full strength. When M closes, a second electric interlock short circuits the holding coil of accelerating contactor $1A$. Being an inductive magnetic circuit, the strength of $1HC$ dies away slowly, and, after the desired time delay, $1HC$ releases and permits $1A$ to close. Then the electric interlock of $1A$ short circuits the holding coil of contactor $2A$, and, in the manner described, the accelerating contactors are closed one after another in sequence and with time delay. The resistors in the circuits of the holding coils prevent line short circuits when the holding coils are short circuited.

Capacitor-timed Acceleration. If separate direct-current timing relays are used, it becomes possible to use standard alternating-current accelerating contactors, and to operate them from the alternating-current supply. The rectifier then has only to supply direct current for the timing relays. These advantages must be weighed against the disadvantage of adding the timing relays to the controller. The complication of the circuit is about the same. Figure 163 shows a controller of this type. In the off position of the controller the coils of the timing relays are all energized through the rectifier, and the contacts of the relays, $1CT$, $2CT$, and $3CT$, are open. These relays are of the inductive-delay type. When their coils are energized, their magnets close immediately, opening the electric contacts. When the circuit to the coil of one of the relays is opened, the coil is not de-energized at once, but is kept energized for a predetermined time by the discharge of the capacitor which is connected across the coil (see Fig. 58). When the contactor M closes, its electric interlocks provide a partial circuit to the coils of the accelerating contactors, but the circuit is not completed because contacts $1CT$, $2CT$, and $3CT$ are open. A second interlock on M opens the circuit to the coil of timing relay $1CT$, and, after a time delay, contact $1CT$ closes. The coil of $1A$ is now energized, and $1A$ closes. Its interlock opens the circuit to the coil of timing relay $2CT$, which, after time delay, closes the circuit to coil $2A$. Similarly, any desired number of accelerating contactors may be closed in sequence.

Series Relays. It is occasionally desirable to use current-limit acceleration in a control for a slip-ring motor, particularly where the motor is a large one and the starting time is long. A large continuous-rolling mill equipped with a heavy flywheel is a good example of such a drive. Such a mill might require a minute or more to come up to speed, and it might be desirable that the motor accelerate as far as it will on each step of the control, before the next step of resistor is cut out of circuit.

Current-responsive relays of the series type are used to control the acceleration (see Fig. 153). The connections for a series-relay con-

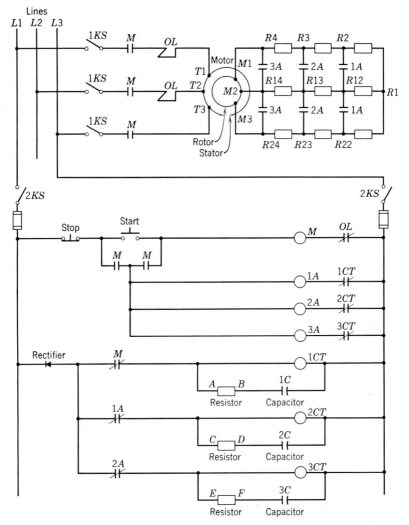

FIG. 163. Method of Timing Acceleration by Capacitor Discharge, with Timing Relays Operated from a Rectifier.

troller are shown in Fig. 164. The series relays have three coils because a three-phase magnetic structure for a relay of this kind is more quiet in operation, and also more positive and accurate than a single-phase magnet.

The initial current inrush flows through the resistor and the coils of relay $SR1$. The relay operates in the same manner as the direct-current relay, opening its contacts before the main contactor interlocks close. The accelerating contactors are of the double-pole type, so that, when $1A$ closes, a step of resistance in each phase is short-circuited. The coils of relay $SR1$ are also short-circuited, and those of relay $SR2$ are connected into circuit. This relay controls contactor

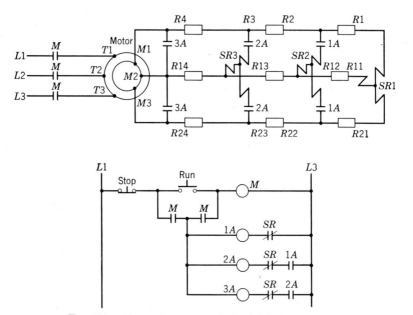

FIG. 164.   Alternating-current Series-relay Acceleration.

$2A$ and, in like manner, the other accelerators are closed, until finally all the resistance is cut out of the circuit by the closing of $3A$.

These relays are not so sensitive as the direct-current series relay, and they require a wider range between the inrush current which opens them and the current at which they are set to close.

Series relays may also be connected in the primary circuit to govern secondary contactors. Such relays are of a different construction as they must be insulated for line voltage. It will be noted that there is practically no voltage between coils of the relays of Fig. 164. The pilot contacts, of course, must be adequately insulated from the coils.

Acceleration by Frequency Relays. When a wound-rotor motor is started, the voltage and frequency at the rotor slip rings are high. The frequency is the same as that of the power supply, and the actual value of the voltage will depend on the design of the rotor winding. As the motor accelerates, voltage and frequency decrease together, until at synchronous speed they are theoretically zero. These characteristics may be used to control the motor acceleration by employing

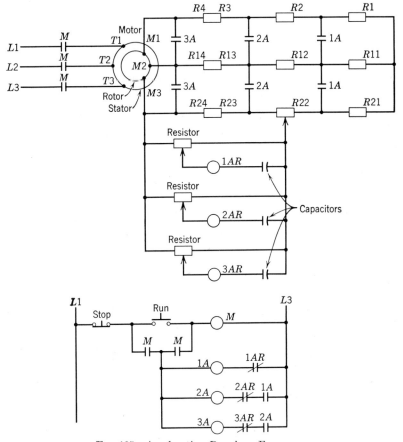

FIG. 165. Acceleration Based on Frequency.

a group of normally closed relays which are arranged to close their contacts at definite values of voltage and frequency. The relays are then used to control accelerating contactors which commutate resistance in the rotor circuit. Figure 165 shows how a potentiometer resistor is connected into the rotor circuit, and the relay coil connected in series with a capacitor, and across the resistor. The combination of resistance, inductance, and capacitance results in a resonant circuit, which means that there is a definite value of frequency at which a relatively very high current will flow. The relays can therefore be made to operate very positively and accurately at a given desired frequency. At the starting frequency the relays open at once. As the frequency decreases, the current in the relay coil increases, until the critical frequency is approached. The current then rises rapidly to double its value, or higher, and, when the critical frequency is passed, current decreases rapidly. The relays are set to close at the desired point on the decreasing current. The nature of the relay characteristic may be seen from the following test values for the current in the relay coil.

Frequency	Amperes
60	0.1
55	0.14
50	0.40
45	0.22
40	0.05
30	0.02

Calculation of Accelerating Time. It is often necessary to calculate the time which will be required to accelerate or decelerate rotating machinery, when the available torque is known, or to calculate the torque which will be required to accelerate or decelerate in a desired time.

If the torque available for accelerating or decelerating is constant throughout the speed range being considered, the time required may be calculated from the equation

$$\text{Time in seconds} = \frac{WR^2(N_2 - N_1)}{308} \times \frac{1}{T} \qquad [1]$$

where W = weight of the rotating part in pounds.
R = radius of gyration of the rotating part in feet.
N_1 = the lower speed in revolutions per minute.
N_2 = the higher speed in revolutions per minute.
T = accelerating or decelerating torque in pound-feet.

In calculations involving motor-driven machines, it is often convenient to express the torque in per cent of the motor full-load rated torque. The equation then becomes

$$\text{Time in seconds} = 0.62 \times \frac{WR^2}{H} \times \frac{(N_2 - N_1)}{1000} \times \frac{S}{1000} \times \frac{100}{T} \qquad [2]$$

In this equation,

W = weight of the rotating part in pounds.

R = radius of gyration of the rotating part in feet.

H = horsepower of the motor.

N_1 = the lower speed in revolutions per minute.

N_2 = the higher speed in revolutions per minute.

S = speed of the motor at full load in revolutions per minute.

T = accelerating torque in per cent of full-load rated torque.

It should be noted that, in any of these calculations, the rotating part is assumed to be driven directly from the motor shaft, and to be rotating at the same speed as the motor. If there is gearing between the rotating part and the motor, this must be taken into account, and the figure used for the WR^2 of the rotating part must be adjusted to a WR^2 equivalent to direct connection to the motor shaft.

$$\text{Equivalent } WR^2 = WR^2 \times \left(\frac{N}{N_b}\right)^2 \qquad [3]$$

where W = weight of the rotating part in pounds.

R = radius of gyration of the rotating part in feet.

N = speed of the rotating part in revolutions per minute.

N_b = speed of the motor shaft in revolutions per minute.

By the use of equation 3, it is possible to calculate the WR^2 of a system including several rotating parts, which are rotating at different speeds. The WR^2 of each part is adjusted to its equivalent WR^2, and the equivalent WR^2 figures are added together to obtain the WR^2 of the whole system.

Equations 1 and 2 apply when the accelerating or decelerating torque is constant, as, for example, when a mechanical brake is used to stop a rotating system. When a motor is used to accelerate a machine, or when dynamic braking is used for stopping, the torque in most cases is not constant. The equations will still apply if the term $1/T$ is replaced by the term $(1/T)$ average, where this term is the average of the reciprocals of the torques available during the accelerating or decelerating period. It is relatively easy to calculate the average of the torques available, particularly since, in most cases, the current peaks during the acceleration are equal. Sufficient accuracy is usually obtained if the speed-torque curves are assumed to be straight lines. However, if the average of T_1 and T_2 is calculated, and this value used in the equations instead of the average of the reciprocals of the torques, a very appreciable error will result. The time calculated could easily be incorrect by 25 per cent. The average of the reciprocals of the torques may be determined from the average of T_1 and T_2 by multiplying the latter by a factor K. The equation for the factor K is

$$K = \frac{2\left(\dfrac{T_1}{T_2} - 1\right)}{\left(\dfrac{T_1}{T_2} + 1\right)\log_e \dfrac{T_1}{T_2}} \qquad [4]$$

where T_1 = highest value of the accelerating torque.

T_2 = lowest value of the accelerating torque.

The use of factor K results in an equivalent torque T_e, which may be used in equations 1 and 2 with accuracy.

$$T_e = KT \qquad [5]$$

T_e = equivalent torque.

T = average of T_1 and T_2.

Figure 166 is a curve showing values for the factor K, plotted against values of T_1/T_2.

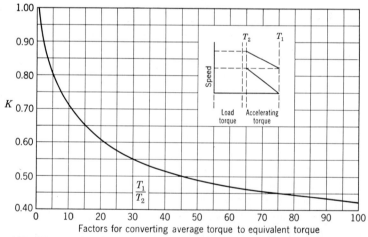

FIG. 166. Factors for Converting Average Torque to Equivalent Torque. (Reprinted by permission from *Factory Management & Maintenance*, Feb. 1937)

If the values of T_1 and T_2, or either of them, vary on the different speed points of a controller, it is necessary to calculate the accelerating time on each step, and then add the times together.

To illustrate the method of using these equations, consider a 100-horsepower 1750-rpm motor which is to accelerate a constant-torque load having a total WR^2, for motor and load, of 500 lb-ft². The controller limits the torque peaks to 150 per cent of motor full-load torque, and on each step the motor accelerates to a speed where the motor torque is 5 per cent greater than the load torque.

The average of the accelerating torques = T =

$$\frac{50 + 5}{2} = 27.5 \text{ per cent}$$

$$\text{The ratio } \frac{T_1}{T_2} = \frac{50}{5} = 10$$

From the curve, $K = 0.71$

From equation 5, $T_e = 0.71 \times 27.5 = 19.5$ per cent

From equation 2,

$$\text{Time in seconds} = 0.62 \times \frac{500}{100} \times \frac{(1750 - 0)}{1000} \times \frac{1750}{1000} \times \frac{100}{19.5} = 48.6$$

If the average torque of 27.5 per cent had been used, the calculated time would have been 34.5 seconds, representing an error of 29 per cent.

The radii of gyration of a few frequently encountered shapes are given here for convenience.

Solid cylinder about its own axis, $R^2 = \dfrac{r^2}{2}$

where r = the radius of the cylinder.

Solid cylinder about an axis through its center, $R^2 = \dfrac{L + 3r^2}{12}$

where L = length of the cylinder.
    r = the radius of the end.

Solid cylinder about axis at one end, $R^2 = \dfrac{4L^2 + 3r^2}{12}$

Solid cylinder about an outside axis,

$$R^2 = \frac{4L^2 + 3r^2 + 12dL + 12d^2}{12}$$

where d = distance from center of gyration to bottom of cylinder.

Hollow cylinder about its own axis, $R^2 = \dfrac{r_1{}^2 + r_2{}^2}{2}$

where r_1 = the inner radius of the rim.
    r_2 = the outer radius of the rim.

References

D. C. Wright, "Frequency Relays and Motor Acceleration for Steel Mill Control," *Iron and Steel Engineer*, May, 1939.

J. D. Leitch, "Two New Methods of Accelerating Electric Motors Automatically," *Transactions AIEE*, 1941, Vol. 60, p. 487.

M. N. Halberg, "How Long to Speed Up or Slow Down?", *Factory Management and Maintenance*, February, 1937.

The author is indebted to Mr. Halberg, and to *Factory Management and Maintenance*, for permission to reprint some of the material in this article.

Problems

1. Draw an elementary diagram for the main and control circuits of a controller for a slip-ring motor, including the following:

Three-pole line knife switch.
Two-pole control knife switch and fuses.
2 three-pole reversing contactors.
3 overload relays.
4 two-pole accelerating contactors.
Resistor.
Low-voltage protective relay.
Master controller having five speeds in each direction.
Mechanically operated time-relay acceleration.

2. Draw an elementary diagram for the main and control circuits of a controller for a slip-ring motor, including the following:

Three-pole line knife switch.
Two-pole control knife switch and fuses.
Three-pole line contactor.
3 overload relays.
2 two-pole accelerating contactors.
2 magnetically-operated timing relays.
Resistor.
Jogging relay.
Start, stop, and jog pushbuttons.

3. Draw an elementary diagram for the main and control circuits of a controller for a slip-ring motor, including the following:

2 three-pole reversing contactors.
3 overload relays.
3 two-pole accelerating contactors.
3 series relays.
Low-voltage protective relay.
Resistor.
Master controller having four speeds in each direction.
Limit switches for slowdown and stopping in each direction.

4. A 50-horsepower 440-volt 61-ampere 3-phase 60-cycle slip-ring motor has rotor characteristics of 200 volts across the slip rings at standstill, and 118 amperes per ring when running at full load. During acceleration the current peaks are 210 per cent of rated current, and the valleys occur at 120 per cent of rated current. The resistor is in three steps, and the time on the steps is in the ratio 55–30–15. The total accelerating time is 20 seconds.

(a) With timed acceleration, what is the setting of the timing relays?

(b) With frequency acceleration, what is the setting of the frequency relays?

(c) With series-relay acceleration, what is the closing setting of the relays?

(d) With inductive acceleration, what is the setting of the relays?

(e) With series-relay acceleration, what is the maximum theoretical opening setting of the relays?

5. A 75-horsepower 550-volt 75-ampere 3-phase 60-cycle 1150-rpm slip-ring motor is used to drive a flywheel having an outer radius of 3 feet and an inner radius of 2 feet and weighing 200 pounds. The accelerating peak torques are 210 per cent of rated torque, and the accelerating contactors are set to close at 110 per cent of rated torque. What is the WR^2 of the flywheel?

6. How long will it take the motor of problem 5 to accelerate the flywheel to full speed, neglecting the WR^2 of the motor itself?

7. If the WR^2 of the motor is 118 lb-ft², how long will it take the motor to accelerate the flywheel?

8. If this motor could be supplied with a controller having a very large number of steps, so that the accelerating peak torque could be kept essentially constant at 210 per cent of rated torque, how long would it take to accelerate motor and load?

9. A 250-horsepower 440-volt 302-ampere 3-phase 60-cycle 850-rpm slip-ring motor is used to drive a load having a WR^2 of 800 lb-ft². The motor WR^2 is 900 lb-ft². The controller has five speed points with peak torques and contactor closing points, as given below. Calculate the time required to accelerate motor and load.

	Contactor Closing Point in per cent of Rated Torque	Peak Torque in per cent of Rated Torque
Initial	...	125
Contactor 1A	100	150
Contactor 2A	100	200
Contactor 3A	110	250
Contactor 4A	110	300

10. A 35-horsepower 550-volt 35-ampere 3-phase 60-cycle 1750-rpm slip-ring motor has a WR^2 of 40 lb-ft². It is geared to a solid flywheel having a WR^2 of 200 lb-ft². The gear ratio is 5 to 1, so that the flywheel speed is 350 rpm. What is the equivalent WR^2 of the system?

11. How long will it take the motor to accelerate the system, if the torque peaks are limited to 166 per cent of rated torque, and the accelerating contactors close at 105 per cent of rated torque?

12. What will be the horsepower required of a motor which will accelerate this system in the same time, if the flywheel is directly connected to the motor shaft?

13. A large mill consists of two rolls which are solid cylinders having a radius of 18 inches, and weighing 2000 pounds each. The mill is driven by a 150-horsepower 850-rpm motor, geared in the ratio of 5 to 1. The WR^2 of the motor is 415 lb-ft². Dynamic braking is applied to the motor to stop the mill, the initial braking torque being six times the rated torque of the motor. How long will it take to stop the rolls?

14. How far will a point on the surface of the roll travel in the time between the pressing of the stop button and the stopping of the roll?

15. A factory wishes to know the WR^2 of a machine which has a number of rotating parts. There are no drawings nor data available. An engineer gears the machine to a 25-horsepower 440-volt 32-ampere 1150-rpm slip-ring motor, having rotor characteristics of 300 volts and 40 amperes. The gear ratio used is 1 to 1. The machine is brought up to speed, and the following readings are taken:

Rotor peak currents	84 amperes
Rotor current when contactors close	44 amperes
Rotor current when running	40 amperes
Time to accelerate	15 seconds

What is the WR^2 of the machine and motor, if the motor torque varies directly with the rotor current?

16. If the rotor current when running had been 20 amperes, what would be the WR^2 of the machine and motor?

17. If the running current is 20 amperes, the factory will probably decide to use a 15-horsepower motor to drive the machine. If the controller is designed to give the same percentage accelerating currents as the controller in problem 15, and the 15-horsepower motor has a WR^2 of 13 lb-ft² less than the 25-horsepower motor, what will the accelerating time be?

18. An extractor has a WR^2 of 2000 lb-ft². It is to be accelerated to a speed of 1800 rpm by a constant torque of 100 pound-feet. Calculate the time required to accelerate.

19. Calculate the time required for the extractor of problem 18 to accelerate from rest to a speed of 100 rpm.

20. Calculate the time required for the extractor of problem 18 to accelerate from a speed of 1700 rpm to a speed of 1800 rpm.

21. Calculate the time required to decelerate the extractor by dynamic braking, the initial braking torque being 600 pound-feet and the final braking torque being zero.

16

THE POLYPHASE SQUIRREL-CAGE MOTOR

Because of its mechanical simplicity, the squirrel-cage motor is ideal for constant-speed applications. It can safely be installed in out-of-the-way places or in places where gas, dirt, or moisture-laden atmospheric conditions prevail, and under these conditions it will perform satisfactorily with little attention. Since the motor has no commu-

FIG. 167. Disassembled View of Wagner Type-CP Totally Enclosed Fan-cooled Motor. (Courtesy Wagner Electric Corporation)

tator and no brushes, and is strongly constructed, it is able to stand high inrush currents without injury, and it is also easy to service and maintain.

Since both the stator and the rotor of a squirrel-cage motor carry alternating current, the motor is non-synchronous, and its speed is not strictly constant. The speed will vary with the load on the motor and with the frequency of the power supply. However, the speed is essentially constant, and the motor does not lend itself readily to speed variation or regulation.

Construction. Figure 167 shows the construction of a squirrel-cage motor. The stator, or stationary member, is a laminated framework into which are wound wire coils for connection to the power supply. The laminations are made of high-grade annealed sheet iron, and the outer framework usually of fabricated steel plate. The rotor also is a laminated structure, having slots into which copper or aluminum bars are fitted. All the bars are connected together at each end by metal end rings. Blowers are used on each end of the rotor to supply cooling air, and air passages are provided in the larger rotors to permit circulation of the air through the rotor iron. The slots in the rotor are usually slightly skewed to reduce magnetic vibration and to insure a uniform torque for all rotor positions. The end plates of the motor, which house the bearings for the shaft, are usually cast of iron or steel. The motor takes its name from the similarity of the rotor construction to that of a squirrel cage. Since there are no brushes, no commutator, and no wire windings, it follows that no connections can be made to the rotor.

Rotating Field. When polyphase alternating current is applied to a stator winding, the resultant magnetomotive force is the vector sum of those phases. The resultant field rotates around the stator at a speed depending on the frequency of the supply voltage. This is shown in Fig. 168, in which the top sketch represents a three-phase two-pole stator winding, the center sketch shows the relation of the phase currents, and the bottom sketch shows the vector relationship.

Referring to the top sketch, winding 1 will create a magnetic field in a north-south direction, varying from a maximum north pole directly north to a maximum south pole directly north. Winding 2 will create a field 120 degrees out of phase with winding 1, having a maximum north pole 30 degrees south of west. Winding 3 will create a field 240 degrees out of phase with winding 1, having a maximum north pole 30 degrees south of east. Referring now to the center sketch, and calling the north direction the positive, or north, pole, it is evident that at point A in the cycle phase 1 is at its maximum positive value, while phase 2 and phase 3 are each at half of their maximum negative value. Adding these vectorially shows that the resultant north pole is at a point in the winding directly north.

At point B the conditions have changed so that the resultant north pole is 60 degrees west of north. At point C in the cycle, the north pole is at 30 degrees south of west, and at point D it is directly south. In the remaining half of the total cycle, the north pole continues to move around the stator winding, until it has returned to its starting point, directly north. Points A, B, C, etc., have been selected for easy calculation. Measurements made from the curves at any point will show the position of the north pole at that point. The demonstration therefore shows that for each complete cycle of the alternating current the stator field rotates 360 electrical degrees, which in the two-pole machine is also 360 mechanical degrees around the winding. If the

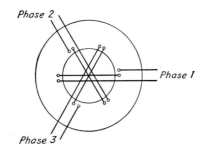

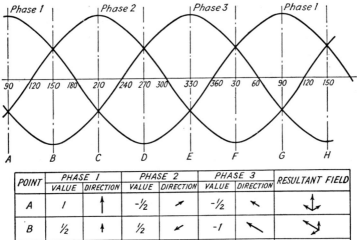

POINT	PHASE 1		PHASE 2		PHASE 3		RESULTANT FIELD
	VALUE	DIRECTION	VALUE	DIRECTION	VALUE	DIRECTION	
A	1	↑	-½	↗	-½	↖	↓
B	½	↑	½	↙	-1	↖	↘
C	-½	↓	1	↙	-½	↖	↗
D	-1	↓	½	↙	½	↘	↑
E	-½	↓	-½	↗	1	↘	↖
F	½	↑	-1	↗	½	↘	↙

Fig. 168. Rotation of a Three-phase Motor Field.

power is supplied at 60 cycles, the speed of field rotation will be 3600 rpm. The three individual phase windings may be located in only a portion of the stator frame, with one or more additional sets of windings located in the rest of the frame, which is just another way of saying that the stator may be wound with two, four, six, or more poles. Since the magnetic field rotates 360 electrical degrees for each cycle and passes through one pair of poles in that period, it is evident that with a four-pole machine the field will rotate completely around the stator in two cycles. The general equation for the speed of rotation is

$$\text{Speed in rpm} = \frac{60 \times \text{Frequency}}{\text{Pairs of poles}}$$

Motor Speed. When power is applied to the stator of the motor, and a rotating field is set up, the squirrel-cage structure of the rotor becomes essentially the secondary of a transformer. A voltage is induced in the rotor bars, its value being determined by the ratio of the stator and rotor turns to the rate of change of the field flux. Current will flow in the rotor bars, in an amount limited by the rotor impedance, and the rotor will be magnetized. As the stator field revolves, the rotor field will be impelled to follow it, and the rotor will start to turn. Considering the two-pole 60-cycle machine, with the rotor stationary, the rate of change of the field cut by any given rotor bar will be 3600 times per minute. As the rotor speeds up, the rate at which the field is cut by a given bar becomes less and less, with consequent reduction in the induced voltage and the generated current. The maximum theoretical speed, called the synchronous speed, is reached when the rotor is revolving at the same speed as the stator field, or 3600 rpm. At that speed there would be no field flux cut by the rotor bars, no induced voltage, and no generated current. There would also be no torque, as the rotor would not be magnetic without current flowing in it, and for this reason synchronous speed can never quite be attained. Some torque is required, even without load on the motor, to keep the rotor turning against friction and windage. The difference between the actual speed and the synchronous speed will be just enough to permit the rotor conductors to cut enough field flux to induce the voltage and current required to produce the necessary torque. This speed difference is called slip.

Standard polyphase squirrel-cage motors are built for 110, 220, 440, 550, and 2200 volts, and for 25 and 60 cycles. The standard speeds available are given in Table 24.

Motor Torque. The motor torque is determined by the design of the machine and in particular by the resistance of the rotor conductors. The standard motor is built with a relatively low-resistance rotor and has a relatively low starting torque and low running slip. A motor built with a relatively high-resistance rotor will have a higher starting torque but will also have a higher slip. Such a motor is called a high-torque motor.

TABLE 24

POLYPHASE SQUIRREL-CAGE MOTORS

Number of Poles	Speed	
	25 Cycles	60 Cycles
2	1500	3600
4	750	1800
6	500	1200
8	...	900
10	...	720
12	...	600
16	...	450

Figure 169 shows typical characteristic curves of a standard squirrel-cage motor. The starting torque is shown as about 145 per cent

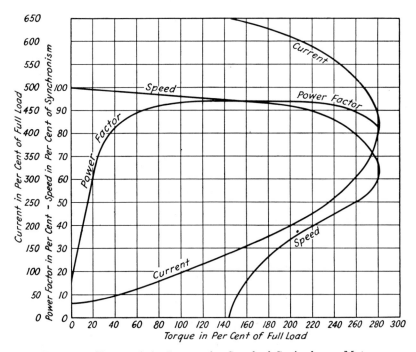

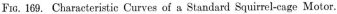

FIG. 169. Characteristic Curves of a Standard Squirrel-cage Motor.

of the normal full-load, full-speed value. It may vary, in different motors, from 110 to 175 per cent. The maximum torque available, called the pull-out torque, is shown as 280 per cent. This value may vary from 200 to 300 per cent of normal. The slip at 100 per cent torque is shown as about 3 per cent of synchronous speed. The inrush current obtained when starting the motor on full voltage, by direct connection to the power supply, is usually from six to ten times full-load running current but may be higher if an exceptionally low-resistance rotor is used.

Figure 170 shows typical characteristic curves of a high-torque squirrel-cage motor. The starting torque is shown as about 200 per cent of the normal full-load, full-speed value. The pullout torque is

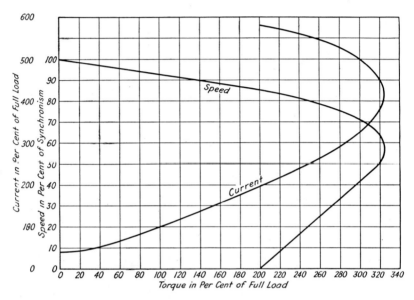

FIG. 170. Characteristic Curves of a High-torque Squirrel-cage Motor.

shown as about 325 per cent, and the slip at full load is about 7 per cent of synchronous speed. Because of the higher rotor resistance, the starting inrush current is relatively low, usually being from 400 to 500 per cent of the normal full-load value. The higher-resistance rotor, therefore, has the advantage of giving a greater starting torque with a lower starting current. The higher running slip, however, results in higher heat losses in the rotor and also causes the motor speed to vary more with changes in the load.

Double-cage Motor. In order to obtain the advantages of both the low-resistance rotor and the high-resistance rotor, motors are built with two squirrel-cage windings embedded in the same rotor core. Such a motor is called a double-cage motor. The rotor bars are placed in the same slots, one layer above the other. The inner squirrel cage is designed to have low resistance and high reactance, and the outer one has high resistance and low reactance. At standstill the rotor current has line frequency, and the larger part of it flows through the low-reactance outer winding. As the motor accelerates, the frequency of the rotor current decreases and the reactance of the inner cage becomes less effective, so that a constantly increasing proportion of the current flows through the inner cage. The total torque is the sum of the torques of the two windings.

Figure 171 illustrates the characteristics of the motor. The starting torque will be from 150 to 250 per cent of the normal full-load

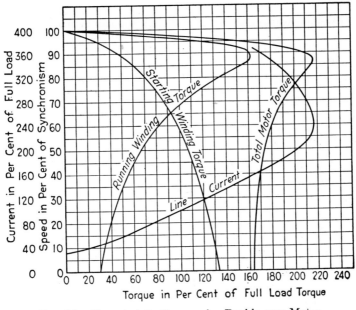

FIG. 171. Characteristic Curves of a Double-cage Motor.

running torque, and the maximum pull-out torque will be from 175 to 225 per cent of normal torque. The slip will be from 3 to 5 per cent of synchronous speed. The starting currents of a motor of this type are low enough to permit the motor to be started directly from the line in sizes up to 40 horsepower without exceeding the limitations set by power companies. Above this size, the inrush, when starting directly from the line, will not exceed that of a standard motor started on 80 per cent voltage.

Starting Methods. Theoretically, there is no reason why any squirrel-cage motor could not be started by connecting it directly to the power lines. If this were done, the inrush current would be from four to ten times the normal running current of the motor. This inrush would not damage the motor, but it might cause too great a disturbance on the power line. It might also impose too great a shock on the machine being started. It is often necessary, therefore, to use reduced voltage starting.

The five common methods of starting squirrel-cage motors are:

1. Across-the-line starting, which connects the motor direct to full line voltage by means of a manually operated switch or a magnetic contactor.

2. Autotransformer starting, which starts the motor at reduced voltage from an autotransformer and then connects it to line voltage after the motor has accelerated.

3. Primary resistor starting, which introduces a fixed or variable resistor in the primary of the motor during the accelerating period and then short-circuits this resistor to apply full voltage to the motor after it has accelerated.

4. Star-delta starting, which necessitates special motor connections. This method gives approximately 58 per cent of line voltage at the motor terminals, 58 per cent full-load current, and 35 per cent torque.

5. Part-winding starting, with which a part of the motor winding is connected to the lines as a first starting step, and, after a time delay, the remainder of the motor winding is connected to the lines.

In addition to these five methods, starting through impedance is sometimes practiced; but, since such starters have very low power factor, relatively very few are used.

Across-the-line Starting. The advantages of across-the-line starters are evident in that they are simple, easy to install and maintain, and inexpensive. Their disadvantage is that the motor draws an inrush current of four to ten times full-load current. With a small motor this does not make any difference, nor does it with a large motor if the power supply is adequate. However, most power companies object to the line disturbance caused by connecting large induction motors directly to the line. The power-generating companies have developed rules and values as suggested practice covering the installation of squirrel-cage motors on central-station distributing systems.

The limits of starting current are generally such that starting devices will be required for motors above 5 horsepower, where the installation consists of a single motor of that size. Instances may occur wherein it is necessary to use a starting device on 5-horsepower motors.

Manual Starters. Ratings for across-the-line manually operated starters (including reversing), with or without overload relay or other auxiliary devices, in any enclosure, for use with any type of induction motor, are given in Table 25.

Several kinds of devices are used for manual motor starters. Where a small compact starter without overload relay is desired, a suitably constructed three-pole snap switch in sizes 00 and 0 is satisfactory.

TABLE 25

RATINGS OF MANUAL LINE STARTERS

Size	Horsepower at 110 volts, Three Phase	Horsepower at 220 volts, Three Phase	Horsepower at 440–550 volts, Three Phase
0	1½	2	2
1	3	5	7½

In sizes 0 and 1, starters are available which are essentially like a magnetic contactor but without the operating magnet and coil. The contactor mechanism is arranged to be closed and opened manually by pushbuttons mounted in the cover of the starter and operating through a positive make-and-break toggle mechanism. These starters are provided with overload relays and are free-tripping, so that the mechanism cannot be held closed on overload.

Controllers of the drum type are widely used, especially in the smaller sizes. They are available for separate mounting on any suitable surface, and also without cover and with head plates suitable for mounting in a cavity in a machine. This type has a pistol-grip handle, which turns an insulated cylinder on which contact segments are mounted. The segments engage stationary contact fingers mounted in the drum frame. They can be arranged with a self-centering spring if it is desired to make contact only as long as the lever is held in the on position. They are also used with a rope drive instead of a handle for such applications as floor-operated cranes and hoists.

Magnetic Starters. The NEMA standard ratings for magnetic across-the-line starters are given in Table 26. The horsepower ratings

TABLE 26

RATINGS OF MAGNETIC ACROSS-THE-LINE STARTERS

Size Numbers	8-hour Open Rating of Contactor, amperes	Horsepower at 110 volts, Three Phase	Horsepower at 220 volts, Three Phase	Horsepower at 440–550 volts, Three Phase
00	..	¾	1	1
0	15	1½	2	2
1	25	3	5	7½
2	50	7½	15	25
3	100	15	30	50
4	150	25	50	100
5	300	..	100	200
6	600	..	200	400
7	900	..	300	600
8	1350	..	450	900
9	2500	..	800	1600

apply also to two-phase three-wire starters, but the current ratings on this type of power supply are reduced to 90 per cent of the three-phase ratings. The ratings apply to all starting, reversing, and throw-over contactors furnished with any type of enclosure, either with or without disconnecting means or other accessories.

When the controller is subject to rapid jogging service or frequent plug-stop service, and so must repeatedly open the stalled-motor current, it is recommended that the starter ratings be reduced in accordance with Table 27. Rapid service is defined as being in excess of five operations a minute.

TABLE 27

Ratings for Jogging Service

Size Numbers	8-hour Open Rating of Contactor, amperes	Horsepower at 110 volts, Three Phase	Horsepower at 220 volts, Three Phase	Horsepower at 440–550 volts, Three Phase
00	..	$\frac{1}{3}$	$\frac{1}{2}$	$\frac{1}{2}$
0	15	$\frac{3}{4}$	1	1
1	25	2	3	5
2	50	5	10	15
3	100	10	20	30
4	150	15	30	60
5	300	..	75	150
6	600	..	150	300

In their simplest and most widely used form, magnetic line starters consist of a three- or four-pole magnetic contactor and a thermal overload relay (see Fig. 172). These devices are mounted in a suitable enclosing case, which may be of the general-purpose sheet-metal construction or may be dust-tight, water-tight, explosion-resisting, or whatever may be required by the installation conditions. Start and stop pushbuttons may be mounted in the cover of the case; then the stop button is usually combined with the overload resetting device. A separately mounted start-stop pushbutton may also be used, and the case mount only the reset button. When both local and remote control are desired, a small three-position switch is mounted in the starter cover to give local control, off, and remote control. The starters are also built in skeleton form, without enclosure, for mounting in a cavity in a machine.

The control circuit is very simple, since it involves only energizing the contactor coil when the start button is pressed and de-energizing it when the stop button is pressed or when the overload relay trips. With a three-wire momentary-contact type of pushbutton, low-voltage protection is obtained. With a two-wire snap-switch type of button, low-voltage release is obtained.

Line starters are also built with self-contained outside-operated disconnect switches. The disconnect switch may be of the knife-switch type or may consist of a set of contactor parts without the operating

Fig. 172. NEMA Size-2 Across-the-line Starter, in NEMA Type-I Enclosure. Cover Removed.

coil and manually operated. Starters are also built with self-contained outside-operated circuit breakers, which act as a disconnect device and a protection against short circuit.

All the above types of line starter are also built for reversing service. The single magnetic contactor is then replaced with a pair of mechanically interlocked contactors. As a rule, only the reset button is mounted in the cover of a reversing starter, the other buttons being separately mounted.

Line starters are made by many manufacturers. Their design is not so simple as it might appear to be, because the designer is always

THE POLYPHASE SQUIRREL-CAGE MOTOR

pulled in opposite directions by the desire to make the device as small and compact as possible and by the desire to make it readily accessible for mounting, wiring, and maintenance. However, the starters are simple, easy to service, inexpensive, and relatively trouble-free, which accounts for the fact that they are probably the most popular item of any control manufacturer's line of apparatus.

Reduced-voltage Starting. The principle of both the autotransformer starter and the primary resistance starter is to reduce the

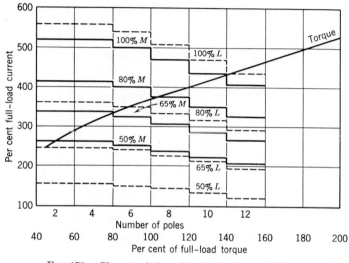

Fig. 173. Characteristics of a Squirrel-cage Motor.

voltage across the motor terminals at starting. Since the current inrush, or starting current, varies almost directly with the applied voltage, the current can be reduced by applying less than full line voltage to start. However, whereas the starting current varies almost directly with the applied voltage, the starting torque varies as the square of the applied voltage. If the applied voltage is reduced 50 per cent, the starting current will be reduced to 50 per cent but the starting torque will be reduced to 25 per cent of the full voltage value. Any starter, therefore, must be so adjusted as to give the proper compromise between the torque which is required and the current which is taken from the line. An examination of the curves in Fig. 173 will show the relation between starting current and torque. The solid curves, marked M, give the starting inrush to the motor in percentage of full-load current for average commercial motors of 2 to 12 poles. The dotted curves, marked L, give the corresponding line currents with an autotransformer starter. The torque curve gives the starting torque, in percentage of full-load torque, for different values of motor-starting current.

For example, consider a 25-horsepower 220-volt three-phase 60-cycle 1200-rpm motor driving an exhaust fan. If it were connected directly to the line, the starting current would be about 500 per cent of the full-load current. The corresponding starting torque would be about 180 per cent of full-load torque. Not nearly that much starting torque is needed; furthermore, we may assume not more than 200 per cent of full-load current to accelerate. By using the 50 per cent tap on an autotransformer starter, the starting current drawn from the line can be kept down to 150 per cent of full-load current. The corresponding inrush to the motor is 250 per cent of full-load current, giving a starting torque of about 45 per cent, which is sufficient in this case. Therefore, by using an autotransformer starter, the current drawn from the line has been reduced from 500 per cent to 150 per cent of the full-load value, keeping within the assumed limitation and still having sufficient torque to start the load.

The Autotransformer Starter. The autotransformer starter consists of two autotransformers connected in open delta, and the motor is

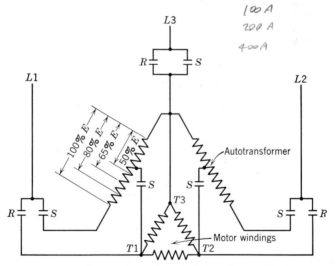

Fig. 174. Connections of an Autotransformer Starter.

connected as shown in Fig. 174. Some manufacturers use three auto-transformers, but two are more general because with two the current in the third phase is only about 15 per cent greater than in the other two phases, and this unbalance is permissible.

Three taps are usually provided, giving 50, 65, and 80 per cent of full line voltage. The motor current varies directly as the impressed voltage; the line current varies as the square of the impressed voltage.

FIG. 175. Manually Operated Autotransformer Starter.

The starting torque consequently varies directly as the line current, neglecting transformer losses. The chief characteristics of the starter as compared to other types are low line current, low power from the line, and a low power factor. A disadvantage is that the torque which is applied remains practically constant for the first step of starting and practically constant at another value for the second step, whereas with the primary resistance starter the torque varies, increasing steadily as the motor accelerates. Another disadvantage is that, in transferring from the tap on the transformer to the line voltage direct, the motor is momentarily disconnected from the line. For the above two reasons acceleration is not so smooth with the autotransformer starter as it is with the resistor type.

Figure 175 shows a manually operated autotransformer. The transformer is mounted at the top, and the contacts at the bottom. The contacts operate under oil. An overload relay is included, and also a low-voltage release magnet.

An automatic transformer starter consists of a five-pole starting contactor, a three-pole running contactor, and a thermal overload relay. The contactors are interlocked mechanically, so that only one can close at a time. A timing relay of the dashpot type is operated by the starting contactor. When the run button is pressed, the starting contactor closes, connecting the transformer to the line and the motor to the taps of the transformer. After a time interval during which the motor accelerates, the timing relay contacts close. The starting contactor is de-energized, and the running contactor energized. The motor is then connected to full line voltage. The transformer is mounted on the rear of the panel, or to the frame or enclosing case.

High-voltage transformer starters function in the same manner as those built for lower voltages. The air-break contactors are replaced by oil-immersed switches, magnetically operated. A potential transformer is included, to apply low voltage for the control circuits. If overload relays are included, as they generally are, they are energized through current transformers. The autotransformer and potential transformer are generally mounted separately.

The Primary-resistor Starter. With the primary-resistor starter the motor is connected to the line through a primary resistor, and the reduced voltage at the motor terminals is obtained by means of the voltage drop across the resistor. Accordingly, the line current is the same as the motor current, and this current, and power taken from the line are much higher than in the autotransformer starter. It follows that the efficiency of this starter is less than that of the autotransformer starter. Its advantages are smoothness of acceleration, high power factor, and low cost in the smaller sizes. The smoothness of acceleration is due to the fact that as the motor accelerates the current taken becomes lower, and consequently the voltage drop across the resistor becomes lower, and the voltage at the motor terminals rises. The torque delivered by the motor is constantly increased as the motor speeds up. The motor will accelerate faster with a given initial torque than when started by an autotransformer.

Furthermore, the motor is not disconnected from the line at the transfer period, but the resistor is simply short-circuited without being

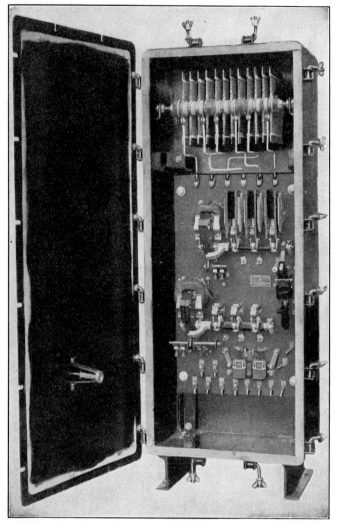

Fig. 176.   Primary-resistance Starter.

disconnected.   Consequently, the motor does not lose speed during the transfer period, and the acceleration is smoother.   So far as cost is concerned the primary-resistor starter is cheaper in the small sizes.

The primary-resistance starter shown in Fig. 176 has time-limit acceleration.   It consists of a main magnetic contactor equipped with magnetic blowouts, and a resistance commutating contactor without blowouts. The resistor is of cast grids and is mounted near the top of the enclosing case in order to keep the heat away from the panel. Pressing the start button energizes the main contactor and connects the motor to the supply lines through the resistance. When the main contactor closes, it operates a dashpot timing relay which, after a set

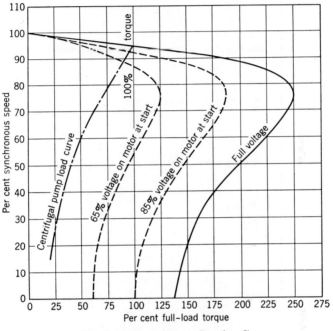

FIG. 177. Primary-resistance Starting Curves.

time, closes its contacts and energizes the resistance contactor. This contactor, in closing, short-circuits the resistance and connects the motor directly to the line. A thermal relay gives overload protection. The device shown on the door is a means for resetting the overload without opening the case.

The curves of Fig. 177 are drawn for different values of primary resistance and show the acceleration of the motor in each case. It is evident that with a light load to start, as for instance a centrifugal pump, the motor will reach nearly full speed with the resistance in circuit. For this reason it is common practice to have only one step of resistance. Two or more steps are sometimes used where it is necessary to limit the increments of current which may be drawn from the line.

A multiplicity of starting steps is obtained in the Allen-Bradley carbon-pile starter (Fig. 178). The resistor of this device consists of a number of graphite disks assembled in a steel tube. When the disks are loose, the contact resistance is very high. The application

FIG. 178. Allen-Bradley Carbon-pile Starter.

of pressure lowers the resistance. A solenoid, operating against an oil dashpot, compresses the disks in a set time. When the solenoid has completed its travel and the disks are fully compressed, an interlock on the solenoid energizes a contactor to short-circuit the resistance. Since direct current is more suitable for operating the solenoid, a rectifier is generally included to supply it.

Table 28 presents a comparison of three types of starters used with a 60-horsepower 440-volt three-phase 60-cycle 900-rpm eight-pole motor.

TABLE 28

Method of Starting	Starting Current Drawn from the Line as a Percentage of Full-load Current	Starting Torque as a Percentage of Full-load Torque
Connecting motor directly to the line full potential	470	160
Autotransformer 80% tap	335	105
Resistor starter to give 80% applied voltage	375	105
Autotransformer 65% tap	225	67
Resistor starter to give 65% applied voltage	305	67
Star-delta starter	158	54
Resistance starter to give 58% applied voltage	273	54
Autotransformer 50% tap	140	43
Resistor starter to give 50% applied voltage	233	43

Table 29 gives the relative characteristics of the autotransformer starter and the resistor starter.

TABLE 29

Line current	Considerably greater with primary resistor for same voltage at motor terminals.
Power factor	Higher with primary resistor.
Power from line	Considerably greater with primary resistor for same voltage at motor terminals.
Torque	With the autotransformer the torque does not change much as motor accelerates. It increases as the motor accelerates with primary resistor.
Smoothness of acceleration	Primary resistor much better.
Size and application	For 20 horsepower and below, primary resistor is satisfactory for almost any condition.
Cost	Primary resistor is generally cheaper.
Ease of control	A slight advantage with primary resistor.
Maintenance	Not much difference.
Reliability	Not much difference.
Safety	Not much difference.
Efficiency	Autotransformer higher, particularly on low-voltage taps.
Line disturbance	Depends on line conditions.

Line Current. The current taken from the line in starting is less with the autotransformer starter than with the primary-resistor starter, particularly on the lower taps; that is, the difference is great on the

50 per cent tap and on the 65 per cent tap, but on the 80 per cent tap the difference is not so great. With a primary-resistor starter the motor current is the line current. With the autotransformer starter, the current is nearly, but not quite, in proportion to the ratio of transformation, the difference being due to the magnetizing current of the transformer. This does not necessarily mean that the line voltage will drop lower when the resistance starter is used or that the line disturbance will be greater.

Power Factor. The power factor of the line at the moment of starting is materially higher with the primary-resistor starter than with the autotransformer. When adjusted to give 65 per cent of line voltage at the motor terminals for starting, the power factor with the primary-resistor starter varies from 80 to 90 per cent, depending upon the motor size, whereas with an autotransformer under the same conditions the power factor of the line varies from 30 to 60 per cent, depending on the size of the motor.

Power from the Line. The power taken from the line is greater with the primary-resistor starter than with the autotransformer. The autotransformer is a voltage-changing device; the primary resistor is an energy-consuming device. Also, the fact that the power factor is high for the primary-resistor starter causes a greater power loss. When line disturbance is not taken into account, and with 65 per cent voltage applied to the motor, the power taken from the line at the moment of starting with an autotransformer is about 50 per cent of that which would be taken with a primary resistor. Similarly, when connected to the 80 per cent tap, the power taken from the line with an autotransformer is about 60 per cent of that taken with a primary resistor. However, if the time taken to accelerate to full speed is considered, the difference in energy taken during the starting period is not so great, because the primary-resistor starter will accelerate the motor in a shorter time than the autotransformer starter will. This is because of the increasing torque as the motor accelerates. As a matter of fact, the power lost by the resistor starter in most installations does not amount to very much in actual cost. Calculations based on a 50-horsepower 220-volt three-phase motor, started by a primary-resistor starter, assuming 5 seconds to start and estimating power at 2 cents per kilowatt-hour, show that the power wasted in the resistor would cost approximately 0.2 cent. It is evident that this motor could be started a great many times each day before the power loss would become much of an item.

Torque. The torque developed by a squirrel-cage motor is independent of the method used to reduce the voltage at its terminals and depends only on the actual voltage impressed on the motor, varying as the square of that impressed voltage. For any application a certain torque is required for starting. This torque will, of course, be obtained with either starter. Therefore, the line current will vary, being greater for the resistor starter. For a definite given line current the torque that will be developed at the motor is materially higher when an autotransformer is used because higher voltage can be applied at the motor terminals with the same line current.

Smoothness of Acceleration. This is the principal advantage of the primary-resistor starter. When the motor is connected to the line through the resistor, a certain inrush takes place. As the motor accelerates up to speed, the current required decreases, automatically increasing the voltage at the motor terminals. Thus the torque at the motor builds up as the motor accelerates. With the autotransformer starter the applied voltage is constant as long as the motor is connected to the transformer tap. Accordingly, the acceleration of the motor is smoother and the motor accelerates faster with the primary-resistor starter. There is no loss of torque while the motor is being accelerated to full speed, since the resistor may be cut out of circuit in one or more steps without opening the circuit, whereas with the autotransformer starter the circuit is opened from the starting to the running position, which causes a momentary high current peak and a drop in speed on the motor.

Size and Application. In general, in considering the application of a squirrel-cage motor starter, the principal question involved is the permissible starting current that may be taken from the line. As mentioned before, the principal power-generating companies developed certain rules for permissible starting current which limit the use of this type of motor on central-station supply lines to 30 horsepower and below. This applies to standard single-squirrel-cage motors. Double-cage motors, having a high-resistance starting winding and a low-resistance running winding, will generally not exceed the safe limits up to 40 horsepower. It is probable that up to and including 20 horsepower the primary-resistor starter may be used under almost any conditions.

For motors larger than 20 horsepower, judgment must be exercised, depending upon the motor application, power supply, etc. If the current and power taken from the line in starting are the main consideration, the transformer type is preferable. If smoothness of acceleration is the principal factor, the primary-resistor type would be chosen. Since the effect of current taken from the line is felt more as the size of motor increases, autotransformer starters are generally used for the larger motors and for high-voltage installations. It is possible to build primary-resistor starters of any size for starting low-voltage squirrel-cage motors.

Cost. For motors of moderate sizes the size and cost of the primary-resistor starter are less than for the corresponding autotransformer starter. This difference varies somewhat with the voltage reduction supplied, since more resistance material is required to reduce the motor voltage to 65 per cent than to 80 per cent.

Ease of Control. There is not much difference in ease of control between the two types of starters. Perhaps a little more skill is necessary with the autotransformer type, because of the requirement that the transfer from the starting to the running step must be made very quickly. Also, in a manually operated primary-resistor starter the starting lever is thrown in one direction only, which tends to eliminate mistakes in starting.

Maintenance and Reliability. In maintenance and reliability there is not much difference between the two types of starters, provided that they are both of the air-break type. An autotransformer of the oil-break type is a little more difficult to maintain. There is a slight further advantage in that, if the resistor should burn out in a primary-resistor starter, the accelerating contactor could be temporarily blocked in and the motor thrown across the line to start in emergency.

Safety. There does not seem to be any advantage in safety for one starter over the other.

Efficiency. Because of the fact that the primary-resistor starter takes more current from the line, and more power from the line in starting, its efficiency of starting is lower than that of the autotransformer starter.

Line Disturbances. The amount of line disturbance caused by starting will depend not only on the amount of current taken from the line but also on the conditions of the line itself: that is, whether its capacity is large or small in relation to the motor being started, the amount of load already on the line, the power factor of the original load, and the starting power factor of the new load. Because of the low power factor of the autotransformer starter, more line disturbance may be caused by its use than by the use of a primary resistor, even though the current drawn from the line is lower. The following demonstration is taken from a paper by B. F. Bailey, published in the *AIEE Journal:*

The current taken in starting an induction motor causes a reduction in the line voltage. If the constants of the line and of the transformer, if one is used, are known, the reduction can be computed by the method shown in Fig. 179. In making this diagram, the effect of resistance has been ignored, since this is usually a minor factor compared with the reactance.

In Fig. 179 the line voltage before the motor is connected to the line is represented by the vector OE. The vector OI represents the starting current lagging by a large angle behind OE. For the purpose of analysis this current may be regarded as divided into two components: the component OI_p in phase with the line voltage, and the current OI_1, lagging 90 degrees behind the voltage. Each of these components generates a voltage at right angles to itself, and proportional to the reactance of the line and transformers. These voltages are represented by XI_p and XI_1.

The terminal voltage applied to the motor then becomes OE_1. The effect of connecting the motor to the line has then been to reduce the voltage from the value OE to OE_1. It will be noted that the component XI_p has but small effect on the absolute value of the line voltage, since it is at right angles to it, but the component XI_1 is directly subtracted from the line voltage. It is therefore apparent that the lagging or wattless component of the starting current is the one that is mainly instrumental in influencing the line voltage. The wattless component of the starting current is decidedly greater with the autotransformer starter than with the resistance-type starter.

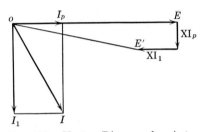

Fig. 179. Vector Diagram for Autotransformer Starting.

Test results on a 10-horsepower motor are given as follows:

	Auto Starter	Resistor Starter
Line current, amperes	75	110
Power factor, per cent	55	86
Lagging component, amperes	62.7	56.5

Although the resistance starter took 47 per cent more line current, the lagging component was only 90.2 per cent as great as with the auto starter. No difference in the momentary voltage drop could be detected, but the disturbance was of shorter duration with the resistance starter. Mr. Bailey concludes that the line disturbance when a motor is started is very nearly the same whether a resistance starter or an autotransformer starter is used.

The autotransformer starter is likely to cause a second line disturbance at the instant when the motor is transferred from the transformer to the line. The magnitude of the current drawn at the time depends upon the exact instant when the transfer is made and upon the length of time required to effect the transfer. As soon as the motor is disconnected from the line, the stator current drops to zero, but the rotor current continues to flow, and a voltage is generated in the stator. This voltage is at a frequency less than line frequency, and so its phase relation with line voltage is constantly changing. If the motor is connected to line at the instant when the two voltages are in phase coincidence, the conditions will be the worse, and a large momentary current will flow. The duration of the current will be short, probably too short to show any effect on lamps, but it may be long enough to have a serious effect upon connected synchronous machinery.

The value of the current may be quite high, as high as four times the inrush current which the motor would take if connected directly to the line when standing still.

Korndorfer Connection. It is possible to avoid opening the motor circuits during the transition from reduced voltage to full voltage.

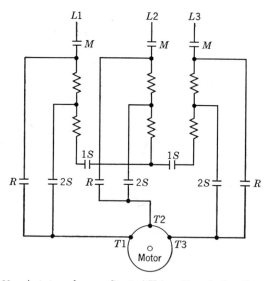

Fig. 180.   Autotransformer Starter Using Korndorfer Connection.

To do this, connections as shown in Fig. 180 are used. The method is known as the Korndorfer connection. With this circuit, contactor M closes first, connecting one side of the transformer windings to the lines, and contactor 1S follows immediately, closing the transformer neutral. Next contactor 2S closes, connecting the motor to reduced voltage. After the motor has had time to accelerate, a timing relay operated by 2S opens the circuit to 1S, which in turn opens the transformer neutral. The motor now runs with sections of the transformer winding acting as inductance in series with the motor. Contactor R then closes, connecting the motor to full voltage by short-circuiting the transformer sections. The last step is to open $2S$, disconnecting the reduced-voltage taps of the transformer.

The method is used to some extent for starting large motors, both induction and synchronous, but is seldom used for smaller motors because of the involved switching required.

Summary. When deciding which type of starter to choose for a given installation, consideration should be given to the various characteristics discussed, and the decision should be based on which of these characteristics are the most important for the installation in question. The questions of power loss during starting, reliability, ease of maintenance, ease of operation, safety, and efficiency will ordinarily not influence the decision. If low line current during starting is the vital requirement, the autotransformer starter should be chosen. If smooth starting, high power factor, or high torque is a vital requirement, then the resistance starter is better. If line disturbance is the criterion, the whole installation and the existing line conditions should be carefully considered. If none of the above factors is of vital interest, the decision will probably be made on a basis of cost.

Part-winding Starters. In order to use the part-winding starting method it is necessary that the motor winding be in two parts, and that at least six terminal leads be provided on the motor. The method is therefore applicable to those motors which are designed for use on either of two voltages, the windings being in parallel on the lower voltage and in series on the higher voltage. For example, a 220/440-volt motor could be used on 220 volts with a part-winding controller. The controller would then be arranged to connect one section of the winding to the supply lines as soon as the starting button was pressed. Then, after a time delay provided by a timing relay, a second contactor would connect the other section of the motor winding to the supply lines, in parallel with the first section.

In this way the starting current is reduced to approximately one-half of what would be required if both winding sections were connected at the same time, as they would be with a standard three-lead motor. The starting torque when the first winding section is connected will be less than half of the torque that would be obtained if both sections were connected at the same time.

Controllers are also built with a step of resistance connected in the circuit of the first winding section. Three starting steps are then available.

Contactors used for part-winding starters need capacity to handle only the circuit which they control, and so may be rated at one-half of the rating that would be required to handle the whole motor. Overload relays are provided for each section of the winding.

Figure 181 shows the connections for a typical controller.

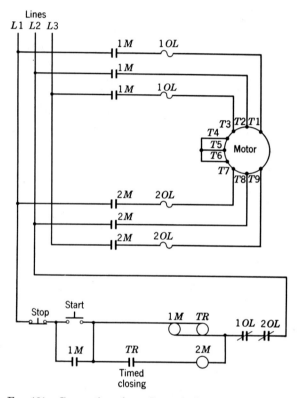

Fig. 181. Connections for a Part-winding Motor Starter.

Reversing. The rotation of a three-phase squirrel-cage motor may be reversed by reversing the line connections to any two of the stator terminals. Similarly, a two-phase machine may be reversed by reversing the line connections to one of the phases. The motor may be plugged for a rapid reversal by connecting it for the reverse direction while it is still running in the forward direction. When this is done, the current inrush obtained is only slightly higher than that obtained when starting from rest.

Reversing controllers for squirrel-cage motors are usually of either the drum type or the magnetic type. The magnetic controller consists of a pair of magnetic contactors, mechanically interlocked so that they cannot both close at the same time, and an overload relay. The controlling pushbutton station has three buttons, for forward, reverse, and stop.

For reversing service, magnetic across-the-line controllers and magnetic reduced-voltage controllers are rated the same as for non-reversing service.

Stopping. The most frequently used method of stopping is simply to disconnect the motor from the supply lines and let it drift to rest. When a quick stop is desired, a magnetic brake may be used. A quick stop may also be obtained by plugging the motor and then opening the reverse contactor just as the motor has stopped and before it starts to reverse. To do this, some sort of switch is required which will close its contacts only in one direction of motor rotation. The switch is coupled to the motor and driven by it. A friction switch of this type is shown in

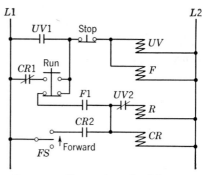

Fig. 182. Connections for Plug-stop Control.

Fig. 28. It is desirable to arrange the control circuits so that a movement of the driven machine by hand will not start the motor.

Figure 182 shows the connections for a plug-stop control. In the off position all contactors and relays are open, and the friction switch *FS* is also open. When the run button is pressed, the undervoltage relay *UV* and the forward direction contactor *F* close. Contact *UV1* maintains them both closed. A normally closed contact on the run button opens the circuit to the reverse-direction contactor *R* and to relay *CR*. Contact *UV2* also opens the circuit to *R*. The motor starts to run forward, and *FS* closes its contacts. When the run button is released, the relay *CR* gets a circuit through *UV1* and the interlock contact *F1* of contactor *F*. *CR* closes, maintaining itself through its contact *CR2*, and opening the circuit to the run button by contact *CR1*. The circuit is now set up for stopping, and when the stop button is pressed *F* and *UV* are de-energized and drop open, disconnecting the motor from the lines. The reverse-direction contactor *R* now gets a circuit through *FS*, *CR2*, and *UV2*, and closes, plugging the motor. The motor slows down and stops, and, as soon as it moves the least amount in the reverse direction, the friction switch *FS* opens its contacts, dropping out R and CR, and finally disconnecting the motor. During the plugging period, operation of the run button cannot do any harm, because $CR1$ is open. With the motor shut down, accidental closing of FS, as by hand rotation of the motor, cannot cause any operation, because $CR2$ is open.

Another method sometimes used for a quick stop is the application of direct current to one phase of the stator winding. The squirrel-cage rotor, turning in a direct-current field, is brought to rest by dynamic braking. If a direct-current supply is available, the current supplied to the stator may be limited by the use of external resistance. When a motor generator set must be installed to supply the direct current, the generator voltage can be adjusted to supply the right amount of current. This method of braking is particularly applicable to drives such as steel-mill roll-type conveyors, where a large number of motors have to be stopped together. The connections for such an arrangement are described in the next paragraph.

Speed Control. The squirrel-cage motor does not readily lend itself to speed variation. There is no way to make any change in the rotor circuits, and the use of resistance in the primary circuits does not accomplish the desired results. The only satisfactory method of speed control is variation of the frequency, and this is seldom attempted because of the expense of the motor-generator set necessary.

The roll tables in steel mills, which are a conveyor consisting of a large number of rolls, each individually driven by a squirrel-cage motor, are generally equipped with variable-frequency speed control. For such an installation, a direct-current motor is used to drive an alternator, and the speed of the set is varied by a rheostat in the shunt field of the motor. The voltage and frequency of the alternator change with the speed of the machines. Each roll motor is provided with its own disconnect switch and overload relay, and all the motors are connected to the alternator supply through a common pair of reversing contactors. If the conveyor has more than one section, each section will have its own reversing contactors. It is then possible to start all the motors of any section together, and to control the speed of all the motors of a section together. A defective motor may be cut out of circuit by its individual switch without affecting the operation of the conveyor as a whole. A separate small motor-generator set is used to supply direct current for braking. The set consists of a squirrel-cage motor operating from alternating-current supply lines, and a direct-current generator. A pair of magnetic contactors connects the generator to one phase of all the roll motors. To bring the conveyor to rest, the reversing contactors are opened, disconnecting the motors from the alternator, and the braking contactors are closed, applying direct current to one phase of the motors. A timing relay is arranged to open the braking contactors after the motors have come to rest.

The Rossman Drive. The Rossman drive is a method of obtaining speed regulation of an induction motor, of either the squirrel-cage or the synchronous type, by rotating both the armature and the field windings. A specially designed motor is required to permit rotation of the armature (normally the stator), which is driven by an adjustable-speed direct-current motor. Since a synchronous speed relation is always maintained between the armature and the field members, the net forward rotation of the field, or normal rotor, will be the difference between synchronous speed and the speed of the rotating armature when rotated in opposite directions. When armature and field are rotated in the same direction, the net forward rotation of the field member will be the sum of the speeds of the two members. The Rossman drive has found its principal application in power plants, for driving forced and induced draft fans and boiler feed pumps. These units are of relatively high rating, running up to 2500 horsepower. The complete installation costs little more than a two-speed motor installation and shows a saving in power consumption which justifies its use.

Voltage and Frequency Variations. The following summary of the effects of variations of voltage and frequency upon the performance of induction motors is taken from the NEMA Standards:

(*a*) Induction motors are at times operated on circuits of different voltage or frequency from that for which the motors are rated. Under such conditions, the performance of the motor will vary from the standard rating. The following is a brief statement of some operating results caused by small variations of voltage and frequency, and is indicative of the general nature of changes produced by such variations in operating conditions.

(*b*) Voltage variations of 10 per cent on power circuits are allowed in most commission rules. However, changing the voltage applied to an induction motor has the effect of changing its proper rating, as far as power factor and efficiency are concerned, in proportion to the square of the applied voltage. Thus a 5-horsepower motor, operated at 10 per cent above its rated voltage, would have characteristics proper for a 6-horsepower motor (6.05 horsepower, to be exact); and at 10 per cent below the rated voltage, those of a 4-horsepower motor (more exactly, 4.05 horsepower). It is obvious that, if the rating of a motor were greatly increased in this way, the safe heating would frequently be exceeded.

(c) In a motor of normal characteristics at full rated horsepower load, a 10 per cent increase of voltage above that given on the name plate would usually result in a slight improvement in efficiency and a decided lowering in power factor. A 10 per cent decrease of voltage below that given on the name plate would usually give a slight decrease of efficiency and an increase in power factor.

(d) The starting and pull-out torque will be proportional to the square of the voltage applied. With a 10 per cent increase or decrease in voltage from that given on the name plate, the heating at rated horsepower load will not exceed safe limits when operating in ambient temperatures of 40 C or less, although the usual guaranteed rise may be exceeded.

(e) An increase of 10 per cent in voltage will result in a decrease of slip of about 17 per cent; a reduction of 10 per cent will increase the slip about 21 per cent. Thus, if the slip at rated voltage were 5 per cent, it would be increased to 6.05 per cent if the voltage were reduced 10 per cent.

(f) Higher than rated frequency usually improves the power factor but decreases starting torque and increases the speed, friction, and windage. At lower than rated frequency, of course, the speed is decreased, starting torque is increased, and power factor is slightly decreased. For certain kinds of motor load, such as in textile mills, close frequency regulation is essential.

(g) If variations in voltage and frequency occur simultaneously, the effects will be superimposed. Thus, if the voltage is high and the frequency low, the starting torque will be very greatly increased, but the power factor will be decreased and the temperature rise increased with normal load.

(h) The foregoing facts apply particularly to general-purpose motors; they may not always be true of special motors, built for a particular purpose, or of very small motors.

Multispeed Squirrel-cage Motors. Although speed regulation of the squirrel-cage motor is not practical, it is possible to get two, three, or four different constant speeds by special arrangement of the stator windings. Two separate and independent windings may be used, each being wound for any desired number of poles. With this arrangement any desired combination of the possible motor speeds may be obtained. Two speeds may also be obtained by regrouping a single stator winding to give a different number of poles. With such an arrangement the ratio of the two speeds is always 2 to 1, as, for example, 1800 rpm and 900 rpm. Three-speed motors have one winding reconnected to give two speeds, and a separate winding for the third speed. Four-speed motors have both windings reconnected.

Multispeed motors may be wound for constant horsepower, constant torque, or variable horsepower and torque.

$$\text{Horsepower} = \frac{\text{Torque (ft-lb)} \times \text{Speed (rpm)}}{5252}$$

With the constant-horsepower design, the torque is inversely proportional to the speed, and the horsepower is the same at each speed. With the constant-torque design, the horsepower varies directly with

Two speed, two winding, three phase

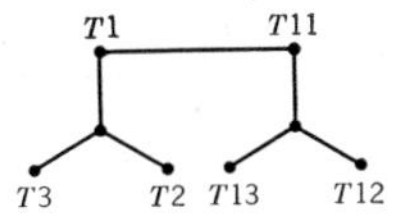

Speed	Connect Lines		
	$L1$	$L2$	$L3$
	To Motor Terminals		
1	$T1$	$T2$	$T3$
2	$T11$	$T12$	$T13$

Two speed, two winding, two phase, four wire

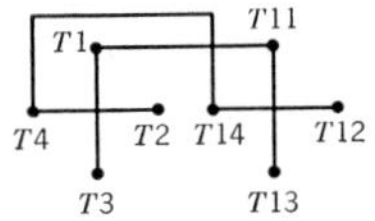

Speed	Connect Lines			
	$L1$	$L2$	$L3$	$L4$
	To Motor Terminals			
1	$T1$	$T2$	$T3$	$T4$
2	$T11$	$T12$	$T13$	$T14$

Four speed, four winding, three phase

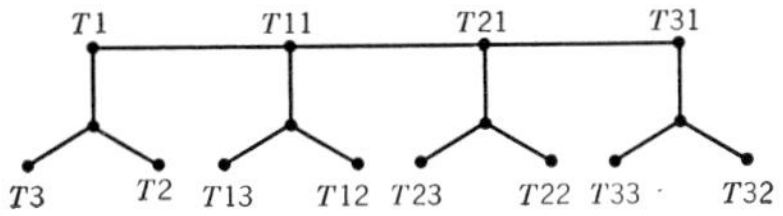

Speed	Connect Lines		
	$L1$	$L2$	$L3$
	To Motor Terminals		
1	$T1$	$T2$	$T3$
2	$T11$	$T12$	$T13$
3	$T21$	$T22$	$T23$
4	$T31$	$T32$	$T33$

FIG. 183.   Multispeed Motor Connections.   Separate-winding Types.

the speed, and the torque is the same at each speed. With the variable-torque and variable-horsepower design, both horsepower and torque decrease with a reduction in speed, the torque varying directly with the speed and the horsepower with the square of the speed. Any of these characteristics can be obtained either by regrouping poles or by

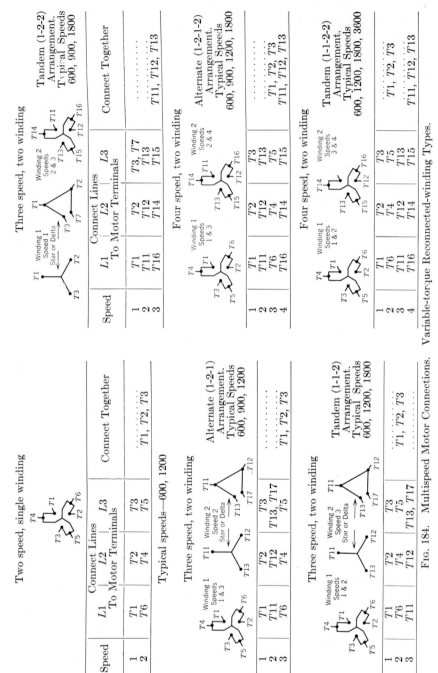

FIG. 184. Multispeed Motor Connections.

Variable-torque Reconnected-winding Types.

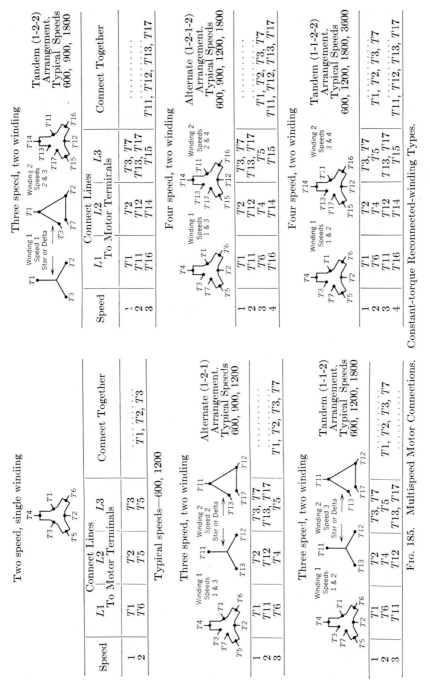

Fig. 185. Multispeed Motor Connections.

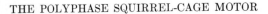

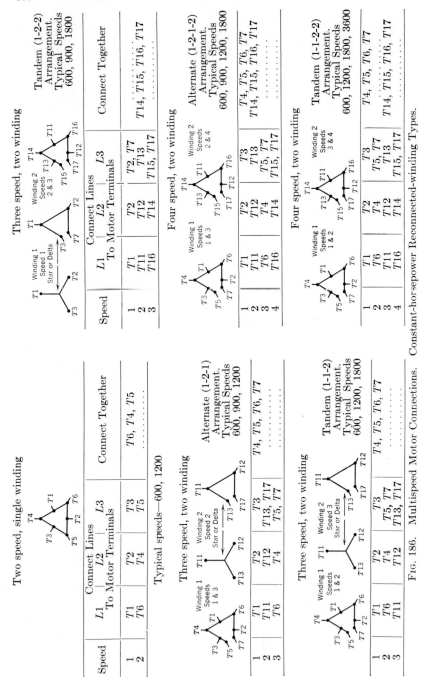

Fig. 186. Multispeed Motor Connections. Constant-horsepower Reconnected-winding Types.

separate windings. Consequent-pole motors are built for three-phase service only; where only two-phase power is available, it is necessary to transform to three phase. This may be done by using Scott-connected transformers. Separate winding motors are built for either two- or three-phase service.

For constant torque the stator windings are connected in series-delta on the low speed and parallel-star on the high speed.

For constant horsepower the windings are connected in parallel-star on the low speed and series-delta on the high speed.

For variable torque and horsepower, the connections are in series-star on the low speed and parallel-star on the high speed.

Figures 183, 184, 185, and 186 show typical arrangements for multi-speed motors.

Manually Operated Controllers. Because of the necessity of switching a number of circuits to obtain the different speeds, a drum-type controller is the most suitable manually operated device. It is not difficult to arrange the contact cylinder and fingers to give any desired switching sequence. A drum, being a compact device, is particularly suited to mounting in or on machine tools, where space is limited. Although the drum can readily provide the switching, auxiliary apparatus is necessary to obtain low-voltage protection, reduced-voltage starting, and overload protection. The larger drums also require a contactor to interrupt the circuit during switching.

Low-voltage protection is readily secured by means of a magnetic contactor, the coil of which is energized through interlocks in the drum as it is moved from the off position, and maintained through an interlock on the contactor. When voltage fails, the drum must be returned to the off position to restart the motor. If an overload relay is used, it will be arranged to trip out the contactor.

Reduced-voltage starting may be secured by substituting any type of reduced-voltage starter, as an autotransformer starter or a primary-resistor starter, for the low-voltage-protection contactor.

There are several methods of using contactors to open and close the motor circuit, and switching only non-arcing circuits in the drum. One method is to incorporate a switch into the drum handle, arranging it to close its circuit only when the drum handle is in one of the running positions. The contactor coil is connected through the switch and so will open whenever the drum handle is moved from one position to another. The switch is arranged mechanically so that the drum handle cannot be moved from one position to another until the switch has been operated and the contactor de-energized. Another method is to use a quick-acting relay, arranged to drop open whenever the drum is moved from one position to another, and to de-energize the contactor. When the drum is again in an operating position, and when the contactor is open, a circuit is again completed to the relay, which closes and re-energizes the contactor. There are also mechanical devices for opening the contactor between operating positions.

To obtain suitable overload protection for a motor with separate speed windings, it is necessary to have one overload relay for each winding. For reconnected variable-torque motors one overload relay per winding is sufficient. For reconnected constant-horsepower motors, and reconnected constant-torque motors, two overload relays per windings are necessary.

Magnetic Multispeed Motor Controllers. Magnetic controllers are used for those applications where the motor is located at a distance from the operator and it is desirable to install the controller near the motor. They are necessary where automatic starting, from a thermostat or other pilot device, is used, and they are desirable for applications where the service is severe. They are made for two-, three-, and four-speed motors, of either the separate-winding or the reconnected-winding type. Though across-the-line starting is generally used, controllers are also built for reduced-voltage starting. These are of the primary-resistance type, a magnetic contactor being provided to short-circuit the resistance during the accelerating period. The resistance contactor is timed by a timing relay. The arrangement is the same as that for a single-winding motor.

The three common forms of control are known as selective, compelling, and progressive.

Selective control permits starting the motor on any desired speed winding. To change the speed of a running motor to any higher speed, it is only necessary to press the desired speed button. To change to a lower speed, it is necessary first to press the stop button and then to press the desired speed button. The shock to machinery when changing speeds is greater when the speed is reduced than when it is increased, and so this control method allows the motor to decelerate somewhat before it is connected at the lower speed.

Compelling control provides that in accelerating the motor from rest it must always be started on the low-speed winding. To reach higher speeds, the pushbuttons must be operated in the sequence of speeds, thus compelling the operator to accelerate the motor gradually. To change to a lower speed, it is necessary first to press the stop button and then to proceed as if starting from rest.

Progressive control provides automatic, timed acceleration of the motor to the selected speed by energizing the speed windings progres-

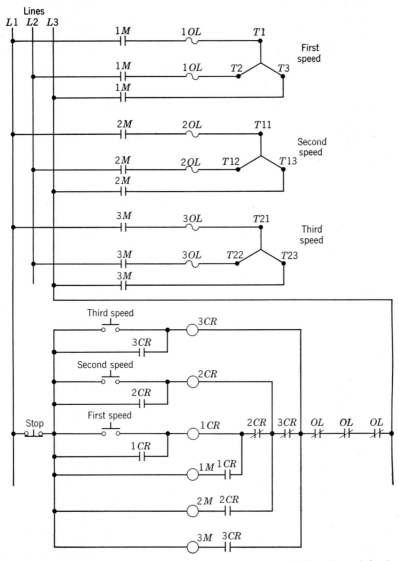

FIG. 187. Connections for a Three-speed Three-winding Full-voltage Selective
Controller.

sively from the lowest to the desired speed. To start the motor from rest, or to change the speed of a running motor to a higher speed, it is only necessary to press the desired speed button; the controller will automatically go from speed to speed until the desired one is reached. To change to a lower speed, it is necessary first to press the stop button and then to proceed as if starting from rest.

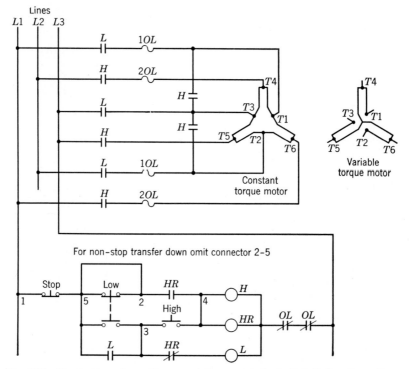

Fɪɢ. 188. Connections for a Two-speed Reconnected-winding Full-voltage Compelling Controller.

All these forms of magnetic starter are provided with overload relays. Low-voltage release is obtained with a two-wire pilot device, and low-voltage protection with a three-wire pilot device. Selector switches with "automatic-off-manual" marking are available, as they are for single-winding motor starters, with the difference that on the "manual" side they have a position for each motor speed.

Figure 187 shows the connections for a selective controller for a three-speed, three-winding motor, starting on full voltage. One control relay and one contactor are required for each winding. The connections are so simple that the operation will be self-evident, and the connections required for a motor with any number of speed windings will also be apparent.

Figure 188 shows the connections for a compelling controller for a two-speed reconnected motor, starting on full voltage. A constant-torque motor will be connected in delta on the low speed and in

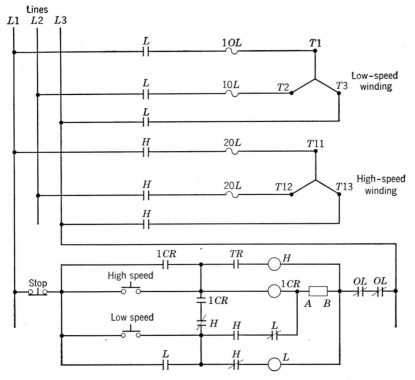

Fig. 189.   Connections for a Two-speed Two-winding Full-voltage Progressive Controller.

parallel-star on the high speed. A variable-torque motor will be connected in single-star on the low speed and in parallel-star on the high speed. Either connection requires a three-pole contactor for the low speed and a five-pole contactor for the high speed. The control connections are again very simple. If it is not desired to stop when changing from high to low speed, a pushbutton having both normally open and normally closed contacts is used, and the connection between points 2 and 5 is omitted.

Figure 189 shows the connections for a progressive controller for a two-speed two-winding motor, starting on full voltage. The contact

TR is a timing relay operated by relay $1CR$. The other contacts of $1CR$ open and close instantaneously.

Considering the various kinds of motors, speed combinations, types of windings, and control schemes, it is evident that there are a good many possible combinations. The three examples given are typical, and any other combinations can be worked out from them.

Application of Squirrel-cage Motors. For reasons already stated, the standard squirrel-cage motor is very popular and is used wherever the installation and service conditions permit. It is not suitable where the starting torque is high but is best applied where the starting load is light. For example, a centrifugal pump, working against a constant head of water, does not start to deliver water until it is well up to speed, and the starting load is low. Fans have similar characteristics. Many machine tools are suitable applications. Motor-generator sets are often driven by these motors.

The high-torque motor is used for slow-speed freight elevators where speed control is not required. It offers good starting torque, simplicity, and low cost. Motors for this service may have as much as 15 per cent slip at full load. Punch presses, printing presses, and washing machines are other applications of the high-torque motor.

The double-cage motor is used where it is desirable to limit the line current when starting, and also where high torque is needed. Crushers, air compressors, and conveyors starting under load are typical applications.

The constant-torque multispeed motor is used to drive printing presses, compressors, dough mixers, tumblers, constant-pressure blowers, conveyors, elevators, and stokers.

The constant-horsepower multispeed motor is used to drive lathes, boring mills, other metal- and wood-working machinery, and similar machines in which a higher torque is required at the low speed.

Variable-torque motors are used to drive machines whose load varies approximately as the square of the speed, as, for instance, fans, blowers, and centrifugal pumps.

When selecting a motor it will be found economical to choose a high-speed motor if possible, and an open motor rather than an enclosed motor if conditions will permit. For example, a 10-horsepower 900-rpm motor weighs about 500 pounds, whereas a 10-horsepower, 1800-rpm motor weighs about 310 pounds. The slow-speed motor takes about 69 per cent more copper, 65 per cent more steel, and 60 per cent more cast or malleable iron. An enclosed motor has a lower horsepower rating than the same size of open motor, which means that for a given horsepower rating the enclosed motor will probably be larger than the open motor. A check on a 100-horsepower motor showed that the partially enclosed design was 43 per cent heavier, taking 20 pounds more of aluminum, 50 pounds more of copper, and 470 pounds more of steel. A fully enclosed motor was about 120 per cent heavier than the open motor.

Design of Primary Resistor. Resistance is used in the primary circuit of a squirrel-cage motor to limit the starting torque or the

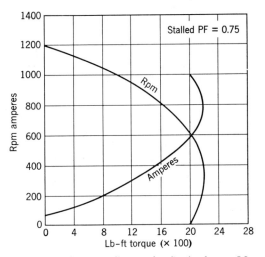

FIG. 190. Speed-torque Curve of a Squirrel-cage Motor.

starting current. It is necessary to have some data on the motor characteristics, which may be obtained from a motor curve like that of Fig. 190. Suppose that with this motor it is desired to limit the starting torque to 600 pound-feet.

From the curve,

E = line voltage = 440.
I_s = stalled current = 1000 amperes.
PF = stalled power factor = 0.75.
T_0 = stalled torque = 2000 pound-feet.

The impedance of the motor is $Z_s = \dfrac{E}{1.73 \times I_s} = \dfrac{440}{1.73 \times 1000} = 0.254$

ohm. Calling the total impedance of motor and resistor Z, the inrush current will be

$$I = \frac{E}{1.73 \times Z} = \frac{440}{1.73Z}$$

$$Z = \frac{440}{1.73I} \qquad [1]$$

The voltage across the motor will be

$$E_m = \frac{Z_s \times E}{Z} = \frac{0.254 \times 440}{Z}$$

$$Z = \frac{0.254 \times 440}{E_m} \qquad [2]$$

Combining 1 and 2 gives

$$\frac{440}{1.73I} = \frac{0.254 \times 440}{E_m}$$

$$E_m = 0.44I \qquad [3]$$

This gives one relation of E_m to I, and it is now necessary to get another equation between them. The torque obtained with the resistance in circuit will be proportional to the current and to the voltage.

$$T = \frac{I \times E_m \times T_0}{I_s \times E}$$

$$600 = \frac{I \times E_m \times 2000}{1000 \times 440}$$

$$E_m I = \frac{600 \times 440 \times 1000}{2000}$$

Reducing this somewhat, we have

$$E_m = \frac{132,000}{I} \qquad [4]$$

Now combining equations 3 and 4 gives

$$0.44I = \frac{132,000}{I}$$

$$I = 548 \text{ amperes} \qquad [5]$$

and, from equation 3, $E_m = 241 \text{ volts} \qquad [6]$

From equation 2, $Z = \dfrac{0.254 \times 440}{241}$

$$Z = 0.465 \text{ ohm} \qquad [7]$$

Referring to Fig. 191, the line AD is drawn at such an angle to the base line AC that the cosine of the angle is 0.75.

Choosing a convenient scale, lay off $AD = 0.254$.

AD is then the impedance of the motor, AB is the motor resistance, and BD the motor reactance. From D draw the line DE parallel to AC, and select the point E so that the line $AE = 0.465$. Then AE is the total impedance of motor and resistor, and DE is the value of the resistor alone. DE will be found to be 0.24 ohm.

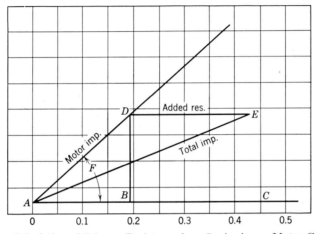

FIG. 191. Calculation of Primary Resistance for a Squirrel-cage Motor Controller.

If the current inrush obtained in starting is the limiting factor, and the torque of secondary importance, the calculations are much simpler. With I known, the total impedance Z is immediately determined from equation 1. The controller resistance is then obtained from the vector diagram in the manner described.

References

A. M. Rossman, "A New System of Speed Control for A-c Motors," *Transactions AIEE,* 1931, Vol. 50, p. 162.

W. I. Bendz, "Comparison of Methods of Stopping Squirrel-cage Induction Motors," *Transactions AIEE,* September, 1938, Vol. 57, p. 499.

H. M. Norman, "Starting Characteristics and Control of Polyphase Squirrel-cage Induction Motors," *Transactions AIEE,* 1926, Vol. 45, p. 369.

H. Littlejohn, "Basic Control Circuits for Squirrel-cage Motors," *Product Engineering,* 1946, Vol. 17, p. 444.

J. A. Jackson, "High-slip Motors," *General Electric Review,* December, 1944.

"Squirrel-cage Motor Starters," *Electrical Contracting,* July, 1944.

Problems

1. What is the synchronous speed of an eight-pole 60-cycle squirrel-cage motor?

2. What is the synchronous speed of a 12-pole 25-cycle 220-volt squirrel-cage motor?

3. At what speed will the motor of problem 2 run if it is connected to a 260-volt 30-cycle supply line?

4. A squirrel-cage motor is driving a machine at 1780 rpm. If the rotor of the motor is removed, and replaced with a rotor having twice the resistance of the original rotor, at what speed will the machine be driven?

5. Referring to Fig. 168, draw a set of curves which will produce a field that rotates in a clockwise direction.

6. Referring to Fig. 190, calculate the ohms of a primary resistor which will limit the inrush current on starting to 450 amperes.

7. What starting torque will be obtained with the resistor of problem 6?

8. If suitable cast-iron grids having a resistance of 0.01 ohm each are available, how many will be required for the resistor of problem 6?

9. It is desired that the motor of Fig. 190 be braked to stop, by the application of direct current to two of the motor leads. It is also desired that the breaking current be limited to 600 amperes. If the direct current is obtained from a small motor-generator set, what will be the voltage of the generator?

10. A four-speed 60-cycle multispeed motor has a two-pole winding and a six-pole winding, each of which may be reconnected. What four speeds will be obtained?

11. Draw an elementary diagram for the control circuits of an autotransformer starter like Fig. 174, consisting of

Five-pole starting contactor.
Three-pole running contactor.
3 overload relays.
Autotransformer.
Start-stop pushbutton.
Timing relay operated by the starting contactor.

12. Draw an elementary diagram for the main and control circuits of a primary-resistor starter, consisting of

Three-pole line contactor.
3 overload relays.
Three-pole accelerating contactor.
3 blocks of resistor grids.
Timing relay magnetically operated.
Start-stop pushbutton.

13. Draw an elementary diagram of a primary-resistor increment starter, consisting of

2 three-pole reversing contactors.
3 accelerating contactors.
3 overload relays.

Resistors in three phases.
Timing relays mechanically operated.
Forward-reverse-stop pushbutton.

14. A manufacturing company requests a quotation on a non-reversing increment starter for a 50-horsepower three-phase 220-volt 122-ampere squirrel-cage motor having a locked-rotor current of 10 times its full-load running current. The power company limits the starting current to 210 amperes per second. Prepare a list of the devices which are required to build the starter.

15. Draw an elementary diagram for the control circuits of a Korndorfer-type starter like Fig. 180.

16. Calculate the ohmic value of a primary resistor for a motor and controller of the following characteristics:

Line voltage	440	
Stalled amperes	1200	
Stalled power factor	0.80	
Stalled torque	2300	lb-ft
Starting torque	500	lb-ft

17. Calculate the ohmic value of a primary resistor for a motor and controller of the following characteristics:

Line voltage	220	
Stalled amperes	1100	
Stalled power factor	0.80	
Stalled torque	1150	lb-ft
Starting amperes	500	

18. Calculate the starting torque with the motor and controller of problem 17.

19. Two squirrel-cage motors are to be used to drive a machine, and it is desired that they divide the load equally between them. What type of motor should be used, and why?

17

THE WOUND-ROTOR MOTOR

The wound-rotor induction motor is like the squirrel-cage motor, but instead of having a series of conducting bars placed in the rotor slots it has a wire winding in the rotor. If the winding is permanently short-circuited, the rotor is just another form of squirrel cage. However, if the ends of the rotor winding are brought out to three continuous slip rings, and brushes are arranged to ride on the slip rings and afford a method of connecting to them, the motor offers possibilities

Fig. 192. Rotor of a Slip-ring Motor. (Courtesy of Reliance Electric and Engineering Company)

for application widely different from the squirrel-cage motor. Strictly speaking, a wound-rotor motor may be of the first-mentioned type, without slip rings, but in this discussion the terms wound rotor and slip ring will be used synonymously to mean a motor with slip rings.

The stator of the wound-rotor motor is of the same construction as that of the squirrel-cage motor. Figure 192 shows the rotor and its slip rings. The brushes are mounted in the end bearing bracket, and connections from them are led to a terminal box on the motor frame.

Since the motor operates on the principle of the rotating stator field, the equation for its speed and the synchronous speeds obtainable are the same as those of the squirrel-cage motor.

In the preceding chapter, it was shown that when a motor is constructed with a relatively low-resistance rotor it will have a low running slip, which is desirable, but will draw a high starting current and will have a low starting torque, which are undesirable features. Conversely, a motor with a relatively high-resistance rotor will have the desirable features of higher starting torque and lower starting inrush, but will have a high slip at full load. With the squirrel-cage rotor, the choice must be made in the design, and nothing further can be done about it. The slip-ring motor, however, offers the possibility of

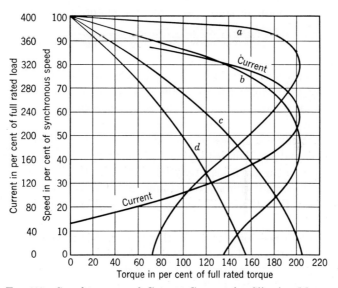

FIG. 193. Speed-torque and Current Curves of a Slip-ring Motor.

connecting an external resistor into the rotor circuit for starting, and then cutting it out of circuit for running, and so obtaining all the desirable characteristics. The external resistance in the rotor circuit also affords a means of speed regulation.

Figure 193 shows the speed-torque curves for a slip-ring motor with various amounts of resistance connected into the rotor circuit. Curve *a* is that of the motor with the rotor short-circuited. The starting torque is about 72 per cent and the starting current is about 350 per cent of full-load current. Curve *b* shows the conditions when a small amount of resistance has been added in the rotor circuit. The starting torque is now about 138 per cent and the starting current 320 per cent. Curve *c* shows the conditions when just enough resistance has been added in the rotor circuit to give the maximum starting torque of about 204 per cent. The inrush current is about 230 per cent. A further increase in the resistance will reduce the starting torque as well as the starting current. Curve d represents a common starting condition, where enough resistance is inserted to allow a starting current of about 150 per cent and a torque of about the same per cent of the rated value. It is, therefore, possible to start a slip-ring motor in the same way that a direct-current motor is started, using enough resistance to limit the starting current to the desired amount and then cutting it out in one or more steps until the motor is fully accelerated and its rotor is short-circuited.

The motor may be reversed by reversing any one phase of the stator windings.

The speed-torque curves show that speed regulation may readily be secured by means of resistance in the rotor circuit. Considering curve d, the motor, if fully loaded, will run at 48 per cent of full speed. At half load it will run at 78 per cent speed. With some resistance cut out, so that curve c applies, the motor will run on full load at 65 per cent speed and on half load at 82 per cent speed. Similarly, any desired speed at a given load may be obtained. It will be noted that the curves become flatter as greater amounts of resistance are inserted, which means that there will be a greater speed change with changes in the load.

To calculate resistors for a slip-ring motor, it is necessary to know the characteristics of the rotor winding: that is, the voltage across the open-circuited slip rings at standstill, and the current in the rotor leads to the slip rings at full load. At standstill, the rotating stator field induces, in the rotor windings, a voltage which is determined by the ratio of stator and rotor turns. The frequency of the rotor voltage will be the same as that of the stator current, which is supply-line frequency. When the rotor starts to turn, the voltage and frequency decrease, finally approaching zero as the rotor approaches synchronous speed. Their value at full running speed depends upon the slip. If the full-load slip is 5 per cent, the rotor voltage and frequency will be 5 per cent of normal, and this voltage will be just enough to cause full-load current to flow against the rotor impedance. So far as calculations for resistors are concerned, it does not make any difference whether the rotor windings are connected in star or in delta; it is only necessary to know the open-circuit voltage and the load amperes.

With an overhauling load, and with the slip rings short-circuited, the motor will run slightly above synchronous speed. With external resistance in the rotor circuit, the speed will be increased.

Controllers for Slip-ring Motors. A controller for a slip-ring motor usually consists of some form of switch or contactor, to connect the primary winding to the supply lines, and some form of resistance-commutating device for the rotor circuit. The controller may be manually operated, semi-magnetic, or fully magnetic. It may be reversing or non-reversing, and it may be for plain starting or for speed regu-

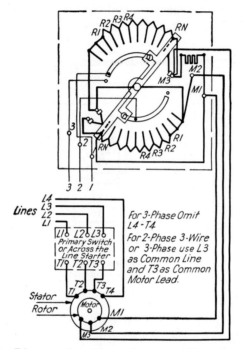

FIG. 194. Diagram of an Alternating-current Face-plate Starter.

lation. Across-the-line starting is not used, as there would be no reason for the more expensive slip-ring motor if its advantages were not exploited. For the same reason, autotransformer starting and primary-resistance starting are not used.

Face-plate Starters. Figure 194 is a diagram of a face-plate starter for the rotor circuit. The starter has a manually operated lever provided with contact brushes on both ends. Two sets of copper segments are mounted on the starter base. The resistor material is connected to the segments, and the lever bridges the two sets. The resistor consists of three sections connected in delta. It is commutated in two phases only, the third section being a fixed step, as this allows a simple construction of the operating lever. The resistor is balanced in the three phases in the initial starting position and in the final running position. The intermediate starting steps are unbalanced. The unbalancing results in a lower torque than would otherwise be obtained, but the resistance is proportioned to offset this somewhat; since this type of starter is used only with small motors, the unbalancing is not a serious matter. The starting lever has a spring to return it to the all-resistance-in position when it is released, and it is provided with a low-voltage-release magnet, the coil of which is connected across two phases of the primary circuit, behind the stator contactor. This in-

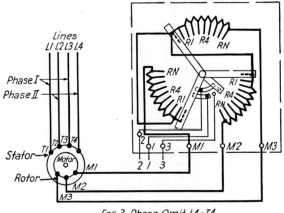

For 3-Phase Omit L4-T4
Use L3 as Common Line.

FIG. 195. Diagram of an Alternating-current Speed Regulator.

sures that the motor will not be started with the resistance short-circuited, as the lever cannot be left in the full on position with the stator circuit open. The stator contactor is a standard across-the-line magnetic starter with thermal overload relay, as used for a squirrel-cage motor.

Face-plate Speed Regulator. A face-plate speed regulator must be arranged to commutate resistance in all three phases at the same time, because the regulator may be left on any resistance point, and all running speed points should be balanced. Running with an unbalanced resistance in the rotor circuit will cause vibration of the motor and driven machinery. It is not so difficult to build a three-arm regulator, because the spring-return feature is not required. The usual practice is not to provide any interlock between the regulator arm and the stator contactor. The resistor is star-connected and is cut out step by step in all three phases. Figure 195 is a diagram of the regulator.

Multiple-switch Starter. Multiple-switch starters for wound-rotor motors are similar in construction to those described for direct-current

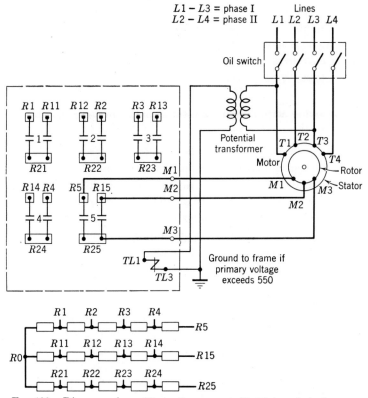

FIG. 196. Diagram of an Alternating-current Multiple-switch Starter.

shunt-wound motors, except that the levers are double-pole and so short-circuit resistance steps in three rotor phases at the same time. A contactor, or circuit breaker, is used with the starter, to close the

TABLE 30

MULTIPLE-SWITCH STARTERS

Horsepower	Number of Steps	Inrush Current in per cent of Full Load	NEMA Resistor Class
75	4	165	135
115	5	165	135
200	6	150	135
300	7	125	134
400	7	100	134
Above 400	8	85	133

stator circuit, and the release magnet coil of the starter is connected on the motor side of the contactor. All the starter levers will then be opened when the stator circuit is opened. Figure 196 is a diagram of the starter, showing how the resistance is commutated. Table 30 gives the approximate number of levers (resistance steps), the inrush currents for various motor ratings, and the resistor class used.

Drum Controllers. Drum controllers for slip-ring motors are made in several types, as follows:

> Non-reversing, with circuits for rotor control only.
> Reversing, with circuits for stator and rotor control.
> Motor driven, with circuits for rotor control only.

All these may be used with a resistor suitable for starting duty only or with a speed-regulating resistor. The manual types may have either a radial drive lever or a straight-line drive lever, or they may be provided with a handwheel drive. The general construction of an alternating-current drum controller is the same as that of a direct-current drum, but the circuits are arranged to commutate resistance in the three rotor phases. The drum starter generally does not cut out resistance in all three phases simultaneously. The number of drum fingers required can be considerably reduced, with corresponding reductions in the size and the cost of the controller, by cutting out steps alternately in the three phases. This unbalances the currents in the three phases and reduces the starting torque somewhat, but neither effect is serious when the drum is used for starting only. Drums for regulating duty have several balanced speed points in addition to some unbalanced points. Figure 197 shows the connections for a drum-type starter. The primary circuit of the motor is not handled in the drum but by an auxiliary magnetic contactor. This contactor may be interlocked with the drum to give either low-voltage release or low-voltage protection, as desired, and in either case the stator cannot be closed unless the drum is in the all-resistance-in position.

Reference to the diagram will show that, with the drum in the off position and with the primary switch closed, the resistances in the three phases are equal. When the drum is moved to the first running point, resistance step $R1–R2$ is short-circuited. On the second point, resistance $R1–R12$ is short-circuited. These two points give unbalanced conditions. On the third point, resistance $R1–R22$ is cut out, and the resistance is balanced again. The same procedure is followed for the remaining points, every third point being balanced. It will be noted that the resistor is star-connected. This is the most common connection.

Reversing drums for slip-ring motors have the reversing contacts included in the drum, these contacts changing the primary circuit of the motor. Oil-immersed primary contacts handle the stator circuits

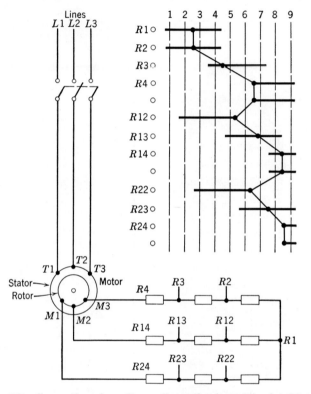

Fig. 197. Connections for a Drum Controller for a Slip-ring Motor.

of 2200-volt motors. The rotor circuits are similar to those of non-reverse drums. A typical drum controller is shown in Fig. 198.

Motor-driven Drums. In some applications, particularly large motors, close automatic speed regulation is desired; for this purpose motor-driven drums are used. Stokers and blowers in power plants and large air-conditioning units are typical examples. The drums usually operate to vary resistance in the rotor circuit, the stator being connected to the power lines through a contactor or circuit breaker. The resistor is usually mounted separately from the drum controller.

FIG. 198. Drum Controller for a Slip-ring Motor.

FIG. 199. General Electric Motor-operated Drum Controller with 20 Balanced Speed Points. Rated at 600 Amperes and 1000 Volts.

NEMA standard sizes for motor-driven drums are given in Table 31. All speed points are balanced.

TABLE 31

MOTOR-DRIVEN DRUMS

8-hour Rating, amperes	Number of Speed- regulating Points
300	13
300	20
600	13
600	20

Figure 199 shows a motor-driven drum with the covers removed from the motor drive and from the contact mechanism. The frame of the drum is of fabricated steel with cast top and bottom plates. The contacts, of copper, are opened and closed by cams on the operating shaft. Each contact arm carries two contacts, both of which are connected to the middle leg of the resistor. They make contact simultaneously with stationary contacts, one connected to each of the outside legs of the resistor. Therefore, the closing of each contact arm short-circuits the resistor at the point to which the contacts are connected.

The motor-operating mechanism consists of a standard fractional-horsepower pilot motor, connected to the drum shaft through suitable gearing. It also includes a positioning switch arranged to insure that the pilot motor, once energized, will run long enough to move the drum from full-on one position to full-on another position. This is sometimes called a step-by-step device, and its purpose is to prevent operation with the drum contacts only partly engaged. Limit switches are also included, to stop the pilot motor at each limit of the drum rotation, and a manually operated lever is provided so that the drum may be operated by hand if for any reason the pilot motor cannot function.

Motor-driven drums are sometimes built with sliding copper contact segments and contact fingers, similar to the manual drum construction (Fig. 74). With this construction it is difficult to get a large number of balanced points, since the required number of contact fingers becomes too great to get into a reasonable space. If unbalanced points are used, commutating resistance in one leg at a time, the drum must be arranged so that these are accelerating points only, and any running position must be a balanced point.

Magnetic Starters. Magnetic controllers used simply for starting a slip-ring motor include a magnetic contactor and overload relay for the stator winding and a suitable number of magnetic contactors to commutate the resistor in the rotor circuit. In starting, the stator contactor is closed when the starting button is operated. Electric interlocks on the stator contactor complete a circuit for the resistor contactors, which close in sequence under the control of some type of accelerating device. Timing relays are most general, but series

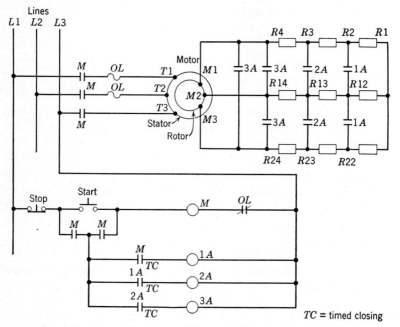

FIG. 200. Connections for a Magnetic Slip-ring Motor Starter.

current relays are also used. If reversing is required, the stator contactor is replaced by a pair of mechanically interlocked contactors, one of which closes in each direction of travel.

The horsepower ratings of these controllers are the same as those of across-the-line starters for squirrel-cage motors, and they are made in sizes from NEMA size 1 (25 amperes) up. Of course, the resistor contactors must be selected to suit the rotor current, which will vary widely with different motors of the same horsepower rating. The resistor is usually connected in star, and three-pole contactors connected in delta are used to short-circuit the sections as shown in Fig. 200. With large motors a delta-connected resistor or parallel-star or parallel-delta connections may be economical. These connections permit the use of smaller contactors, and in the larger sizes the difference in the cost of one size of contactor over another is considerable. In the smaller sizes the difference in cost is not so great, and the saving does not warrant the extra complication of the circuit.

Speed Regulation. Speed regulation may be secured by means of the same kind of controller, except that the resistor contactors are arranged to be individually energized from a master controller or some form of multipoint pilot device. The resistor must then be designed for continuous duty on any point.

Speed Setting. Speed setting is desirable on printing presses and some other machines. This means that the speed-regulating master

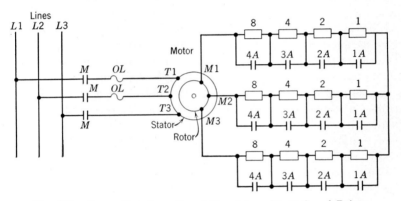

Fig. 201. Connections for a Speed Regulator with 16 Speed Points.

may be left on any desired speed, and, when the motor is stopped and restarted from the pushbutton station, it will run at the speed at which it was originally running. There is no difficulty about this if the amount of speed reduction is small, but if it is large the resistor required for the speed reduction will limit the starting current to an amount too low to start the motor. A printing press, for example, may have a point in its cycle at which a very high torque is required. When the press is running, the inertia of the machinery will carry it through the high-torque point easily; but, if it happens to stop at that particular point, it will take a high torque to restart it. The difficulty may be overcome by connecting a so-called high-torque contactor into the rotor circuit at the point which will short-circuit just enough resistance to provide the maximum motor torque. When the starting button is operated, the high-torque contactor closes at the same time that the line contactor closes, and it remains closed as long as the operator keeps his finger on the button. When the motor has accelerated, the operator releases the button and the high-torque contactor opens, inserting additional resistance as determined by the setting of the speed-selecting master.

If a relatively small number of speeds is desired, one resistor contactor is used for each speed point, but, if a large number of speeds is necessary, that arrangement would result in a large and expensive controller. To secure a large number of speeds with a small number of contactors, the resistor steps are tapered in ohmic value according to a geometric ratio, and contactors are closed in various combinations instead of a fixed sequence. For example, with four resistor steps, the ohmic values of the steps would be in the ratio 1, 2, 4, 8, and there would be four contactors, one arranged to short-circuit each step. Referring to Fig. 201, if the total resistance were 15 ohms, closing contactor 1 only would leave 14 ohms in circuit. Closing 2 only would give 13 ohms. Closing numbers 2, 3, and 4 would give 1 ohm. It will be evident that with the four contactors it is possible to get 16 speeds. Using five contactors, it is possible to get 32 speeds.

Crane and Hoist Control. Magnetic control for a crane bridge or trolley motor is made up of a pair of magnetic reversing contactors with a disconnecting knife switch and suitable overload relays for the motor stator, and a number of magnetic contactors to commutate resistance connected in the rotor winding. A multipoint master gives about 5 speeds in each direction. The first point in either direction closes one of the direction contactors, and, with all resistance in circuit, about 80 per cent torque is obtained. This is a low-torque starting point and also a plugging point. Succeeding positions of the master close the rotor contactors in sequence, giving successively higher speeds, until on the last point the rotor is short-circuited. The rotor contactors may be controlled either by series current relays or by any of several methods of timing. The resistor is usually star-connected, so that two-pole contactors may be used to commutate it. The stator contactors may be either two three-pole devices or three two-pole devices. The latter is preferable, as one contactor may be used as a main contactor, closing in both directions; it will then permit stopping the motor if a ground or other fault prevents the direction contactor from opening.

When a crane hoist is equipped with a wound-rotor motor, and the gearing is such that the load will overhaul and drive the motor when lowering, some special provision must be made to permit safe handling of the load in the lowering direction. Small cranes which do not require accurate stopping or spotting of the load may simply be equipped with a foot-operated brake, no provision being made for a slowdown before stopping. Some cranes are equipped with a device called a load brake, which remains released as long as the motor is driving the load down but automatically sets to provide a braking action when the load begins to overhaul the motor. With either of these arrangements, the control need be only simple reversing equipment, as previously described. Brakes for retarding the load are subject to a good deal of wear and to heating, and so, particularly for larger motors, methods of obtaining electric braking have been developed. Two methods are common, one known as countertorque lowering or plugging lowering, and the other as the unbalanced-stator method.

Countertorque Lowering. Figure 202 shows the connections for a controller with the countertorque method of lowering a load. The controller has the following devices:

H	Two-pole hoisting contactor
L	Two-pole lowering contactor
M	Two-pole main contactor
OL	2 overload relays
KS	Main and control circuit knife switches
$1A$–$2A$–$3A$	3 single-pole speed-selecting contactors
$4A$–$5A$–$6A$–$7A$	4 double-pole speed-selecting contactors
SR	A three-coil series relay
UV	Double-pole undervoltage relay
$1C$	Double-pole control relay

The resistor steps $R1$, $R11$, and $R21$ are so high in ohmic value that it is not necessary to delay or control the operation of contactors $1A$, $2A$, and $3A$ by any accelerating means. Contactor $4A$ is controlled by the series relay SR. No method of controlling $5A$ and $6A$ is shown. Any of the common accelerating means, timing relays, series relays, frequency relays, etc., may be used for that purpose.

The undervoltage relay is closed in the off position of the master; thereafter it maintains its own circuit and sets up a circuit for one side of coils M, H, and L. If power fails, or if an overload occurs, UV opens, and the master must be returned to the off position to restart.

To hoist, the master is moved to the first position in that direction, and contactors M, H, $1A$, $2A$, and $3A$ close. The resistor remaining in circuit will allow a starting torque of about 80 per cent of full-load torque. This is provided to permit taking up a slack cable. On the second point contactor $4A$ closes, increasing the torque to about 150 per cent of full-load torque. The series relay SR is set to remain closed and does not delay the closing of $4A$. However, if the motor had been running in the lowering direction and was then plugged to the hoisting direction, the relay would function on the high inrush

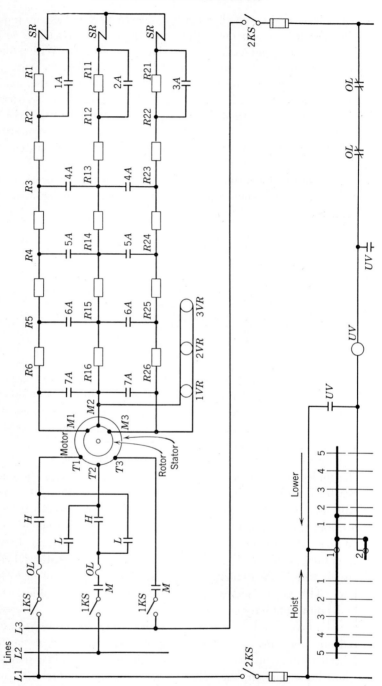

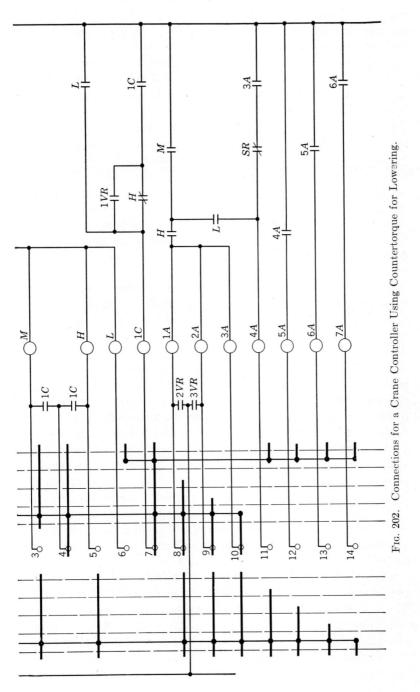

FIG. 202. Connections for a Crane Controller Using Countertorque for Lowering.

current and would delay the closing of 4A. Contactor 4A is, then, the plugging contactor, and resistor steps $R2$, $R12$, and $R22$, are the plugging resistor steps. On the third and fourth points hoisting, contactors 5A and 6A are closed, further increasing the speed. Contactor 7A closes on the fifth point, and the motor runs at full speed. The operator may move the master back or ahead to any hoisting point, selecting the one that gives him the speed he desires.

On the first point in the lowering direction, contactor M closes, but the motor is not energized because L does not close. No other contactors are closed on this point or on points 2, 3, and 4. Nothing happens until point 5 is reached, and on that point the motor is energized in the lowering direction by the closing of contactor L. If the master is left on that point, contactors 4A, 5A, 6A, and 7A will close in sequence, under the control of their accelerating means, and the motor will be brought up to full speed. This point is used to drive down an empty hook or a light load. It may also be used to lower an overhauling load, and the lowering speed will then be a little higher than synchronous speed. On the fifth point the relay 1C is energized by a circuit through an interlock contact of L.

Now, if the master is moved back to point 4, L will open and H will close, circuit for H being made through the contacts of 1C. All the seven rotor circuit contactors are opened and the motor is connected for hoisting, but with a high resistance in the rotor. The torque in the hoisting direction is too low to hoist the load, but, since it is opposing the pull of the overhauling load, it acts as a brake and retards the speed. Moving the master back to point 3 will further increase the braking torque by closing 1A and decreasing the resistance in the rotor circuit. The speed will be decreased. On point 2 contactor 2A closes, further increasing the braking torque, and similarly on point 1 contactor 3A closes, increasing it again. The master may be moved back or ahead to any of the first four points, increasing or decreasing the braking torque to secure the desired control of the load, and on these points the motor will be connected in the hoisting direction so long as the load is heavy enough to overcome the hoisting torque applied.

When the master is moved to the off position, the magnetic brake (not shown) is set to stop the motor. Contactors M, H, 1A, 2A, and 3A are kept energized until the motor stops, so that the countertorque may assist the brake. This is done by the relay 1VR, which may be a voltage relay or a frequency relay, having its coil connected across the rotor of the motor and set to open at a voltage or a frequency corresponding to practically zero speed.

Referring to Fig. 203, which shows the speed-torque curves obtained with a controller of this kind, it will be evident that the curves on the countertorque points are rather flat, so that changes in the load will result in relatively great changes in speed. Also, if the operator

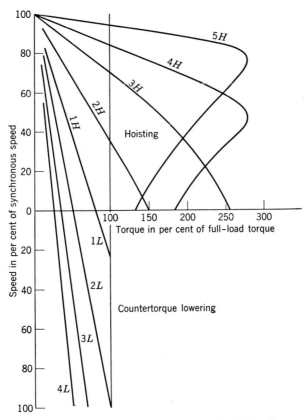

Fig. 203. Speed-torque Curves for a Crane Controller Using Countertorque for Lowering.

misjudges the load and tries to lower with too little retarding torque, the motor is likely to overspeed dangerously. Relays $2VR$ and $3VR$ are used to guard against this possibility. They are voltage or frequency relays, like $1VR$, and have their coils connected across the rotor slip rings. Relay $2VR$ is set so that, if the master is on point 3 and the motor begins to overspeed, the relay will close and energize contactor $2A$. If the speed is still too high, relay $1VR$ will close and energize $3A$.

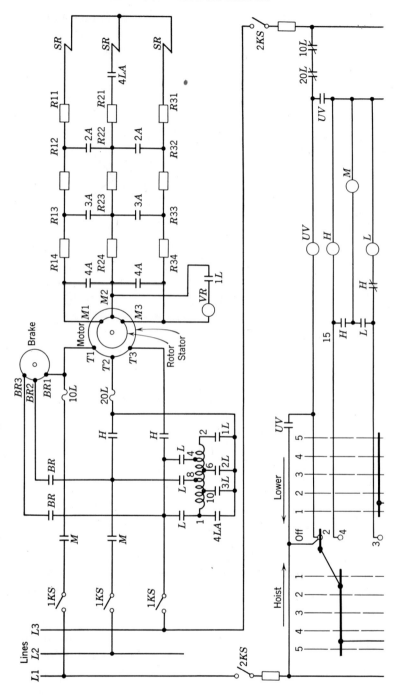

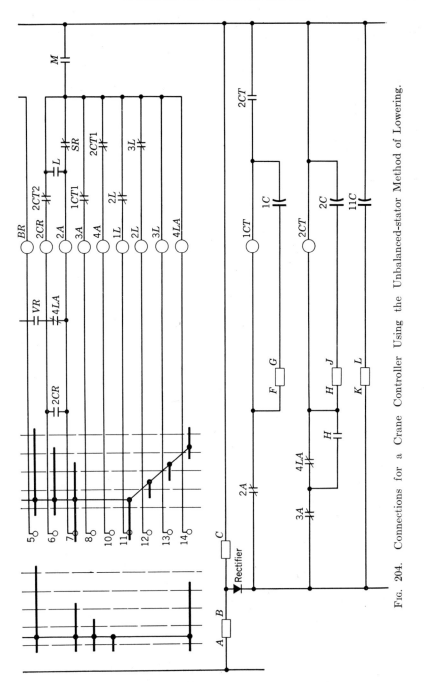

Fig. 204.   Connections for a Crane Controller Using the Unbalanced-stator Method of Lowering.

Countertorque control is used for cranes and hoists, for coal-handling bucket hoists, and for car-hauling hoists in mines. It offers a method of obtaining speed control of an overhauling load electrically. It requires more contactors and relays than a straight reversing controller, and it also requires about 50 per cent more resistor material.

Unbalanced Stator Method. Figure 204 shows the connections for a hoist controller with the unbalanced-stator method of control. In hoisting, the circuit is the conventional three-phase arrangement, with resistance connected in the rotor circuit for speed regulation. In lowering, the voltages applied to the stator are unbalanced. An autotransformer is connected across two of the power lines, and a series of contactors connects the motor to one of several voltage taps. Voltages both lower and higher than normal are applied.

When a motor stator is connected to an unbalanced voltage supply, the effect is the same as if two rotating fields were produced, rotating in opposite directions. One tends to rotate the motor clockwise; the other counterclockwise. The relative strength of the two fields may be varied by varying the amount of unbalance of the stator voltages and by varying the resistor in the rotor circuit. The resultant torque on the motor shaft is equal to the algebraic sum of the two opposing torques. The system is comparable to two identical motors mechanically coupled to the same load and connected for rotation in opposite directions. Such a system could be made to run at any desired speed, and in either direction, by varying resistance in the two rotor circuits.

By properly selecting the unbalancing voltage and the rotor-circuit resistance, steep speed-torque curves, like those of a direct-current dynamic lowering hoist, may be obtained. Typical curves are shown in Fig. 205, and it will be evident that their characteristics are much more desirable than those of the reverse-torque method of control.

In hoisting, the low torque on the first point is obtained with all rotor resistor in circuit and with one phase of the rotor open. This is a slack cable take-up point. The other four curves show the torques and speeds obtained by successive closing of the rotor circuit contactors. On all these points the stator voltage is balanced.

In lowering, the first, second, and third speeds are obtained by the selection of suitable taps on the transformer and with a rotor circuit resistance of 50 per cent of E/I. The stalled torque of 10 per cent on the first point is selected to provide a minimum lowering speed without applying enough reverse torque to hoist an empty hook. The fourth and fifth speed points are obtained with full voltage on the motor and rotor resistances of 50 and 100 per cent of E/I, respectively. When transferring from the third to the fourth speed point, the total resistance is first inserted to reduce the current inrush and the motor is permitted to accelerate along curve 5L. A timing relay then operates to reduce the resistance and transfer the motor operation to curve 4L.

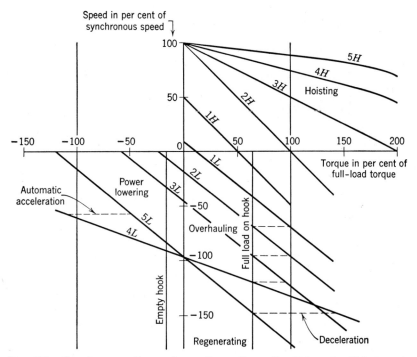

Fig. 205. Speed-torque Curves for a Crane Controller Using the Unbalanced-stator Method of Lowering.

Referring to the diagram of Fig. 204, the following is a list of the devices used:

M	Double-pole main contactor
H	Double-pole hoist contactor
L	Three-pole lower contactor
1L–2L–3L	3 single-pole contactors for changing transformer taps
4LA	Double-pole contactor for transformer and resistor connection
2A–3A–4A	3 double-pole resistor contactors
10L–20L	2 overload relays
UV	Double-pole undervoltage relay
BR	Double-pole brake relay
1CT–2CT	2 condenser-type timing relays
SR	Three-phase current relay for plugging
2CR	Single-pole control relay
VR	Single-pole voltage or frequency relay
1J–2J	Condensers for the timing relays
11J	Smoothing condenser for rectifier

The hoisting operation is as follows:

In the off position, relay UV closes and thereafter maintains its own circuit.

On the first point, contactors M, H, and relay BR close.

The brake is released, and the motor starts with one rotor phase open.

On the second point, contactor $4LA$ closes, closing the complete rotor circuit.

On the third point, contactor $2A$ closes, increasing the torque and speed.

On the fourth point, contactor $3A$ closes, further increasing the speed.

On the fifth point, contactor $4A$ closes, short-circuiting the rotor for full motor speed.

If the master is moved rapidly, the closing of the accelerating contactors will be delayed by the timing relays $1CT$ and $2CT$.

The lowering operation is as follows:

On the first point, contactors L, M, and relay BR close, followed immediately by contactors $2A$ and $1L$. The stator of the motor is then connected to the lines through tap 2 of the transformer, and unbalanced voltages are applied to the three phases. The rotor resistor is balanced at about 50 per cent of E/I. Relays $1CT$ and $2CT$ are energized, and relay $2CR$ is prevented from closing. The speed-torque curve for this point is curve $1L$.

On the second point, contactor $1L$ is opened and contactor $2L$ is closed. The stator is now connected to tap 6 of the transformer, and the applied voltages are unbalanced to a different degree. The curve for this point is $2L$.

On the third point, contactor $2L$ is opened and contactor $3L$ is closed. The stator is now connected to tap 10 of the transformer, and the unbalance of the applied voltages is again changed.

The curve for this point is $3L$.

When the master is moved to the fourth point, contactors $3L$ and $2A$ are opened and $4LA$ is closed. The applied stator voltages are unbalanced, and the rotor circuit resistance is increased to 100 per cent of E/I. The motor characteristic is now shown by curve $5L$. An interlock contact of $4LA$ de-energizes the relay $2CT$, and after a time interval $2CT$ operates, closing the circuit to $2CR$, and through $2CR$ to $2A$. When $2A$ closes, the resistance is again reduced to 50 per cent of E/I and the motor characteristic is that shown by curve $4L$. This method of transfer avoids an objectionable current inrush which would be obtained with an empty hook, if the transfer were made directly from curve $3L$ to curve $4L$. On the fifth point of the master, relay $2CR$ and contactor $2A$ are opened. This provides an increase in the lowering speed to about 150 per cent of rated motor speed, with full load on the hook, as shown by curve $5L$.

Deceleration is accomplished by moving the master back step by step to any desired point. If the master is moved to the off position when the motor is running at a low speed, all relays and contactors except UV drop open, and the motor is disconnected and the brake set to hold the load. If the speed of the motor is not low, the relay VR will remain closed, maintaining the circuit to contactors L, M, $1L$, and $2A$, and so providing a negative torque to stop the motor. At or near zero speed, VR opens and all contactors are de-energized.

Braking with Direct Current. The idea of applying direct current to one phase of the stator winding to obtain a braking torque when lowering a load is old in the art but, to the best of the author's knowledge, has not been used to any great extent. This is probably because of the extra motor-generator set required and the fact that the direct current must be supplied by a generator specially built for the particular application. The controller is of a conventional reversing design, as used to control the bridge or trolley motions of a crane, with the addition of a double-pole contactor for connecting the direct-current supply to one phase of the motor stator when lowering.

With direct current so applied, and with an overhauling load turning the motor, a voltage is generated in the rotor, and current flows in the rotor windings and through the resistor connected in the rotor circuit. The energy of the falling load is dissipated as heat in the resistor, and dynamic braking is secured.

The braking effect may be varied from the master controller in either of two ways. The rotor circuit resistance may be varied by closing the accelerating contactors, one at a time. The more usual method is to vary the voltage of the direct-current generator by changing the strength of its field. Small relays controlled from the master are used for this purpose. The second method permits adjustment of each speed point to the exact value desired, whereas, with the first method, the speeds are fixed by the design of the resistor, which is determined by the requirements of hoisting.

In order to develop full-load retarding torque, it is necessary to apply direct current equal to 100 to 130 per cent of the normal stator current. The direct voltage required is determined by the current and by the resistance of the stator. A rough approximation of the direct-current power required would be one-eighth of the power of the hoist motor. The direct voltage might be about 32 volts for a 550-volt alternating-current supply. In order to permit driving down an empty hook or a light load, one point on the lowering side of the master is arranged to disconnect the direct current and accelerate the motor to full speed on alternating current.

Ratings. For any of the above-described crane and hoist controllers, NEMA standard ratings are given in Table 32. These ratings are for contactors in the motor primary, or stator, winding.

TABLE 32

RATINGS OF CRANE CONTROLLERS

8-hour Rating, amperes	Crane Rating, amperes	Hp at 220 volts	Hp at 440 and 550 volts
50	50	15	25
100	133	40	75
150	200	60	125
300	400	150	300
600	800	300	600
900	1200	450	900
1350	1800	600	1200

Accelerating contactors should be equipped with blowouts and should have a crane rating of not less than the full-load secondary (rotor) current of the motor. When used for motor secondary control, the ampere rating of a three-pole alternating-current contactor, with its poles connected in delta, is 1.5 times its standard crane rating.

The number of accelerating contactors exclusive of the plugging contactors for reversing controllers, and of the low-torque contactor for hoist controllers, is as follows:

Motor Horsepower Rating	Minimum Number of Accelerating Contactors
15 and less	2
16 to 75	3
76 to 200	4
Above 200	5

Electric Load Brake. The thrustor-operated brake, described in Chapter 20, may be used as an electrically operated load brake to control the speed of an overhauling load. A reversing magnetic controller, having a resistor connected in the rotor circuit and a set of accelerating contactors to commutate the resistor, is used. In hoisting, the motor of the thrustor brake is connected to the stator side of the main motor and so operates at full voltage and frequency to release the brake. The slowest lowering speed is obtained by opening the rotor circuit of the motor and connecting the thrustor motor to the rotor slip rings. Since the hydraulic pressure of the thrustor is obtained by means of a straight-blade impeller acting as a centrifugal pump, the pressure varies approximately as the square of the speed of the thrustor motor. The speed of that motor is determined by the frequency of the power supplied to it or, in other words, by the speed of the main motor. With the main motor rotor circuit open, the motor will not deliver any torque. A light overhauling load will turn the motor slowly, the frequency at the slip rings will be high, and the brake will be almost entirely released. A heavy overhauling load will turn the motor faster, the frequency at the slip rings will be lower, and the brake will be partially set. The degree of braking obtained will be determined by the load.

The second lowering point gives a higher speed by closing one phase of the rotor-circuit resistor. The motor delivers a low torque, and the net torque is the difference between the torque of the motor and that of the brake. The third point gives a still higher speed by connecting in the entire three-phase resistor and so increasing the motor torque. On the fourth and fifth points the thrustor is transferred to the stator side of the motor and the brake is completely released. The speeds will be above synchronous speed in an amount determined by the amount of resistance in the rotor circuit and by the amount of the overhauling load.

Speed Adjustment by Concatenation. Two induction motors are said to be connected in concatenation, or cascade, when their shafts are rigidly coupled together and when the secondary winding of the first motor is electrically connected to the primary winding of the second motor. When the motors are connected so that they tend to revolve in the same direction, they are said to be in direct concatenation; when they tend to revolve in opposite directions, they are said to be in differential concatenation. The change from one to the other is accomplished by reversing one phase of the secondary winding of the first motor. One of the motors must be of the slip-ring type; the other may be either a squirrel-cage or a slip-ring motor. With two motors in cascade, a total of four economical speeds is available. Either motor alone may be connected to the line, or the two may be connected in direct or differential cascade. In cascade the motors will run at a speed equivalent to that of a motor having the same number of poles as the two motors together, adding the poles for direct cascade and subtracting for differential cascade. The speed in cascade may be determined from the equation

$$\text{Rpm} = \frac{\text{Frequency} \times 120}{P1 + P2}$$

$P1$ is the number of poles of the first motor, and $P2$ of the second motor.

Cascade control is not very practicable. The exciting volt-amperes of the set will be the sum of those of the individual motors. The reactance also will be the sum of those of the two machines. With two equal motors, the combined output at pullout will be less than half of the output of one machine alone. The losses of the set will be the sum of those of the two machines, so that the efficiency will be low. A differential cascade set will not have sufficient torque to accelerate but must be brought up to speed by the second motor alone.

The Kraemer System. There are several methods of controlling the speed of a slip-ring motor which necessitate auxiliary machines. The general principle is the introduction of a countervoltage into the rotor circuit of the motor to increase the slip at any given load and speed. The slip energy, which is lost with resistance control, is saved with these control systems, being either returned to the line as electric energy or converted to mechanical power and applied to the shaft of the main motor. The cost of the auxiliary machines limits the use of these systems to large motors, where the energy saved will justify their cost. They are used for main mill drives in steel mills, where the motors may be from 500 to several thousand horsepower in rating, for the cutter motors on large dredges, and for similar applications.

Figure 206 shows the arrangement of a constant-horsepower Kraemer system. The main motor is started as a conventional slip-ring motor by the use of a resistor in the rotor circuit. When the motor is up to speed it is disconnected from the starting resistor by the opening of contactor S, and the rotor is connected to the alternating-current winding of a rotary converter by the closing of the running contactor R. An auxiliary direct-current motor, mechanically connected to the shaft of the main motor, has its armature connected to the direct-current winding of the converter. The field windings of the converter and the direct-current motor are separately excited. The voltage applied by the converter to the main motor rotor is determined by the countervoltage of the direct-current motor, which may be regulated by varying the strength of the motor field. The speed of the main motor may then be controlled from the direct-current motor field rheostat. Some power-factor correction may be obtained by over-exciting the converter field.

The direct-current motor, instead of being coupled to the shaft of the main motor, may be coupled to a separate generator, connected to return power to the supply lines. With this arrangement the system delivers constant torque.

With either arrangement any desired speed reduction may be obtained, the size of the auxiliary machines becoming larger as the required speed reduction increases. For example, if the system is to provide 50 per cent reduction in speed, the direct-current motor must be capable of delivering half of the main motor rating at half of its speed, and it will be as large as the main motor. Most Kraemer sets are used to provide 25 to 35 per cent speed reduction, with 50 per cent as a practical maximum.

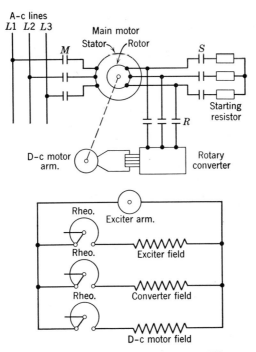

FIG. 206. Connections for a Constant-horsepower Kraemer System.

Since the frequency of the power supplied to the slip rings approaches zero as the speed approaches synchronism, the Kraemer system becomes unstable at speeds near synchronism. For this reason the system is usually limited to operation at speeds below synchronism.

The initial cost of the system is less when 60-cycle power and high machine speeds are used. The constant-horsepower drive will cost less than the constant-torque drive, because of the additional machine required by the latter. It is general practice to bring out both ends of the rotor windings of the main motor, using six slip rings on motor and converter, as this connection results in a less costly converter. With this exception the machines for the Kraemer system are of standard design, as used for many other purposes; this is a decided advantage of the system.

The Scherbius System. Figure 207 shows the arrangement of a Scherbius drive. The system uses two special machines, one for speed regulating and the other for carrying the system through the unstable speed range near synchronism to speeds above synchronism. The regulating machine is similar in construction to a direct-current gen-

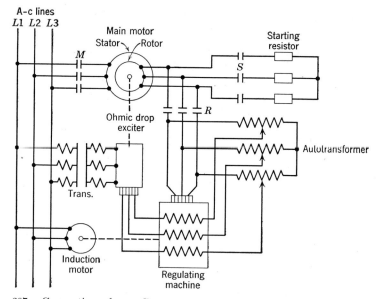

Fig. 207. Connections for a Constant-torque Double-range Scherbius System.

erator and is coupled to an induction motor. The other machine is called the ohmic-drop exciter and is coupled to the shaft of the main motor. The regulator receives its field excitation partly from the slip rings of the main motor, through an autotransformer, and partly from the ohmic-drop exciter. It delivers a three-phase voltage of the same frequency from its alternating-current commutator to the main-motor slip rings.

Speed regulation is obtained by changing the autotransformer tap connections and so varying the field strength of the regulating machine, the field strength determining the value of the voltage applied to the main-motor slip rings. At speeds below synchronism, power flows from the main-motor rotor to the regulating machine, which drives the induction machine as a generator and returns power to the lines.

If the field of the regulating machine is reversed, the direction of power flow will be reversed and the entire system will operate at speeds above synchronism, but provision must be made to carry the system through the unstable range near synchronism. The exciter for that purpose is mounted on the extended shaft of the main motor. It has the same number of poles as the main motor, so that its frequency of rotation is the same. It delivers a constant voltage from its commutator to the field windings of the regulating machine. At speeds near synchronism, when the frequency is approaching zero, this voltage furnishes enough excitation to the regulating machine to enable it to supply current to the main-motor rotor. Since the only opposition is the ohmic drop of that circuit, the machine is known as an ohmic-drop exciter. The current supplied is in excess of that required to drive the load, and it provides the torque necessary to carry through the unstable period into stable speeds above synchronism.

As compared to the Kraemer system, the Scherbius system has the disadvantage of requiring two special machines of types used for that purpose only. It has the advantage of operating readily both below and above synchronism. No direct-current excitation is necessary, all power being drawn from one source of supply. The system is satisfactory for either 60 cycles or 25 cycles, the cost of the regulating machines being greater for 60 cycles. The maximum speed range available for 60 cycles is 2 to 1, whereas for 25 cycles it is 5 or 6 to 1. The cost of the system increases with the speed range. The power factor will be 90 to 95 per cent, or higher, but is not subject to adjustment.

Frequency-changer System. Figure 208 shows the arrangement of a frequency-changer system. The frequency changer is a machine similar in construction to the ohmic-drop exciter of the Scherbius system. It is driven by a small synchronous motor which supplies its mechanical losses. The synchronous motor has the same number of poles as the frequency changer. The slip rings of the frequency changer are connected to the stator of another synchronous motor, which is coupled to the shaft of the main motor and which has the same number of poles as the main motor. The function of the frequency changer is to convert the frequency of the synchronous motor to that of the main-motor rotor without affecting the voltage. Since it rotates at synchronous speed, with slip frequency applied to its commutator, the slip-ring frequency will be the same as that of the synchronous motor, or the difference between line frequency and slip frequency. The terminal voltage of the synchronous motor may then be varied by increasing or decreasing its field strength. This will similarly vary the voltage impressed on the main motor rotor, resulting in a change in the speed of the whole drive.

The frequency-changer system may also be arranged to deliver a constant torque. The frequency changer is then driven from the main

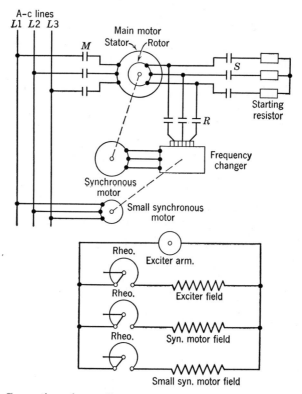

Fig. 208. Connections for a Constant-horsepower Frequency-changer System.

motor shaft, and its slip rings are connected to the power lines through a tap-changing transformer. The synchronous motor is not required. The speed is varied by changing the tap connections to the transformer.

This system has the disadvantage of requiring a special machine, the frequency converter, which is not in general use for other purposes. Its use is confined to 25-cycle power systems and to relatively small speed ranges (10 to 15 per cent on each side of synchronism), although it will carry through the synchronous speed and operate above synchronism. The size and cost of the auxiliary machines are greater at low synchronous speeds and increase with the range of speed control required. The power factor is 90 to 95 per cent and is subject to some adjustment by shifting the brushes of the frequency changer.

Application of the Wound-rotor Motor. The wound-rotor motor is useful where high starting torque with low starting current is desired. Heavy loads can be started slowly and smoothly, without undue line disturbance. It is also used where speed regulation is desired, as on fans, centrifugal pumps, stokers, and printing presses.

The disadvantages of the motor, as compared to the squirrel-cage motor, are the complications of machine, control, and wiring, introduced by the rotor connections, and the higher cost of the motor and control.

The motor is particularly applicable to cranes, hoists, coal-handling bridges, and similar applications, where speed control of a variety of loads is required and where overhauling loads must be safely lowered.

Design of Resistors. Slip-ring Motor. Accelerating. Resistance is used in the secondary circuit of slip-ring motors for acceleration, plugging, and speed regulation. The ohmic value of the resistance is based on the voltage generated in the secondary windings and on the full-load secondary current. The voltage and current, being matters of motor design, vary widely in motors of the same size but of different manufacture. The data for any particular motor, obtainable from the manufacturer, will be given either in volts and amperes or in ohms and amperes. If given in volts and amperes,

E = voltage across the slip rings at standstill.

I = amperes in the secondary winding at full load.

If given in ohms and amperes, the value of ohms is that which would allow full-load amperes to flow, with voltage equal to the open-circuit voltage at standstill. The open-circuit voltage may then be determined from the equation

$$E = R \times I \times 1.73 \tag{1}$$

The values given for the secondary volts and amperes may be checked from the equation

$$\text{Efficiency} = \frac{\text{Hp} \times 746}{E \times I \times 1.73} \tag{2}$$

If the efficiency as calculated from this equation is less than 85 per cent, or greater than 100 per cent, the data are probably incorrect and should be checked with the manufacturer of the motor.

what of power facto??

The controller resistance may be connected in star or in delta. If connected in star, the resistance in each phase is

$$R = \frac{E}{1.73I_s} \qquad [3]$$

where I_s is the starting inrush current.

If connected in delta,

$$R = \frac{1.73E}{I_s} \qquad [4]$$

The resistance taper may be either calculated or determined graphically in the manner described for the shunt motor. The torque may be assumed to be proportional to the secondary current, within practical limits. On the basis of equal inrushes on each point of the controller, and of cutting out the steps when the secondary current falls to 120 per cent, the inrushes and taper shown in Table 33 will apply. One hundred twenty per cent is selected as a safe point to cut out the steps in series relay control. If the current is allowed to drop lower, the inrushes will, of course, also be lower.

TABLE 33

RESISTOR TAPER FOR SLIP-RING MOTORS

Number of Steps	Secondary Inrush	Primary Inrush	Taper of Resistance Steps in per cent of Total
1	320	300	100
2	250	230	70–30
3	210	195	55–30–15
4	180	165	40–30–20–10
5	166	155	34–26–19–13–8
6	155	150	29–23–18.5–13.5–9.5–6.5

Plugging. The total resistance required for plugging is

$$Rt = \frac{1.8E}{1.73I_p} \qquad [5]$$

where I_p is the plugging inrush.

The plugging step is the difference between the total resistance and the accelerating resistance.

Speed Regulating. The speed of a slip-ring motor is inversely proportional to the resistance in the secondary circuit and to the secondary current. The resistance required to give a desired speed reduction is

$$R = \frac{E \times S}{1.73I \times 100} \qquad [6]$$

where S = the slip, or percentage speed reduction.
       I = the current at the reduced speed.

This value of R is the total resistance, including the motor and line drop, and S is the slip as compared to synchronous or no-load speed.

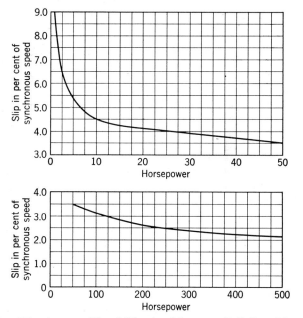

FIG. 209. Average Slip of Slip-ring Motors at Full Rated Load.

For most applications the line drop may be disregarded. Figure 209 shows average values for motor slip at full load. The resistance of the motor may be calculated from these values, and the equation

$$R_m = \frac{E \times S_m}{1.73I \times 100} \qquad [7]$$

where R_m is the resistance of the motor.
       S_m is the motor slip at full load, in per cent of synchronous speed.
       E is the voltage across the slip rings at standstill.
       I is the full-load rotor current per phase, in amperes.

The use of these average values will give sufficient accuracy for most applications. The slip is lower for motors with a small number of poles, and higher for motors with a large number of poles. The values of Fig. 209 are average for 8-pole motors. Values for 4-pole motors would be about 30 per cent lower, and for 16-pole motors about 30 per cent higher. Where extreme accuracy is necessary, actual values for the motor in question should be obtained from the motor manufacturer.

References

M. H. Morgan, "Adjustable-speed Main Roll Drives," *Iron and Steel Engineer,* October, November, 1928.

A. K. Bushman, "Adjustable-speed Main Roll Drives," *General Electric Review,* October, 1923.

C. W. Kincaid, "Variable-ratio Frequency-changer Sets," *Electric Journal,* June, 1928.

B. W. Jones, "Unbalanced Resistance and Speed-torque Curves," *General Electric Review,* September, 1948.

S. A. Vincze, "Three-phase Induction Motors; Views on Starting, Reversal, and Electrical Braking," *Electrician,* 1947, Vol. 139, pp. 541, 605, 689, 768.

H. Gibson, "Wound-rotor Machine Operation," *General Electric Review,* April, 1948.

N. L. Schmitz, "Control of Slip-ring Motors by Means of Unbalanced Primary Voltages," *Transactions AIEE,* 1947, Vol. 66, p. 1103.

N. L. Schmitz, "Application of Low Frequency to Industrial Control Problems," *Transactions AIEE,* 1948, Vol. 67, Part II, p. 1571.

Problems

1. If a wound-rotor motor has a synchronous speed of 1800 rpm and its full-load running speed is 1710 rpm, what is the per cent slip at full-load?

2. If the resistor of a wound-rotor motor controller is designed to obtain 50 per cent speed at 50 per cent torque, what will be the starting torque with the motor at rest?

3. The voltage measured across the slip rings of a 50-horsepower wound-rotor motor at standstill is 260 volts. The motor is 95 per cent efficient. What will be the rotor current in each phase when the motor is operating at full rated load?

4. A wound-rotor motor having the characteristics of Fig. 169 has a rotor voltage at standstill of 175 volts and a rotor current of 75 amperes at full rated load. How many ohms are required in each phase of a star-connected resistor which will enable the motor to produce the maximum possible torque when starting from rest?

5. At what per cent of synchronous speed will the motor run if the resistor is left in circuit and the motor is fully loaded?

6. The manufacturer of a wound-rotor motor says that its rotor characteristics are 230 volts and 1.33 ohms. What is the rotor full-load current? If this is a 50-horsepower motor, what is its efficiency?

7. How many ohms per phase will be required in a star-connected resistor which will limit the initial starting current to 150 per cent of full-load current?

8. How many additional ohms will be required to limit the current to the same value when the motor is plugged?

9. How many ohms will be required in a resistor which will cause the motor to run at 80 per cent speed when 80 per cent loaded?

10. An 1800-rpm wound-rotor motor has secondary characteristics of 250 volts and 150 amperes. When it is running with a resistor in the rotor circuit, a voltmeter measures 75 volts between slip rings. What is the motor speed?

11. A control manufacturer receives an order for controllers for five slip-ring motors. The rotor characteristics are given as follows:

> A   25 horsepower, 115 volts, 98 amperes.
> B   30 horsepower, 1.40 ohms, 75 amperes.
> C   50 horsepower, 200 volts, 85 amperes.
> D   100 horsepower, 1.48 ohms, 150 amperes.
> E   200 horsepower, 2.30 ohms, 600 volts.

Which of these may be accepted as correct, and which are in error?

12. A 150-horsepower slip-ring motor has rotor characteristics of 550 volts and 120 amperes. Calculate the ohms in each step of a two-step resistor, star-connected, which will allow a starting inrush of 250 per cent of rated current. Use a taper of 70–30.

13. Calculate an equivalent resistor for the motor of problem 12, except using two steps each connected in delta, the two deltas being in parallel on the second step.

14. A 100-horsepower slip-ring motor has rotor characteristics of 550 volts and 80 amperes. Its resistance is 5 per cent of E/I. Calculate the ohms required in a star-connected resistor to give 180 per cent inrush on the first starting point.

15. For the motor of problem 14, calculate the ohms in the last two steps of a resistor which will cause the fully loaded motor to run at 85 per cent of rated speed with the last step in circuit, and at 75 per cent of rated speed with the last two steps in circuit.

16. A controller for a motor driving a printing press uses the circuit of Fig. 201. The motor is rated 10 horsepower, 440 volts, three phase, 60 cycles, and the rotor characteristics are 300 volts and 15 amperes. Neglecting motor resistance, calculate the ohms required in each step of a resistor which will permit a total speed reduction of 75 per cent of rated speed.

17. A 20-horsepower slip-ring motor has a controller which gives the characteristic curves of Fig. 193. If the rotor characteristics are 300 volts and 30 amperes, how many ohms will be required in each leg of a star-connected resistor which is designed to give the maximum possible starting torque on the first point?

18. What current would be obtained if the motor of problem 17 is plugged when it is running at half speed?

19. A 75-horsepower slip-ring motor, with rotor characteristics of 400 volts and 78 amperes, is driving a centrifugal pump which has the load characteristics of Fig. 65. Calculate the ohms in each step of a star-connected resistor which will give the operating curves shown in Fig. 65, using a graphical method to derive the resistance taper.

20. Referring to problem 19, what current will be obtained on each step of the resistor, if the resistor is used for speed-regulating duty?

21. A 100-horsepower slip-ring motor has rotor characteristics of 550 volts and 80 amperes. The resistor which is used with it consists of three sections, each consisting of 120 cast-iron grids connected in series. The motor is rewound to have rotor characteristics of 275 volts and 160 amperes. How should the resistor be rearranged to suit these characteristics?

22. A factory has a 40-horsepower slip-ring motor which has been used to drive a machine which required speed control. The motor is to be transferred to another machine which does not require speed control, and the owner asks whether he may now use an autotransformer starter to control the motor. Can this be done, and if so what must be done to the motor?

23. A 25-cycle slip-ring motor has a slip of 5 per cent at full load. What is the frequency of the rotor current under those conditions?

24. An 1800-rpm slip-ring motor on an elevator has a slip of 5 per cent at full load. At what speed will it run when lowering full load, assuming 100 per cent efficiency of the hoisting mechanism?

25. How much resistance, in per cent of E/I, would have to be used in the rotor circuit to permit the elevator to lower a full load at 150 per cent of synchronous speed?

18

SINGLE-PHASE MOTORS

General Description. Single-phase motors are used in large numbers, particularly in fractional-horsepower sizes. Since a single-phase stator winding does not produce a rotating field, a motor provided with that winding only will have no starting torque. Once started, the rotor will set up a pulsating field, which will lag the stator field by 90 degrees and which will be approximately equal to the stator field in strength. The net result will be a rotating field that will keep the motor running in the direction in which it is started. The motor is, then, provided with some form of starting winding, arranged to produce a field out of phase with the stator field, and so produce a starting torque. When the motor has reached 75 or 80 per cent of synchronous speed, the starting winding may be opened, either by a centrifugal switch in the motor or by a relay on the motor controller.

Single-phase motors are more complicated and, therefore, in general, larger and more costly than polyphase motors of the same rating. They find a wide field of application where single-phase power only is available, as in homes and small shops. Typical applications are vacuum cleaners, sewing machines, stokers, food mixers, fans, pumps, small wood- and metal-working tools, portable drills, and countless others.

Types. Single-phase motors are identified by the method of starting which they employ; they fall into one of the following types.

Split phase
Resistance start
Reactor start
Capacitor start
Capacitor
Series (universal)
Repulsion
Compensated repulsion
Repulsion-start induction
Repulsion induction

Motor Ratings. NEMA standard ratings for fractional-horsepower single-phase motors are given in Table 34.

TABLE 34

RATINGS OF FRACTIONAL-HORSEPOWER MOTORS

Brake horsepower	60-cycle Speeds		25-cycle Speeds	
	Synchro-nous	Approximately Full Load	Synchro-nous	Approximately Full Load
1	3600	3450		
¾	3600	3450		
¾	1800	1725	1500	1425
½	3600	3450		
½	1800	1725	1500	1425
½	1200	1140		
⅓ ¼ ⅙ ⅛ ¹⁄₁₂ ¹⁄₂₀	3600	3450		
	1800	1725	1500	1425
	1200	1140		
	900	860		

NEMA standard ratings for open and semi-enclosed, continuous-duty, constant-speed, single-phase, integral-horsepower motors are given in Table 35.

TABLE 35

RATINGS OF INTEGRAL-HORSEPOWER MOTORS

Horsepower	60 cycles Synchronous Speeds				Horsepower	25 cycles Synchronous Speeds			
1		1800	1200	900	1	3000	1500	1000	750
1½	3600	"	"	"	1½	"	"	"	"
2	"	"	"	"	2	"	"	"	"
3	"	"	"	"	3	"	"	"	"
5	"	"	"	"	5	"	"	"	"
7½	"	"	"	"	7½	"	"	"	"
10	"	"	"	"	10	"	"	"	"
15	"	"	"	"	15	"	"	"	"
20	"	"	"	"	20	"	"	"	"
25	"	"	"	"					

Standard voltages for all the above motors are 115 and 230 volts, and standard frequencies are 25 and 60 cycles.

Controller Ratings. Rating of Manually Operated Controllers. Ratings of enclosed, across-the-line, manually operated starters for single-phase motors are given in Table 36.

Rating of Magnetic Controllers. The NEMA ratings of across-the-line magnetic controllers for single-phase motors, given in Table 37,

TABLE 36

RATINGS OF MANUAL CONTROLLERS

NEMA Size	8-hour Rating, amperes	Horsepower at		
		110 volts	220 volts	440–550 volts
0	15	1	1½	1½
1	25	1½	3	5

apply to either two-pole or three-pole contactors for reversing or non-reversing service.

TABLE 37

RATINGS OF MAGNETIC CONTROLLERS

NEMA Size	8-hour Open Rating of Contactor, amperes	Horsepower at		
		110 volts	220 volts	440–550 volts
00	..	½	¾	..
0	15	1	1½	1½
1	25	1½	3	5
2	50	3	7½	10
3	100	7½	15	25

The ratings for reduced-voltage starters are the same as shown in the table, except that these starters are not made in sizes 00 and 0.

When magnetic controllers are used on plug-stop or jogging duty at a rate in excess of five operations per minute, it is recommended that the ratings be reduced to those given in Table 38.

TABLE 38

RATINGS OF CONTROLLERS FOR JOGGING DUTY

NEMA Size	8-hour Open Rating of Contactor, amperes	Horsepower at		
		110 volts	220 volts	440–550 volts
00	..	¼	⅓	..
0	15	½	¾	¾
1	25	1	2	3
2	50	2	5	7½
3	100	5	10	15

The Split-phase Induction Motor. The split-phase induction motor is one of the more popular types, being widely used in fractional-horsepower sizes.

It obtains its starting torque from an auxiliary winding, which is displaced in magnetic position from the main winding and is connected in parallel with the main winding. The auxiliary or starting winding is disconnected by a centrifugal switch, built into the motor and set to open when the motor has reached about 75 or 80 per cent of synchronous speed. The motor may be started in either direction by interchanging the connections of the starting winding; once started, it will continue to rotate in the starting direction.

The starting torque of a split-phase motor varies with the size and speed of the motor, 150 per cent of rated torque being an average value. The starting torque of motors designed for infrequent service will be higher.

Split-phase motors may be wound for two speeds by means of two independent sets of running and starting windings.

The control for these motors is usually very simple, being just a snap switch or some form of manually operated device which connects the motor to the line to start and disconnects it to stop. An overload relay is built into some types of starting switch.

Resistance-start Motor. A resistance-start motor is a form of split-phase motor having a resistance connected in series with the starting winding. The starting circuit is opened when the motor has attained a predetermined speed.

Reactor-start Motor. A reactor-start motor has two windings, as described above, and in addition a reactor connected in series with the running winding during the starting period. When the motor reaches about 75 per cent of full speed, the reactor is short-circuited, and at the same time the starting winding is opened. The purpose of the reactor is to reduce the starting current without substantially reducing the starting torque. The centrifugal switch in the motor has to be a single-pole double-throw device.

The Capacitor-start Motor. A capacitor-start motor is a form of split-phase motor having a capacitor connected in series with the auxiliary winding. The rotor is a squirrel cage, like that of a polyphase motor. The current in the main stator winding lags behind the line voltage; the current in the auxiliary winding leads the line voltage. With suitably designed windings and a suitable capacitor, the two currents will be approximately 90 degrees apart electrically and approximately equal in value. Consequently, the motor will have operating characteristics similar to those of a two-phase motor. The starting current of the motor will be less than that of an equivalent split-phase motor, and the starting torque will be more than twice that of the split-phase motor. The efficiency will be high, and the power factor practically 100 per cent. These characteristics have made the capacitor-start motor very popular, particularly for drives requiring high starting torque, such as refrigerator compressors. The auxiliary winding of small motors is opened by a centrifugal switch when the motor has reached 75 or 80 per cent of synchronous speed. Larger motors may have a separately mounted relay for that purpose.

Since the size of the capacitor required is inversely proportional to the voltage, it is advantageous to keep the voltage relatively high on the starting winding. Some manufacturers wind all motors for 220 volts on the starting winding and supply a small transformer for that winding when used on 110 volts. This has a further advantage in permitting the use of the same control equipment and the same capacitor for all applications.

The Capacitor Motor. A capacitor motor is defined by the American Standards Association as a single-phase induction motor with a main winding arranged for direct connection to a source of power and an auxiliary winding connected in series with a capacitor. The capacitor may be connected into the circuit through a transformer, and its value may be varied between starting and running.

The effect of a capacitor in the circuit when running is to increase the efficiency and power factor and to make the motor run more quietly. The common practice is to have two capacitors: one for starting, which is cut out when the motor is up to speed, and one for running, which is left in circuit. Another method of obtaining the same result is to increase the voltage across the capacitor during the starting period by connecting it to an autotransformer. The transformer may be left in circuit or may be cut out after starting.

Control for Capacitor Motors. The control equipment for a capacitor motor is usually built in two separate units, one consisting of the starter proper and the other of the capacitor and the devices associated with it. The capacitor unit is supplied by the motor manufacturer, but the starter unit is generally purchased separately by the ultimate user of the motor. The starter unit may be any form of line starting device suitable for induction motors. A magnetic contactor with thermal overload relay is frequently used for remote control. A safety switch, or any of the many types of manual starters for small motors, is satisfactory. The control apparatus supplied with the capacitor unit depends on the method of commutating the starting winding. The following are typical forms of control:

1. Capacitor permanently in circuit.
2. Capacitor cut out after starting:
   (a) By current relay.
   (b) By time relay.
   (c) By voltage relay.

3. Part of capacitor cut out after starting:
   (a) By current relay.
   (b) By time relay.
   (c) By voltage relay.
4. Autotransformer, commutated after starting:
   (a) By current relay.
   (b) By time relay.
   (c) By voltage relay.

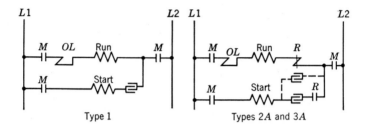

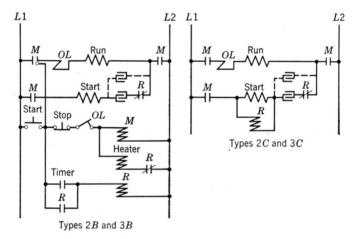

FIG. 210. Connections for Capacitor Motors.

5. Autotransformer, opened after starting:
   (a) By current relay.
   (b) By time relay.
   (c) By voltage relay.

In the diagrams (Figs. 210 and 211) the starting unit is represented by the magnetic contactor M and the thermal overload OL. No auxiliary control is required for type 1; the auxiliary control for types 2 and 3 is the same.

For current control, a current relay has its coil in series with the running winding and a normally open contact in series with the starting capacitor. The initial inrush, when the motor is connected to the line, closes the relay, connecting the capacitor into circuit. When the motor comes up to speed and the current falls, the relay opens, cutting out the capacitor. The relay is adjusted to close at approximately

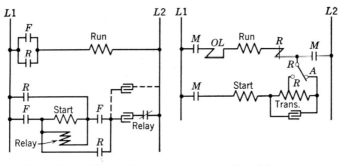

Types 2C and 3C reversing   Type 4A

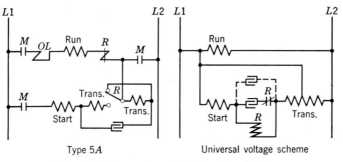

Type 5A   Universal voltage scheme

FIG. 211. Connections for Capacitor Motors.

300 per cent of normal full-load running current and to open at approximately 200 per cent. The starting inrush in the capacitor circuit is 2 to 2½ times rated motor current, and the current at the time the circuit is opened is approximately 30 to 50 per cent of rated motor current. Since the relay coil remains in circuit, the relay will close if the motor tends to stall under load, and the capacitor will be re-inserted. This is not undesirable, as it increases the pullout torque of the motor from approximately 150 to approximately 210 per cent, and so helps to avoid stalling on a peak load. However, the starting capacitor cannot be left in circuit very long, as its rating is usually limited to 5 minutes' service.

There are a number of methods of obtaining time control for starting, generally based on the use of a thermal timing device, because that is the least expensive type of timer. The thermal timer may be made of a piece of bimetal on which a heating coil is wound, or the heating current may pass through the bimetal itself. The action of the device is the same as that of a thermostat. The heater may be connected in the motor circuit or directly across the line or through a transformer across the line. Since the thermal relay is a slow make-and-break device, a relay is generally used with it to handle the motor circuit, and a contact of the same relay may be used to cut off the thermal relay after it has operated. In the arrangement shown in the diagram, the heater of the thermal relay is connected across the line in parallel with the main contactor coil. The contact of the thermal relay energizes a small control relay which opens the capacitor circuit and cuts off the heater.

Control by voltage requires a shunt relay which is normally closed. The coil may be connected across the starting winding of the motor or across the capacitor. The relay is set to open on approximately 120 per cent of line voltage, to hold on normal voltage, and to close if the voltage falls below 90 per cent of normal. The starting capacitor will be re-inserted in case of heavy overload. The voltage scheme also permits plugging the motor in reversing. Connections for this arrangement are shown in the diagram, the contacts F and R being those of the forward and reverse switches. Current control does not work very well for plugging, because the current in the running winding is not the same for forward and reverse connections.

The advantage of an autotransformer to raise the voltage on the capacitor is a considerable saving in the cost of the capacitor. A double-throw relay is required to commutate the transformer. Referring to the diagram, the relay is normally in position a, and when the motor is connected to the line the relay moves to position b. This connects the transformer so that a high voltage is impressed on the capacitor. When the motor is up to speed, the relay returns to position a, reducing the voltage on the capacitor to a value suitable for running. The relay may be of the current type as shown, or of the voltage type, in which event the coil would be connected across the starting winding of the motor. Time-limit control may also be used, the connections then being similar to those shown for type $2b$.

The control for arrangement 5 is similar to that for type 4 except that the transformer winding is in two sections and the relay is connected between the sections so that it will disconnect the transformer entirely after the motor is up to speed. Current, voltage, or time relays may be used.

The last sketch on the diagram shows the arrangement when the starting winding is always operated at the same voltage, regardless of line voltage.

Universal Motor. A universal motor, as defined by the American Standards Association, is a series-wound or a compensated series-wound motor which may be operated either on direct current or single-phase alternating current at approximately the same speed and output. These conditions must be met when the direct and the alternating voltages are approximately the same and the frequency of the alternating current is not greater than 60 cycles per second.

The general construction of the motor is the same as that of a direct-current series motor, and its speed and torque characteristics are also practically the same. The non-compensated motor has field and armature windings connected in series. The compensated motor has an additional winding, also in series with the armature, which improves its operating characteristics by making them more nearly alike on direct and alternating current. The motor is built to stand very high running speeds, and its speed characteristics make it suitable for such applications as vacuum cleaners, portable drills, motor-driven carving tools, and sewing machines. Some motors are equipped with built-in speed governors which hold the speed relatively constant.

Commutation difficulties limit the use of the series motor to low voltages, generally not over 300 volts. The reactance is also a limiting factor, so that it is impractical to design such a motor for frequencies above 25 cycles, except in small sizes. The majority of them are, therefore, of small capacity, and the control required is simple. A snap switch or similar device is sufficient to connect and disconnect the motor. For larger sizes, a magnetic contactor and thermal overload relay may be used. Speed regulation may be obtained by means of a series resistance, for example, the treadle-controlled rheostat of a sewing machine.

Control designers find the series motor useful to drive speed-regulating rheostats for larger motors when these devices are to be operated automatically or by pushbuttons from a remote point. The series motor is then provided with two field windings, and three lead wires are brought out from the motor. One lead wire connects to one side of the armature. The other side of the armature is connected inside the motor to one end of each field winding. The other ends of the two fields are brought out as leads. The armature is then connected to one supply line, and a double-throw pilot device connects either one or the other of the fields to the other supply line. One field is arranged to run the motor forward, and the other backward.

Repulsion Motor. The American Standards Association defines a repulsion motor as follows:

A repulsion motor is a single-phase motor which has a stator winding arranged for connection to the source of power, and a rotor winding connected to a commutator. Brushes on the commutator are short-circuited and so placed that the magnetic axis of the rotor winding is inclined to the magnetic axis of the stator winding. This type of motor has a varying speed characteristic.

The motor is similar to a series motor, and its operating characteristics are similar to those of the series motor. The commutation is better, particularly at speeds near synchronism. The motor may be reversed by shifting the brushes. Otherwise it is controlled in the same manner as the series motor, and the same devices are used.

Compensated Repulsion Motor. The compensated repulsion motor is the same as the simple repulsion motor, except that it has a third winding for compensating purposes. The field winding and the compensating winding may be connected in series and the armature short-circuited, or the field and armature windings may be in series with the compensating winding short-circuited.

The Repulsion-start Induction Motor. A repulsion-start induction motor has the same windings as a repulsion motor, but at a predetermined speed the rotor winding is short-circuited to give the equivalent of a squirrel-cage winding. The motor, therefore, starts as a repulsion motor but operates as an induction motor with constant-speed characteristics. The stator core is laminated and is wound with a single winding. The rotor is wound and is supplied with a commutator. The brushes may be shifted to reverse the direction of rotation. The commutator bars are short-circuited by a centrifugally operated device which, at the predetermined speed, moves into contact with the under side of the commutator bars.

The speed-torque curve is similar to that of a series motor during the starting period, and after the rotor is short-circuited the curve assumes the shape of the curve of a squirrel-cage motor. If plugged, the motor will not reverse but will continue in the same direction. To reverse by changing stator connections, the motor must be allowed to slow down enough to reset the centrifugal device.

Repulsion-induction Motor. A repulsion-induction motor is defined by the American Standards Association as a form of repulsion motor which has a squirrel-cage winding in the rotor in addition to the repulsion motor winding. A motor of this type may have either a constant-speed or a varying-speed characteristic.

The motor, therefore, has a wound stator, and a wound rotor with a commutator. It has brushes which are short-circuited, but no device to short-circuit the commutator, or, in fact, any centrifugal device. The squirrel-cage winding of the rotor is under the main armature winding, and it may be made of high-resistance or low-resistance material. The resistance will affect the torque characteristic just as in a squirrel-cage motor. The starting torque of the motor is high, and the torque does not drop off very much until the motor is up to about 85 per cent of synchronous speed. From that point the torque drops to rated torque at synchronous speed. At no load the motor will run a little above synchronous speed. The motor may be plugged for reversal by interchanging the stator connections.

Types of Controllers. Face-plate starters are used for the larger commutator-type motors. They are similar in construction to those for direct-current motors, and they allow a starting current of about 150 per cent of full-load current. The resistor material is self-contained in the controller.

Manually operated across-the-line starters are made for motors rated 1½ horsepower on 110 volts, 3 horsepower on 220 volts, and 5 horsepower on 440 and 550 volts. They consist of a switch, manually operated by buttons, and a thermal overload relay.

Drum controllers are also used for starting and reversing across-the-line service. They are built up to 5 horsepower on 110 volts and 10 horsepower on 220, 440, and 550 volts.

Magnetic across-the-line starters are similar to those for polyphase motors, having a magnetic line contactor and a thermal overload relay. They are made both in the simple form and with a self-contained disconnect switch which is usually operable from a lever on the outside of the starter enclosure.

Reduced-voltage starters, usually of the resistance type, are used for the larger motors. They are of the same construction as those for polyphase squirrel-cage motors.

A controller for regulating the speed of a repulsion motor by varying the applied voltage is shown in Fig. 212. A transformer is connected to the power supply, and a number of taps are connected to the buttons of a selector switch. This switch is of a special construction, having freedom of motion in a plane parallel to the panel and also, in a lesser degree, in a plane at right angles to the panel. A spring holds the lever tightly against the contact buttons. There is a star wheel, or hill-and-valley device, under the lever, and a roller on the lever rides on the star wheel. When the lever is moved from one button to another, it does not simply slide across them, as that would short-circuit a portion of the transformer winding. The star wheel forces the lever away from the contacts, and so lifts it from one button and places it down on the next button.

The pushbutton is also of a special design. When the start button is pressed, contacts A and C close and B opens. This connects the transformer to the line and connects the motor to a selected tap on the transformer which will supply enough voltage to give a high

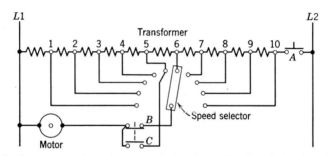

FIG. 212. Connections for a Speed-regulating Controller for Single-phase Motors.

starting torque. Releasing the start button opens contact C and closes contact B, disconnecting the motor from the high-torque tap and connecting it to a tap determined by the setting of the speed-selecting lever. Contact A remains closed, being latched in position. Pressing the stop button releases the latch and opens contact A, disconnecting all circuits. This speed-regulating controller is widely used for the control of small printing presses and fans. It is made for motors rated up to $1\frac{1}{2}$ horsepower on 110 volts and 2 horsepower on 220 volts. Speed regulation to 50 per cent of synchronous speed is the usual practice.

References

H. R. West, "Theory and Calculation of the Squirrel-cage Repulsion Motor," *Transactions AIEE*, 1924, Vol. 43, p. 1048.

L. C. Packer, "Universal-type Motors," *Transactions AIEE*, 1925, Vol. 44, p. 587.

B. F. Bailey, "The Condenser Motor," *Transactions AIEE*, 1929, Vol. 48, p. 596.

C. G. Veinott, *Fractional-horsepower Electric Motors*, McGraw-Hill Book Company, 1939.

C. T. Button, "Single-phase Motor Theory—Correlation of the Cross-field and Revolving-field Concepts," *Transactions AIEE*, 1941, Vol. 60, p. 507.

E. B. Kurtz, "Dynamic Characteristics of a Single-phase Induction Motor," *Transactions AIEE*, 1940, Vol. 59, p. 801.

Problems

1. A garage door is to be opened and closed by a single-phase series motor of the split-field (two fields) type. Make an elementary diagram of the circuit, using up, down, and stop pushbuttons, two double-pole control relays, and two single-pole limit switches.

2. Make an elementary diagram of the same circuit with the addition of a second set of pushbuttons and a transfer switch which in one position permits operation from both sets of buttons, and in another position permits operation only from the station inside the garage.

3. A motor-operated rheostat is driven by a universal-type split-field series motor. In one direction the motor runs at full speed, but in the other direction it runs at a reduced speed obtained by the use of variable resistors in series and in parallel with the armature. Make an elementary diagram of the circuit, using momentary-contact fast and slow pushbuttons, two single-pole limit switches, two control relays, and two variable resistors.

4. The draft door of a furnace is operated by a repulsion-induction motor which is non-reversing. It drives a cam which causes the door to be fully opened after 180 degrees of travel, and fully closed after 360 degrees of travel. Make an elementary diagram of the circuit, using a three-wire thermostat, a limit switch geared to the cam, and the necessary control relays (see Fig. 131).

19

THE SYNCHRONOUS MOTOR

Construction. Synchronous motors have an armature winding connected to an alternating-current supply line, and a field winding connected to a direct-current supply line. They also have a third winding which is short-circuited. It is possible to make either the armature

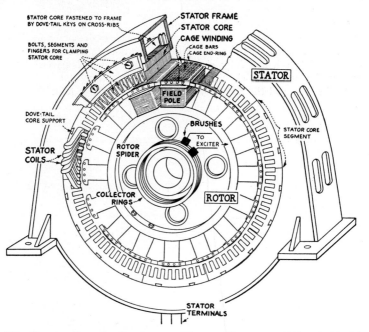

STATOR CORE FASTENED TO FRAME
BY DOVE-TAIL KEYS ON CROSS-RIBS

STATOR FRAME

STATOR CORE

CAGE WINDING

BOLTS, SEGMENTS AND
FINGERS FOR CLAMPING
STATOR CORE

CAGE BARS

CAGE END-RING

STATOR

DOVE-TAIL
CORE SUPPORT

FIELD
POLE

STATOR
COILS

ROTOR
SPIDER

BRUSHES

TO
EXCITER

STATOR CORE
SEGMENT

COLLECTOR
RINGS

ROTOR

STATOR
TERMINALS

FIG. 213. Construction of a Synchronous Motor. (Courtesy of Electric Machinery Manufacturing Company)

or the field stationary, but the common practice is to make the armature stationary and the field rotating. The armature winding is the more complex and is subject to the voltage of the alternating-current supply, which, with large motors, may be as high as 13,200 volts. It is advantageous mechanically to have this winding stationary, and it is also easier to insulate it and to insulate and protect the armature leads. The field winding is energized at 115 or 230 volts, and the slip

454

rings to which the supply lines feed are subject to this relatively low voltage, and so are easy to construct and insulate.

Figure 213 is a vertical cross-section of a synchronous motor like that of Fig. 214. The outer frame is of laminated punchings, having

Fig. 214. Synchronous Motor. (Courtesy of Electric Machinery Manufacturing Company)

1. Stator frame.	6. Field winding.
2. Core clamping plates.	7. Starting cage winding.
3–4. Stator winding.	8. Shaft.
5. Terminal box.	9. Bearing pedestal.

a series of slots around the inner periphery in which the armature winding is placed. The rotating member is a spider mounted on the motor shaft, to which the cores of the field poles are keyed or bolted. The cores are usually of laminated steel, and the field coils are wound around them. Slots are provided in the ends of the field poles in a direction parallel to the motor shaft. Copper bars are placed in the slots, and the ends of the bars on each side of the poles are connected together by an end ring to form a short-circuited squirrel-cage winding. A motor constructed as described is called a salient-pole machine, and the great majority of synchronous motors follow this pattern.

It is also possible to build a motor having stationary salient-pole field windings and a rotating armature. Another possible construction is an embedded field winding wound into slots in laminated punchings like the armature windings. Either armature or field may be the rotating member. This design is seldom used for motors but is advantageous for high-speed turboalternators, as it eliminates much of the windage losses caused by salient poles.

Speed. The speed of a synchronous motor is determined by the number of poles for which the motor is built and by the frequency of the power supply. The equation for the speed is

$$\text{Rpm} = \frac{\text{Frequency} \times 60}{\text{Number of pairs of poles}}$$

The motor will run only at this synchronous speed. If there is a change in the load, there will be an instantaneous change in speed, lasting for a very few cycles, but the average speed will be the same. Table 39, showing standard speeds, is included for ready reference.

TABLE 39

Synchronous-motor Speeds

Number of Poles	Speed		
	25 Cycles	50 Cycles	60 Cycles
2	1500	3000	3600
4	750	1500	1800
6	500	1000	1200
8	375	750	900
10	300	600	720
12	250	500	600
14	214	428	514
16	188	375	450
18	166	333	400
20	150	300	360
22	136	273	327
24	125	250	300
26	115	231	277
28	107	214	257
30	100	200	240
32	94	188	225
36	83	167	200
40	75	150	180

The forty-pole 25-cycle machine is the slowest standard motor of that frequency.

The 50-cycle motor is built in standard sizes to 76 poles and 79 rpm.

The 60-cycle motor is built in standard sizes to 90 poles and 80 rpm.

At any given frequency it is, of course, impossible to obtain speeds higher than those of the two-pole machine.

Torque. Table 40 shows the normal torque characteristics for general-purpose 60-cycle synchronous motors, as given in NEMA Motor and Generator Standards.

TABLE 40

SYNCHRONOUS-MOTOR CHARACTERISTICS

	Speed rpm	Torque Per Cent of Normal Full-load Torque		
		Starting	Pull-in	Pull-out
1.0 power factor to and	1800	110	110	150
including 200 hp	1200–514	110	110	175
1.0 power factor 250 to	1800–514	110	110	150
500 hp, inclusive				
1.0 power factor 600 hp	1800–514	85	85	150
and larger				
0.8 power factor to and	1800	125	125	200
including 150 hp	1200–514	125	125	250
0.8 power factor 200 to	1800–514	125	125	200
500 hp, inclusive				
0.8 power factor 600 hp	1800–514	100	100	200
and larger				

The starting torque is with rated voltage applied to the motor terminals. The pullout torque is with rated voltage and normal excitation supplied. The normal torques for frequencies other than 60 cycles are the same as those for 60-cycle ratings having the same number of poles.

The synchronous motor in itself has no starting torque. One purpose of the short-circuited winding in the field poles is to provide torque for starting. A motor provided with such a winding, and with the field circuit de-energized, starts by induction as a squirrel-cage motor and will reach a speed slightly below synchronism. At that point the field may be energized, and the motor will then pull into synchronism. The squirrel-cage winding also serves to damp out momentary speed changes with changes in load, and for that reason it is generally known as a damper winding. It is also called an amortisseur winding. If the resistance of the damper winding is relatively low, the starting torque will be low, but the motor will approach synchronous speed rather closely. Increasing the resistance of the damper winding will increase the starting torque, but the motor will not approach synchronism so closely. The low-resistance winding is the more effective for damping.

If the torque required by the load exceeds the pullout value, the motor will drop out of synchronism. When this happens, the average torque becomes zero and the motor comes to rest. Typical speed-torque curves are shown in Fig. 217.

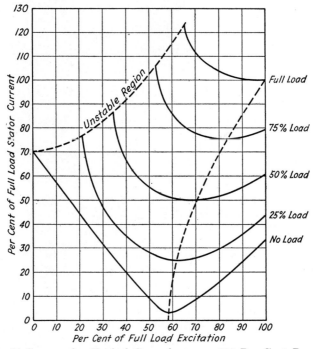

Fig. 215. V Curves of a Typical General-purpose 100 Per Cent Power Factor Synchronous Motor.

Power Factor. The power factor of a synchronous motor may be changed by varying the strength of the direct-current field. Normal excitation is that which produces unity power factor. Underexcitation causes the motor to take a lagging current. Overexcitation results in the motor's taking a leading current. The excitation required to produce any given power factor varies, increasing as the load increases.

Figures 215 and 216 are typical sets of curves showing the excitation required to produce desired power factors at different loads. These are called V curves. Lines drawn through points of equal power factor are called compounding curves.

Advantages. Synchronous motors are sturdy in construction, both electrically and mechanically, and may be wound for high operating voltages. The air gap between rotor and stator may be relatively large, which decreases the chance of rotor and stator striking.

The possibility of running at a leading power factor is an important advantage. For example, a synchronous motor driving a line shaft,

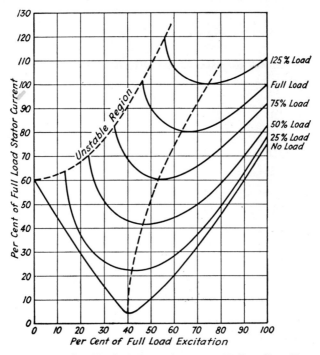

FIG. 216. V Curves of a Typical General-purpose 80 Per Cent Power Factor Synchronous Motor.

in a shop full of induction motors, will materially improve the power factor of the whole installation, at the same time driving a load.

The efficiency of the synchronous motor is higher than that of the induction motor, particularly for slow-speed motors. The efficiency-load curve of a synchronous motor is relatively flat, so that the efficiency at light loads is better than that of a lightly loaded induction motor.

Constant speed may be an advantage, if that is a requirement of the application.

Low starting torque, the necessity of restarting if the motor drops out of synchronism, and the necessity of a direct-current supply are the principal disadvantages.

Application. Synchronous motors are ideal for constant-speed, continuous-running applications where the required starting torque is low. Typical applications are: line shafts, motor-generator sets, air and ammonia compressors, centrifugal pumps, blowers, crushers, and many types of continuous processing mills. When the required starting torque is too great for the motor, a magnetic clutch may be installed

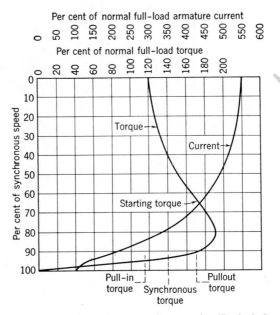

FIG. 217. Speed-torque and Speed-current Curves of a Typical General-purpose Synchronous Motor.

between the motor and its load. The motor is then brought up to synchronous speed while unloaded, after which the load is applied by energizing the clutch.

General Starting Method. To start a synchronous motor it must be brought up to synchronous speed, or nearly so, with the direct-current field de-energized, and at or near synchronism the field must be energized to pull the motor into step. A small induction motor may be mounted on the shaft of the synchronous motor for bringing it up to speed. The induction motor must have fewer poles than the synchronous motor, so that it may reach the required speed. If the exciter which supplies the field is mounted on the motor shaft, it may be used as a direct-current motor for starting, provided that a separate direct-current supply is available to energize it. However, since most synchronous motors are polyphase and are provided with a damping winding, the common practice is to start them as squirrel-cage motors, the torque being supplied by the induced current in the damper winding. Like squirrel-cage motors, they may be connected directly to the line or started on reduced voltage. When they are started on reduced volt-

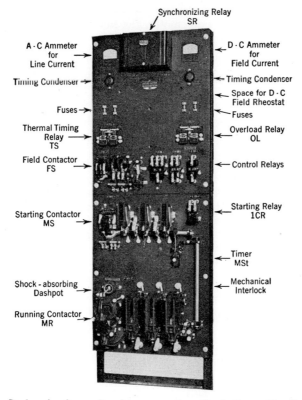

Synchronizing Relay
SR

A · C Ammeter
for
Line Current

D · C Ammeter
for
Field Current

Timing Condenser

Timing Condenser

Space for D · C
Field Rheostat

Fuses

Fuses

Thermal Timing
Relay
TS

Overload Relay
OL

Field Contactor
FS

Control Relays

Starting Contactor
MS

Starting Relay
1CR

Timer
MSt

Shock - absorbing
Dashpot

Mechanical
Interlock

Running Contactor
MR

Fɪɢ. 218.   Reduced-voltage Synchronous-motor Controller with Current-time Method of Synchronization.

age from an autotransformer, the usual practice is to close the starting contactor first, connecting the stator to the reduced voltage, then, at a speed near synchronism, to open the starting contactor and close the running contactor, connecting the stator to full line voltage. A short time later the field contactor is closed, connecting the field to its supply lines. The field may be energized before the running contactor has closed, which will result in a little less line disturbance, but the pull-in torque will be lower.

Since the shunt field winding consists of a large number of turns, special precautions must be taken to insure against a high voltage being generated in it during starting. When the field winding is stationary, as in rotary converters, switches are provided to break it up into sections and so keep down the generated voltage. This method is not practical when the field is rotating, because of the extra slip rings which would be necessary. The usual practice is to short-circuit the field through a discharge resistor, during starting. When the exciter is driven by the synchronous motor, the field may be connected to the exciter before starting and left so connected during starting, because the exciter voltage builds up slowly as the motor accelerates. Motors started in this way usually have a heavy damping winding around the field poles. When a discharge resistor is used its design must be determined by the motor manufacturer, as the ohmic value has a marked effect on the pull-in torque. A reduced-voltage synchronous-motor controller will, in general, consist of the following devices (see Fig. 218):

A starting contactor to connect the stator to reduced voltage.
A running contactor to connect the stator to the line.
An autotransformer to supply the reduced voltage.
A contactor to connect the field to the direct-current supply.
A time-, current-, or frequency-controlled accelerating relay.
An overload protective relay.
A relay to cut the motor off the line if it fails to pull into synchronism.
A field rheostat to adjust the excitation.
A field discharge resistor.
Relays to protect against voltage failure of either alternating or direct current.
Control circuit fuses.
A voltage transformer to supply a safe voltage for the control circuits.
Ammeters to read the alternating load current and the direct field current, to enable the operator to adjust for desired power factor.
A pushbutton station.
Additional instruments, as watt meter, power-factor meter, and voltmeter, are sometimes desired.

Instead of an autotransformer to supply the reduced voltage, any of the methods for starting squirrel-cage motors may be used. These include starting resistance in the stator circuit, starting reactance in the stator circuit, and combinations of reactance and autotransformer. The Korndorfer system of autotransformer connection is also possible.

Synchronizing Means. It will be evident that the control problem specific to the synchronous motor is in the means chosen for transferring the control connections when the motor has reached a speed near synchronism. There are a number of common methods, most of them being based either on time, current, or frequency, or on combinations of these factors. Some of the more common ones are described.

Timed Synchronization. With this method the acceleration and synchronization are based purely on time. Some form of timing relay is operated by the line contactor and started when that contactor closes. When the set time has passed, the relay contacts close and, with across-the-line control, energize the field contactor. The time relay is set for a time long enough to insure that the motor has approached synchronous speed. A reduced-voltage controller will include two such timing relays, one operated by the starting contactor and energizing the running contactor, and the other operated by the running contactor and energizing the field contactor.

Synchronization Based on Frequency. Figure 219 is a simplified diagram of a synchronous-motor controller arranged for starting the motor directly across the line and synchronizing by a relay operating at a selected frequency. All devices such as instruments and overload relays which are not pertinent to the immediate discussion have been omitted. In this diagram:

M is a three-pole line contactor having two normally open interlock contacts, M_a and M_b.

FS is a field contactor having two normally open contacts, and one normally closed contact.

$1CR$ is a control relay having two normally open contacts.

FR is a synchronizing relay having one normally closed contact.

X is a small reactor.

F-D is a field discharge resistor.

When the start button is pressed, the relay $1CR$ closes. One of its contacts provides a maintaining circuit for the relay, and the other contact provides a circuit to energize the line contactor M. When M closes, its main contacts close ahead of its interlock contacts and energize the stator of the motor. Current at supply frequency is induced in the field winding and flows through the discharge resistor and the coil of relay FR. A small proportion of this current flows through the reactor X, but the amount is limited because the frequency is high. Relay FR closes at once and is fast enough to open the circuit to relay FS before the interlock contact M_b closes. Let us, for the moment, neglect the interlock M_a, and the associated coil on FR. Since the reactance of the coil of FR is much lower than that of X, the relay will remain closed at all but very low frequencies. As the motor accelerates, the frequency of the induced current in the field winding decreases, and as it decreases an increasing amount of it flows through

X, until at a speed close to synchronism most of the current is flowing through X. At this point there will no longer be enough current flowing through the coil FR to keep the relay armature closed, and it will open. Field contactor FS then closes, energizing the field and opening the field discharge circuit, and the motor pulls into synchronism.

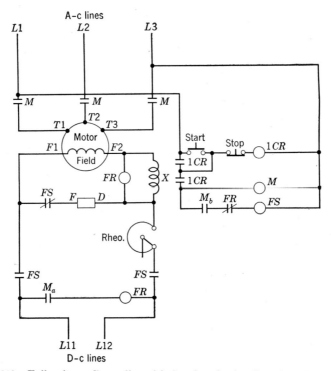

Fig. 219. Full-voltage Controller with Synchronization Based on Frequency.

This is a workable scheme in itself, but the addition of another coil on FR, which is energized by a constant direct current when M_a closes, is a further refinement. This coil polarizes the relay, and its armature will open only when the magnetic effect of the two coils is approximately equal and in opposition. As the motor nears synchronism and the speed of the rotor approaches that of the revolving stator field, the poles of the rotor pass the stator poles relatively slowly. As each pair of poles passes, there occurs a relative position which is most favorable for synchronizing, as when a north pole of the rotor is directly aligned with a south pole of the stator. Polarizing of the synchronizing relay provides a means not only of energizing the field at a speed near synchronism but also of energizing it at a point in the alternating-current wave which is most favorable to synchronism.   If the motor should pull out of step because of an overload or for some other reason, alternating current would again be induced in the field winding, and the *FR* relay would close its armature, open contactor *FS*, and permit the motor to speed up and resynchronize.

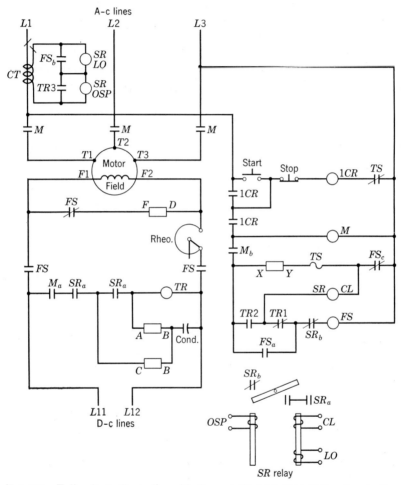

F<small>IG</small>. 220.   Full-voltage Controller with Current-time Method of Synchronization.

Current-time Method of Synchronization.   Figure 220 is a simplified diagram of a synchronous-motor controller similar to that shown in Fig. 219, but using a synchronizing method based on current and time. In this diagram:

M is a three-pole line contactor having two normally open interlock contacts, M_a and M_b.

FS is a field contactor having two normally open contacts, one normally closed contact, and three interlock contacts, FS_a and FS_b normally open, and FS_c normally closed.

$1CR$ is a control relay having two normally open contacts.

F–D is a field discharge resistor.

TR is a timing relay which operates instantaneously when voltage is applied to its coil but is delayed in operation when de-energized. The time delay is obtained by discharging a capacitor through the relay coil, and high resistance A–B. A relatively low resistance, C–B, is used to charge the capacitor rapidly when TR is energized. The relay has one normally closed contact, $TR1$, and two normally open contacts, $TR2$ and $TR3$.

TS is a thermal timing relay having one normally closed contact.

SR is the synchronizing relay having three coils and three contacts. Coils OSP and LO are series coils, responsive to the current drawn by the motor. They are operated through a current transformer, CT. Coil CL is a shunt coil. The relay has a walking-beam contact member, which is moved by either of two plunger elements and which will remain in either of two positions. It is not biased by springs. If, for instance, coil OSP is energized, its plunger will lift, rotating the walking-beam to open contact SR_b and close contact SR_a. If coil OSP is now de-energized, the plunger will drop, but the relay contacts will remain as they are. To reclose SR_b and open SR_a, the other plunger must be operated by coil CL. Coil LO is opposed in action to CL and tends to prevent the plunger from lifting.

When the start button is pressed, the relay $1CR$ closes. One of its contacts provides a maintaining circuit for the relay, and the other contact provides a circuit to energize the line contactor M. When M closes, its main contacts close ahead of its interlock contacts and energize the stator of the motor. Inrush current flows through the current transformer, and SR coils LO and OSP are energized. Coil LO holds down the right-hand plunger of SR, and coil OSP lifts the left-hand plunger. Contact SR_a is closed, energizing TR and charging the capacitor. Contact SR_b is opened. Coil CL is energized by interlock M_b, but not until after coil LO has been energized. Coil CL therefore cannot operate the right-hand plunger. When TR is energized, its contact $TR1$ opens, and contacts $TR2$ and $TR3$ close. Coil OSP is short-circuited, and its plunger drops, but the relay contacts do not change position. As the motor accelerates the inrush current decreases, with corresponding decrease in the current through coil LO. The relay is set so that, when the motor current has reached a value of approximately 175 per cent of normal current, the pull of coil CL will overcome that of coil LO, and the right-hand plunger will lift, closing contact SR_b and opening SR_a. The opening of contact SR_a

disconnects the timing relay coil, and timing begins as the capacitor discharges slowly through the coil.

Each contact of the timing relay is separately adjustable, and the capacitor discharge method is accurate and constant.

After a set time the contact $TR1$ closes, completing the circuit to energize the field contactor FS, which closes. This energizes the motor field, and the motor is pulled into synchronism. Contacts $TR2$ and $TR3$ are set to open a little later, after the surge of current, which occurs during synchronizing, has ended.

The motor has now been accelerated and brought into synchronism, and the synchronizing means, that is, relays SR and TR, are back in their original positions. However, coil CL has been opened by interlock FS_c, and coil LO has been short-circuited by interlock FS_b. Coil OSP is still in circuit, and if, for any reason, the motor should pull out of synchronism, the resulting surge of current will operate relay SR, opening the field contactor and starting the synchronizing process over again. If the load conditions should be such that the motor cannot pull into synchronism on the original start or on an attempt to restart, the timing relay TS will open the control circuit and cut the motor off from the line, preventing damage to the starting winding. The relay is a thermal device which is energized when the line contactor is closed and the field contactor open. It is usually set to trip out if the motor fails to synchronize within 30 seconds, and is reset manually. Some device of this nature is included as a safety feature on most synchronous-motor controllers; it will, of course, work with any method of synchronizing.

With any control scheme depending on a changing quantity, such as the lessening inrush current during acceleration, the control relay must be set a little above the final value, to insure that it will always operate. When the current relay does operate, the motor has not quite reached the proper synchronizing speed, although it is very close to it. The time relay functions to permit the motor to accelerate the remaining relatively small amount.

Reduced-voltage Starting. A reduced-voltage starter using this method of synchronizing is generally arranged so that the above-described relays control the running, or full-voltage, contactor. The field contactor is interlocked behind the running contactor and energized by the timing relay a short time after the run contactor closes. However, on resynchronizing after a pullout, the running contactor remains closed and the synchronizing device controls the field contactor. Figure 221 shows this arrangement.

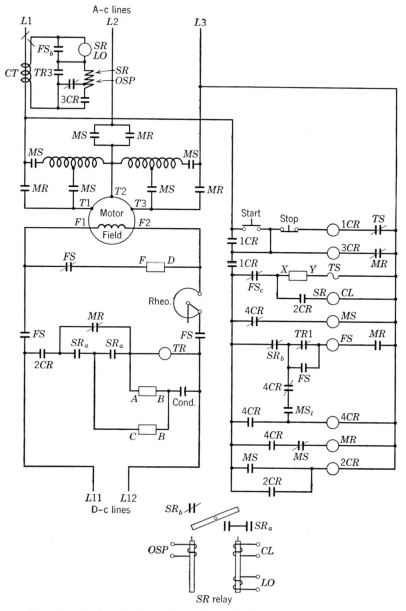

Fig. 221. Reduced-voltage Controller with Current-time Method of Synchronization.

When the start button is pressed, relays $1CR$ and $3CR$ close, followed by the starting contactor MS. This is a five-pole contactor which connects the motor to a reduced-voltage tap of the autotransformer and connects the autotransformer to the power supply. Relay SR operates to close contact SR_a and open contact SR_b.

The purpose of relay $3CR$ is to change the pull of coil OSP, so that it will operate the same on a reduced starting inrush as it will on full inrush during a pullout of synchronism. Relay $2CR$ is energized by an interlock contact on MS and, after closing, provides its own maintaining circuit. Relay $2CR$ energizes timing relay TR and coil CL. The timing relay closes, but relay SR does not operate until the motor has accelerated and the current in coil LO has dropped to 175 per cent. When the inrush current has dropped, relay SR operates, setting up a circuit to the coil of relay $4CR$. However, this relay does not close until the circuit is completed by the closing of MS_t, which is a delayed-time contact operated by the starting contactor MS. In form it is a dashpot time relay, which, instead of having a coil to operate it, is mechanically connected to MS and so closes its contacts in a set time after MS closes. Relay $4CR$, which controls the transfer from reduced voltage to full voltage, is therefore itself controlled by both current and time. When it closes, the starting contactor MS is opened and the running contactor MR is closed. The autotransformer is disconnected, and the motor is connected to full line voltage. An interlock contact on MR opens the coil circuit of timing relay TR. After the set time has elapsed, contact $TR1$ closes, followed by field switch FS, and the motor is synchronized. Contact $TR3$ now opens, and conditions are set up for resynchronizing if a pullout should occur. Since relay $4CR$ is self-maintaining, the running contactor MR will remain closed, and starting contactor MS open, and the resynchronizing will be effected by the opening, and subsequent reclosing, of the field contactor only.

Slip-frequency Method of Synchronizing. Figure 222 is a diagram of a full-voltage controller using a method of synchronizing based on slip frequency.

The synchronizing relay SR is a device having two separate magnetic circuits, each with a coil to energize it. One coil is connected in the power line, through a current transformer, so that it responds to the motor current. The other coil is a shunt coil, having a small rheostat in series with it, to permit adjustment of its magnetic pull. The moving element of the relay is a rotating shaft having two armatures, one in each magnetic circuit, and arranged so that one coil and magnet tend to rotate the shaft clockwise, and the other coil and magnet tend to rotate it in the opposite direction.

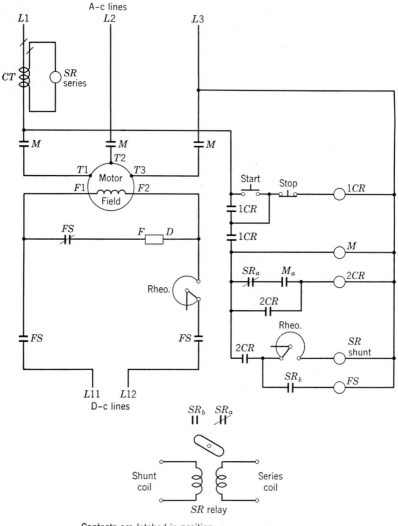

Contacts are latched in position.
Movement of rotating arm counterclockwise trips latch.
Movement of rotating arm clockwise resets contact and latch.

FIG. 222. Full-voltage Controller with Synchronization Based on Slip Frequency.

The contacts of the relay are not directly operated by the rotating shaft but are latched in position. Slight rotation of the shaft has no effect on the contacts, but a sufficiently great rotation will trip the latch, closing one contact and opening the other. Similarly, a sufficient rotation in the opposite direction will reset the latch and the contacts.

The relay is designed and set so that the torques of the two armatures are approximately equal when the voltage is at normal value and the current has dropped to a value which indicates that the motor speed is high enough for synchronizing.

Referring to the diagram, operation of the start button closes relay $1CR$ and line contactor M. The main contacts of M close ahead of the interlock contact M_a, and the resulting motor inrush current operates relay SR, opening contact SR_b and closing contact SR_a. Interlock M_a closes, followed by relay $2CR$, which has a self-maintaining circuit. Another contact of $2CR$ energizes the shunt coil of relay SR and partially sets up a circuit for the field contactor FS. The motor now accelerates, and the current in the series coil of SR decreases, until the pull of the two relay armatures is nearly equal. Since the starting winding of the motor is not continuously equal, but is spaced by the salient field poles into groups of turns, the motor current will pulsate at a frequency proportional to the rotor slip. At a speed near synchronizing speed, the slip is low, and the current pulsations will cause the relay to be subjected to an oscillating torque, as the series coil is momentarily stronger or weaker than the shunt coil.

When a body is subjected to an oscillating force it will not in general move back and forth, as might be supposed, but will have a progressive motion in the direction in which it first starts to move. The movement per cycle of the oscillating force is proportional to the peak value of the force and inversely proportional to the square of the frequency. As the motor approaches synchronizing speed, the relay armature starts to move and eventually moves far enough to trip the latch and operate the relay contacts. The field contactor is then energized and the motor synchronized. If a pullout occurs, the inrush current will cause the relay to reset, opening the field contactor, and then re-synchronizing will occur.

It will be evident that this method of synchronizing is essentially a current-time method. If it is assumed that the relay is adjusted to start moving at 95 per cent of synchronous speed, and that the load conditions will permit the motor to continue to accelerate, the motor might reach 96 per cent speed before the relay contacts operate. However, if the load conditions will not permit the motor to accelerate beyond 95 per cent speed, the relay will eventually operate at that speed. Under low-voltage conditions, a motor will require a longer than normal time to reach synchronizing speed, because the accelerating torque will be below normal. The relay under discussion will provide a longer time on low voltage and a shorter time on high voltage. If the relay were subject only to the pull effect of the two opposing coils, this would not be true, because a reduction in voltage would reduce their pull equally. However, the relay is actually operated by a series of impulses from the pulsating current, which impulses are superimposed on the normal pull of the coils. The value of these impulses will vary as the voltage varies, resulting in a difference in the operating time of the relay.

Synchronization Based on Power Factor. The changing characteristic of the power factor during acceleration may be utilized to apply the motor field at the proper time for synchronizing. When the motor is first energized, the power factor is low, the average probably being between 20 and 50 per cent lagging. As the motor accelerates, the power factor increases, and it also fluctuates above and below the average value, the fluctuations decreasing in frequency as synchronizing speed is approached.

The synchronizing relay is arranged to operate subject to these power-factor characteristics. It has two opposing coils, which are connected through current and potential transformers, as shown in Fig. 223, so that they respond to change in motor current and to power factor. Coil A tends to keep the relay open, and coil B tends to close it. When the motor has approached synchronizing speed, the motor current has decreased, and the power factor is relatively high but fluctuating. These conditions favor the B coil, and with each fluctuation the relay closes its contact momentarily. At first the contacts do not remain closed long enough to actuate the coil of relay TR, but, as the period of the fluctuation increases, the contacts remain closed longer on each cycle, until they are finally closed long enough to cause TR to operate. When this happens, TR provides a maintaining contact for itself (TR_a) and also energizes the field contactor FS (TR_b), and the motor pulls into synchronism.

Contacts TR_a and TR_b are instantaneous in operation, but TR_c is delayed in closing. The delayed contact TR_c is used to set up the proper conditions to control a pullout. As soon as the motor field is applied, the power factor rises, and it may go over to a leading value, depending on the load on the motor. The synchronizing relay resets and normally will not operate again. In order to prevent it from operating on momentary overloads or momentary voltage drop, a resistor is inserted in the B coil circuit by means of an interlock contact on FS. If a pullout occurs, because of a sustained overload or voltage dip, the synchronizing relay contacts will close, this time short-circuiting the coil of TR and causing TR and FS to open. Conditions

are then the same as they were during acceleration, and the motor
will resynchronize.

It will be evident that the relay described must be connected for
the proper phase relationships. Though the relay itself and the circuits

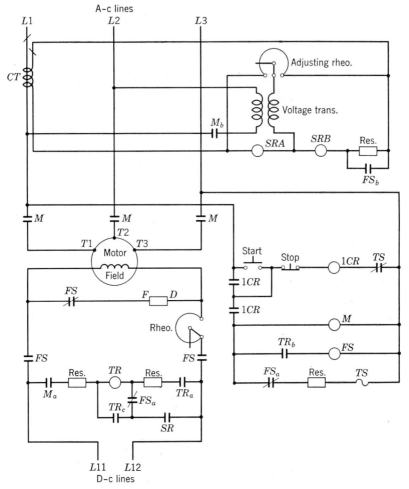

FIG. 223. Full-voltage Controller with Synchronization Based on Power Factor.

relative to it are simple, the vector analysis of its operation is involved
and for that reason is not included here.

Other Methods of Synchronizing. The above-described methods of
synchronizing illustrate the various factors, such as current, time,
frequency, and power factor, upon which the operation of synchronizing

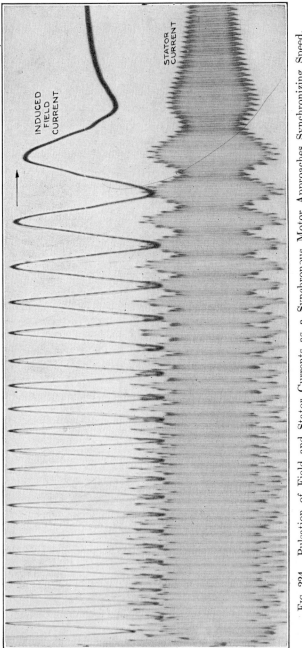

FIG. 224. Pulsation of Field and Stator Currents as a Synchronous Motor Approaches Synchronizing Speed.

relays is based. There are other methods, and other devices, based on these factors and combinations of them, and applying the principles described. There are also other phenomena on which synchronization might be based, and it appears likely that the future may show further development of new methods and devices.

Reversing and Plugging. A synchronous motor may be reversed by reversing one phase of the stator winding, in the same manner as an induction motor. Synchronous motors are not used for applications requiring rapid reversal, because such applications do not require a constant running speed and therefore they would present no advantages. Plugging is used, however, to obtain a quick stop. The field is disconnected from the power supply, and one phase of the stator is reversed. Some form of plugging relay is used to drop out the reversing contactor and disconnect the stator from the line just as the motor reaches zero speed. The method is the same as that for a squirrel-cage induction motor.

Dynamic Braking. Synchronous motors may be brought to rest quickly by dynamic braking. The dynamic-braking resistor consists of three sections, one end of each section being connected to each of the motor stator terminals. The other ends of the sections are open when the motor is running but are connected together through a double-pole normally closed contactor during braking. These spring-closed contactors are mechanically interlocked with the line contactor, so that the stator must be disconnected from the power supply before the braking circuit is closed. The field circuit remains closed, and the rotating field induces currents in the stator windings, which currents flow through the braking resistor. In this way the energy of the rotating field is dissipated as heat in the resistor, and the rotor is brought to rest. The time required to stop the motor depends on the amount of its stored kinetic energy and on the rate of dissipation, the latter being controlled by the design of the braking resistor. The resistor is designed to suit the required conditions of each application, the usual value for the stator current during braking being between two and three times normal full-load motor current. A timing relay opens the field contactor and disconnects the field after the motor has stopped.

Rossman Drive. For a description of this method of obtaining speed regulation, see Chapter 16.

Fynn-Weichsel Motor. The Fynn-Weichsel motor (Fig. 225) is a self-excited synchronous motor combining the desirable characteristics of both the synchronous motor and the induction motor. The rotor is provided with slip rings and also with a small commutator. It has two windings, one in the bottom of the slots being connected to the commutator, and the other in the top of the same slots being connected to the slip rings. The stator also has two windings, which are 90 electrical degrees apart. One of these windings is short-circuited when running, and the other is connected to brushes riding on the commutator.

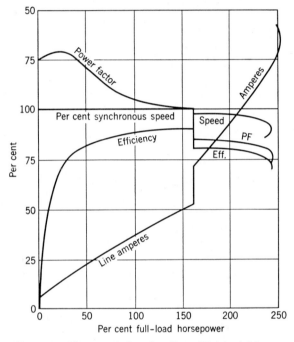

Fig. 225. Characteristics of a Fynn-Weichsel Motor.

To start the motor, line voltage is applied to the rotor through the slip rings. Resistance is connected in both of the stator windings. Induced currents are generated in the stator windings, and the motor starts. As it approaches synchronous speed, the rotor commutator winding begins to become effective and pulls the motor into synchronism. The motor then runs as a synchronous motor, with two exceptions. In a true synchronous motor the direct current must be supplied from a separate source and must be adjusted to give the operating power factor desired. The Fynn-Weichsel motor generates its own direct current, which is automatically proportioned to the motor's requirements for best operation. The second difference is in the pullout torque. A synchronous motor, when loaded beyond its pullout point, will stop. The Fynn-Weichsel motor pulls out of synchronism at about 150 per cent load and then continues to run as an induction motor. If the load is decreased below 150 per cent, the motor will pull back into step again.

The starting torque of this motor is about 150 per cent of normal torque, with a starting current of 150 to 200 per cent of full-load current. With increased starting current it will develop up to 250 per cent of full-load torque.

The motor is built in sizes up to 200 horsepower and for voltages up to 550.

References

McLenegan and Ferris, "Synchronous Motors—Design and Application to Meet Special Requirements," *Transactions AIEE,* 1931, Vol. 50, p. 607.

Shoults, Crary, and Lauder, "Pull-in Characteristics of Synchronous Motors," *Transactions AIEE,* 1932, Vol. 51, p. 424.

H. A. Winne, "Application of Synchronous Motors to Steel Mill Main Roll Drives," *General Electric Review,* June, 1926.

H. Weichsel, "A New Alternating-current General-purpose Motor," *Proceedings AIEE,* April, 1925.

J. Housa, "Fully Automatic Starting of Synchronous Motors," *Electrician,* 1949, Vol. 142, p. 427.

L. A. Umansky, "Applying Synchronous Motors to Main Roll Mill Drives," *Iron and Steel Engineer,* June, 1936.

Problems

1. What is the synchronous speed of a 16-pole 440-volt 50-cycle synchronous motor? At what speed will it run without any load? What will be its speed when overloaded 25 per cent? What will be its speed if the voltage drops to 400 volts?

2. If the starting torque of a synchronous motor is 120 per cent of rated torque when starting across the line, what will the starting torque be when starting with a primary-resistance starter which reduces the line voltage to 70 per cent of normal?

3. A synchronous motor field is drawing 20 amperes when connected to a 230-volt supply line. If the field is disconnected, and immediately connected across a resistor of 23 ohms, what is the maximum induced voltage to which the field windings might be subjected?

4. The stored energy in the rotor of a synchronous motor is 1 million watt-seconds. If the motor is to be stopped in 20 seconds by dynamic braking, what will be the wattage dissipated in the braking resistor at the start of the braking period?

5. A 100 per cent power factor motor has a field winding of 30 ohms resistance, which is to be supplied from a 230-volt circuit. How many ohms will be required in a field rheostat which will permit 100 per cent power factor to be obtained with any load from zero up to full rated load? (See Fig. 215.)

6. How many ohms would be required in a rheostat for the motor of Fig. 216, the rheostat in this case permitting 80 per cent power factor to be obtained over the range from zero load to 125 per cent load? Field resistance 30 ohms and supply voltage 230.

7. Make an elementary diagram for a reduced-voltage autotransformer-type synchronous-motor controller, using synchronization based on frequency.

8. Make an elementary diagram for a reduced-voltage primary-resistance-type synchronous-motor controller, with dynamic braking and with synchronization based on frequency.

9. A machine is driven by a six-pole 440-volt 60-cycle synchronous motor, which is supplied from a motor-generator set used for that purpose only. It is found necessary to run the synchronous motor at 660 rpm. What voltage and frequency must the generator deliver?

10. A controller like that of Fig. 218 has been built for a 100-horsepower 220-volt 60-cycle synchronous motor. The owner now desires to use the controller with a 150-horsepower 440-volt 60-cycle motor having the same field characteristics. Which of the following items will have to be changed?

MS contactor coil	A-c main circuit wiring
MR contactor coil	Control wiring
Main contacts of MR	TS relay coil
Overload relay coils	$1CR$ relay coil
D-c ammeter	Interlock fingers on FS
A-c ammeter	FS contactor coil
Fuses	Timing condensers

11. A continuously running, non-reversing mill for rolling steel slabs is subjected to a very heavy load each time a slab starts to enter the rolls. To cushion the load on the driving motor at this time, the mill is equipped with a heavy flywheel. Two motors of identical rating are available, one a synchronous motor, and the other a wound-rotor motor. Which should be used, and why?

20

MAGNETICALLY OPERATED BRAKES

In many applications of electric motors the ability to stop quickly and accurately is important. Electrically operated brakes are widely used for that purpose, either in connection with dynamic braking or as the sole means of stopping. Brakes are also necessary on hoists, cranes, elevators, and similar machines, to hold the load after stopping.

The essential parts of a brake are the friction material, shoes or band, wheel, operating device, and mounting parts. Most brakes are electrically released and spring-set, so that the brake will be set in case of an electrical failure or a power interruption. It is occasionally advantageous to make the brake electrically set. A typical example of this arrangement is the application of brakes to the individual rolls of a printing press. The motor is stopped by dynamic braking, and the brake coils are connected in the dynamic-braking circuit, so that the brakes are set by the dynamic current and released as soon as the motor has stopped.

Brakes are of the shoe, the disk or the band type. The shoe-type brake has the friction material mounted on two shoes, which apply on opposite sides of the brake wheel. The shoes cover approximately half of the wheel circumference. They are operated independently and are independently adjustable. The shoe brake requires only a small movement to release, the travel of the operating magnet being approximately 0.04 inch for each shoe. The short stroke gives fast operation and also reduces shock and hammer blow when releasing or setting.

The disk brake is arranged for mounting directly to the motor end-bell. The brake lining is fastened to a steel disk which is supported by a hub keyed to the motor shaft. The disk rotates with the motor. When the brake is set, a spring pulls a stationary steel member into contact with the rotating disk. Although brakes have been built with a number of disks, the general practice is to have only one. Since the air gaps must necessarily be small, the use of more than one disk increases the chance of the brakes dragging when released. Disk brakes are limited to relatively low torque ratings.

479

The band brake has the friction material fastened to a band of steel which encircles the wheel and may cover as much as 90 per cent of the wheel surface. The increased braking surface permits a lower pressure per square inch, with consequent reduction of wear of the lining. This is offset somewhat by the fact that the braking pressure is not equal over the whole band, as a wrapping action may occur when the brake sets. The band brake requires a longer stroke to release it.

Lining Materials. The following description of the lining materials for electrically operated brakes, and of the wheels, is taken from a paper by H. E. Hodgson, published in the *Iron and Steel Engineer*, February, 1931, and the facts are the same today.

The basic material in all cases is asbestos. In all but molded types it is fashioned into a thread around a brass wire. Generally some cotton is used to make the thread more easily formed. The woven linings are made so that in effect there are several layers of woven fabric tied together by occasional strands of woof which pass through all layers. The fabric is then impregnated with a binder, which will serve as a matrix to cement the strands and fibers together; tar, asphalt, sugar, silica, rubber, and various polymerizing oils are, or have been, used. Then heat and pressure are applied to cure the binder and reduce the lining to the final shape and condition. In this process the thickness which will give longest life per unit of material may be limited by the wearing process, by the penetrating process of the binder, or by the press capacity. The woven lining is reasonably flexible and can easily be formed to suit wheel surfaces. Its surface is rather rough, and the high spots must be worn down before maximum friction is delivered. In the molded type, the asbestos fibers are mixed with a binder and other constituents. Sometimes short pieces of brass wire are used to reinforce the product. The mixture is then formed in molds to the desired shapes. The molds are customarily heated to cure the binder. Molded linings are hard, dense, uniform in thickness, and smooth surfaced. They must be formed to the shape in which they will be used. They are not so easily fastened to the carrying surface as either of the other types and may break.

In the folded and stitched type of lining the strands are loosely woven into a rough open cloth, which is filled with the binder by the frictioning process. In the frictioning process the cloth is passed between metal rolls. The binder material is fed into the bite of the rolls, and it adheres to them to some extent, so that it is pulled through with the cloth and forced into all spaces in the cloth. Usually only one surface is filled at a time, and two passes are required to cover both surfaces. The friction cloth is folded together in the necessary number of sheets to build up to the desired thickness. The sheets are loosely stitched to make further handling during the subsequent operations easier. The stacks are then subjected to heat and pressure for curing and producing a uniform thickness. The folded and stitched linings are reasonably flexible and will not break while being riveted to the carrying surfaces. The surface is moderately smooth.

The fundamental requirement in all types is that the binder must permeate the fabric and form a matrix to support the relatively weak fibers of asbestos. The binder must stand the temperature which develops when the wheel slides against the friction lining under pressure, and it must remain mechanically strong enough to support the asbestos. When linings are worked too hard the wear rate is multiplied in all types. There is a critical temperature which, if exceeded, causes rapid failure of the lining. It does not appear that the wear rate is especially affected at any value below the critical temperature of the particular lining. When the critical temperature is exceeded in the woven lining, the woof cuts away, and the binder is either not strong enough to hold the pieces or it vaporizes out, and strands of the warp fly out along the short loops of woof.

The molded type scuffs away.

The folded and stitched type separates between layers, and partial layers flake off.

The problem is to know what is the limiting severity of service to give economic results.

The adhesion or coefficient of friction can be regulated by the manufacturer; it appears mainly to be a function of the binder in combination with the asbestos. The coefficient is not exact; it will vary, in a given sample, over a range of 1.6 to 1. The factor depends quite largely on the condition of the metal surface which opposes the lining as well as on the lining itself. Roughly, the life is progressively shorter as the coefficient of friction increases. Temperature effects, oil effects, and water effects produce variations in results. There is a light service condition where a film of metal oxide will form on the lining face, practically eliminating the lining wear and increasing the frictional coefficient to as high as 0.8. This can be obtained with almost any type of friction material if the right conditions are provided, but the conditions represent such low energy consumption per unit of area that it is not practical to embody them in industrial apparatus. We have previously pointed out that it would require three to ten times the present accepted friction area to produce these conditions.

TABLE 41

COMPARATIVE RESULTS WITH LININGS

Type of Lining	Coefficient of Friction	Lining Wear, Characteristic Range	Order of Wear Effect on Wheels	Wheels with Which Tests Were Made
Woven	0.36–0.75	9,000– 100,000	Hard	Steel castings untreated and steel castings hardened
Molded	0.3 –0.6	43,000– 73,000	Harder	0.20–0.30 C casting untreated
Folded and stitched	0.36–0.75	22,000–1,250,000	Hardest	All wheels and all service conditions

Brake Wheels. Materials for brake wheel must be strong and flexible but must break sharply if their strength limit is exceeded. In other words, it is desirable to have the elastic limit and the ultimate strength high and close together. The relation of diameter and length must be considered. The surface area of the wheel is fixed by the heat to be dissipated. A narrow wheel will have a high WR^2, whereas a wide wheel may be more difficult to machine.

In operation, brake wheels heat up unequally. The source of heat is between the lining and the wheel, and the heat flows through the wheel to meet a cooling current of air at the inside of the wheel; consequently the wheel expands unequally in proportion to the inequality of temperature in the wheel. Elasticity is required to stand the inequality of expansion. The particles in the wheel should retain their strength up to fairly high temperatures, and when their strength is exceeded they should break away in infinitesimal grains and not foul the lining. Cast-iron wheels have been tested in three forms— semi-steel, nickel cast iron, and a so-called graphite cast steel, which is very similar in appearance to cast iron but can be hardened. Steel wheels have been tested in 20-point carbon casting, 45-point carbon casting without heat treatment, low carbon with some manganese casting, 5-point carbon forged wheel, 45-point carbon casting-hardened, 60- to 75-point carbon rolled steel plate formed for the rim and hardened, untreated alloy steel, and mild steel carburized and case-hardened.

With low pressures and low energy consumption, the wear characteristics go very high; for example, a ½-inch-wide leather belt with a half wrap on a wheel running at 1200 rpm with a slip speed of 294 feet per minute and a 10-ounce pull on the leather belt operated continuously for three months with no measurable wear of the leather. On another brake similar to this, a $\frac{1}{32}$-inch-thick band operated a year at 200 rpm, equivalent to 100 feet per minute slip speed, with no apparent wear of the band. It will be noted from a study of the tabulation that the wear characteristic values have a ratio as high as 60 to 1, depending upon the condition of the brake wheel and the temperature. The range of a single lining on a single type of wheel is approximately 5 to 1.

The general indicated conclusions are that cast-iron wheels are not elastic enough for wide ranges of temperature. Surface cracks develop, and under extreme conditions cracks will progress through the rim, caused by the inequality of stresses due to the varying expansion in the rims. In ordinarily mild service the wheel surface polishes, thus producing very good conditions for long life of wheel and lining. Another feature is that, in order to get the same rigidity, the weight must be increased approximately 50 per cent. This adds to the flywheel effect and is undesirable. Owing to the lower breaking strength, the permissible speed of rotation is less for the cast-iron wheel than for the steel wheels.

Steel, whether of low or high carbon content, without heat treatment, under easy service conditions, with light pressure and low speeds, will ordinarily become polished and produce long wheel and lining life. There is a gradual improvement in wheel performance as the carbon content increases, but it was indicated from tests that with pressure in the range from 30 to 50 pounds per square inch and normal velocities, representing fair severity of service, steel without heat treatment tends to drag, and particles bed into the lining. Then the scoring of the wheel progresses rapidly.

Hardened steel, even though the hardness does not exceed 40 Scleroscope, apparently produces better lining life than cast iron in the ratio of about 4 to 3, without danger of cracking. The cost of the hardened or heat-treated wheel is certain to be somewhat above that for a casting, since the wheel must be machined close to finished size before it is heat-treated, and then it must finally be finished after heat treatment, so that two sets of operations are required in the manufacture of the wheel, instead of the single set which is needed for the untreated wheel. Also the final grinding operation on the hardened wheel surface requires somewhat longer than a machined finish on an untreated wheel. The heat treatment itself adds something to the cost. However, in view of the economies to be gained from the increased length of lining and wheel life, it appears that on a majority of installations it would be an economical plan to buy the hardened-steel wheels.

Finally, then, cast iron will be satisfactory, with any lining, for light service and limited speeds; untreated cast steel will be satis- factory, with some linings, for light service and fairly high speeds; hardened steel will be satisfactory, with any lining, for all service conditions. Lining life varies over a wide range, depending more on wheel condition than on severity of service, except that severity of service finally affects the wheel condition.

Fig. 226.   Direct-current Direct-acting Shoe Brake.

Operating Mechanisms—Direct Current. Direct-current brakes may be operated by a solenoid or by a direct-operating magnet. A solenoid operates against a spring through suitable linkages. A combination of weight and spring may be used, the solenoid lifting the weight, which rests on the base of the brake when the brake is set. The torque delivered at the wheel is regulated by adjusting a spring. In the direct-operating type the armature of the electromagnet is an integral part of one of the brake-shoe arms. The field member of the magnet is connected to the opposite shoe arm by a rod which passes over the brake wheel. When the brake is applied, the armature and field are forced apart by a spring located in the center of the magnet field, and the brake shoe attached to the armature is forced against the wheel. Simultaneously, the magnet field pulls the opposite shoe against the wheel. The intensity of the braking force is regulated by varying the adjustment of the spring in the magnet field. Adjustment for wear of the lining is made by varying the length of the rod above the brake wheel. The rod is threaded at one end, and the length is varied by turning a nut. Provision is also made for equalizing the clearance of the two shoes.

The operating coils of either solenoid or direct-acting magnetic brake may be wound for series or shunt connection and for continuous or intermittent duty. If series-wound, the coil is connected in the motor circuit and operated by the motor current. The coil is wound to suit the horsepower and duty rating of the motor with which the brake

Fig. 227. Alternating-current Solenoid-type Shoe Brake.

is to be used, and for intermittent duty it is designed to lift the brake on about 40 per cent of full-load current and hold it released on about 10 per cent of full-load current. For continuous duty the coil will require about 80 per cent of full-load current to lift the brake. Intermittent-duty series brakes are rated as either ½-hour duty or 1-hour duty, corresponding to the method of rating intermittent-duty series motors.

Shunt-wound brakes are wound for either intermittent or continuous duty. Intermittent duty is understood to mean 1 minute on and 1 minute off, or the equivalent, the longest continuous application of voltage not to exceed 1 hour. These brakes will release at 85 per cent of normal voltage when adjusted for rated torque. Since shunt-wound coils have a greater inductance than series-wound coils, the shunt brakes are ordinarily not so fast in releasing. In order to increase the speed of operation, it is customary to wind the shunt coil for a voltage lower than line voltage and to use a resistance in series with it. The coil is usually wound for one-half of line voltage, but it may be wound for a voltage as low as one-tenth of line voltage in order to get extremely fast release. A relay may then be used to insert the

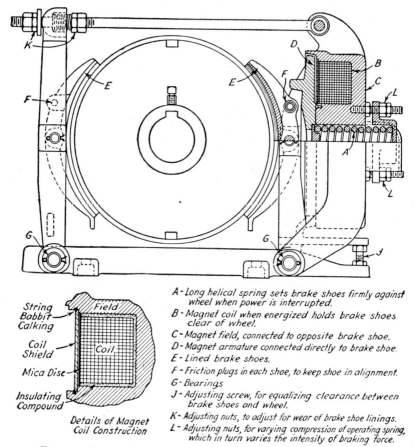

String Babbit Calking
Coil Shield
Mica Disc
Insulating Compound

Field
Coil

Details of Magnet Coil Construction

A - Long helical spring sets brake shoes firmly against wheel when power is interrupted.
B - Magnet coil when energized holds brake shoes clear of wheel.
C - Magnet field, connected to opposite brake shoe.
D - Magnet armature connected directly to brake shoe.
E - Lined brake shoes.
F - Friction plugs in each shoe, to keep shoe in alignment.
G - Bearings
J - Adjusting screw, for equalizing clearance between brake shoes and wheel.
K - Adjusting nuts, to adjust for wear of brake shoe linings.
L - Adjusting nuts, for varying compression of operating spring, which in turn varies the intensity of braking force.

FIG. 228. Direct-current Direct-operated Shoe Brake Construction.

resistance. The relay is normally closed around the resistance, and its coil may be connected in series with the brake. When voltage is applied, the inductance of the brake winding retards the rise of current. As soon as the current has built up, the relay operates and inserts the series resistance. Another frequently used method is to insert the resistance by means of a timing relay. With this arrangement the brake will release even more quickly than with a permanent series resistance. The smaller brakes, up to a 10-inch-diameter wheel, do not ordinarily require partial voltage coils, but their use is general on the larger brakes.

Series brakes have several advantages in addition to that of fast operation. The series coil, being of heavy wire, is less likely to give trouble than a fine-wire shunt coil; and, since the voltage per turn is low, the insulation is not likely to break down. The coil is in series with the motor armature, so that if the armature circuit is opened the brake will set. This is an important safety feature in connection with hoists or other machines where there is an overhauling load, as a broken resistance grid or a loose wire connection might open the armature circuit and allow the load to drop. The wiring to the brake is simple, as the brake is mounted on the motor and connected to it.

Shunt brakes are used in connection with machines which have a widely varying load, when the armature current is not always great enough to keep a series brake released. It is possible to obtain some measure of protection against an open armature circuit by using a series relay with the shunt brake. The coil of the relay is connected in the armature circuit, and the contacts in series with the brake coil. When the motor is started, the inrush current will close the relay, and the relay will close the circuit to the brake. An interlock on the brake is used to bypass the contacts of the series relay, so that the brake will remain energized if the series relay opens on low armature current. This arrangement protects only against releasing the brake with the armature circuit open; it does not protect against opening the circuit after the motor has started.

Operating Mechanisms—Alternating Current. The three principal forms of alternating-current brake-operating mechanisms are the solenoid type, the torque-motor type, and the thrustor type.

The alternating-current solenoid brake is similar to the direct-current solenoid type, except that the solenoid frame must be laminated to reduce eddy currents. Since the alternating-current flux passes through zero twice every cycle, the pull of the magnet is not constant. Shading coils, similar to those on alternating-current contactors, must be used to provide a pull during the change of direction of the main flux. Even with shading coils it is difficult to design a solenoid mechanism which will be quiet in operation and free from vibration. Another disadvantage of the solenoid is that it draws a heavy current at the first application of voltage, when the magnetic gap is open. In general, solenoids are used only for the smaller brakes, although polyphase solenoids are sometimes used for the larger sizes.

The torque-motor mechanism utilizes a specially wound polyphase squirrel-cage motor, which may be stalled without injury to the wind-

Fig. 229. Alternating-current Brake, Operated by Torque Motor.

Fig. 230. Disk Brake.

ings and without drawing excessively heavy currents. The motor drives a ball jack, which translates the rotary motion of the motor to a straight-line motion and releases the brake. The motor then stalls, holding the brake in the released position until the motor circuit is opened. The brake is set by a spring, which overhauls the torque motor. The slight flywheel action of the rotor tends to eliminate shock

Fig. 231. Clark Thrustor-operated Band Brake.

when the brake sets. A slip clutch, constructed as a part of the ball-jack mechanism, also acts to prevent shock at the end of the brake movement. The brake is quiet in operation, as the pull of the motor is uniform, and there is no open magnetic circuit. The current taken from the line is not great and is practically uniform throughout the stroke. A small brake of this type requires 110 volt-amperes, compared to an inrush of 2000 volt-amperes for a solenoid brake of the same rating. A large size requires 1520 volt-amperes, compared to 21,000 for the corresponding solenoid brake. A disadvantage of this brake in comparison with the solenoid type is that the torque motor must always be operated in the same direction, which necessitates an extra relay on a reversing controller and extra trolley wires when used on a crane.

The operation of the thrustor is quite different from that of the mechanisms which have been described. The thrustor is essentially a motor-driven centrifugal pump, which operates on oil in a cylinder. The pump motor is of the polyphase squirrel-cage type. When energized, the motor forces oil under a piston, which, in rising, moves a lever and releases the brake. To set the brake, the motor is de-energized, and a spring forces the piston to its original position. The return movement of the piston is cushioned by the inertia of the operator motor and pump, and so the brake is set without severe shock. The pump impeller has straight blades, and it pumps equally well in either direction of rotation.

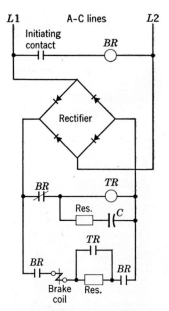

FIG. 232. Connections for Operation of a Direct-current Brake on Alternating Current.

Operation with Rectifiers. Since the direct-current operating mechanisms are so much simpler than alternating-current mechanisms, particularly in the larger sizes, there has been an increasing use of rectifiers to supply direct current for the brake on an alternating-current installation. Selenium-disk-type dry rectifiers are generally used.

Figure 232 shows the connections for a control of this type. The brake relay *BR* is energized by the closing of a contact in a master controller, or on the motor control panel. The closing of *BR* energizes the brake through the rectifier and also sets in motion a timing relay *TR* which, after a short time delay to permit the brake to operate, inserts a resistor into the brake coil circuit. Since the brake requires more current to release than it does to remain released, the current may be reduced in this way, permitting the use of the minimum size of rectifier. The timing relay shown is one of the condenser-discharge type. Any type giving an accurate timing of a second or so is satisfactory.

Mechanical Parts and Mounting. The frame and mechanical parts of a brake are usually made of steel and must be strong enough to withstand the shocks and jars of frequent operation. The structure must also be rigid so that the brake shoes and wheel will stay in proper alignment and so that side strains on the motor shaft will be avoided. Springs afford the best means of setting the brake, as they have relatively little inertia. Where a weight is used, it is customary to provide a dashpot or some similar means of cushioning the shock in setting.

Brakes may be mounted either on the floor or on the frame of the motor. There is some difference of opinion as to the preferable method, and the choice is probably best made from a consideration of the application in question. The advantages of floor mounting are:

> Lower first cost.
> More rigid mounting.
> Less strain on the motor frame.

The advantages of mounting on the motor are:

> No special foundation is required.
> The brake is automatically aligned with the motor.
> The brake will not get out of alignment with the motor.
> The brake and motor can be handled as a unit.
> Less floor space is required.

Determination of Brake Size. There are three factors which must be considered in rating a brake, or in selecting the correct brake for a given application.

The first factor is the mechanical strength of the brake, or the retarding effort which it can deliver. This is determined by the force with which the spring holds the shoes against the wheel, the radius of the wheel to which the force is applied, and the coefficient of friction between the lining and the wheel face. The torque required of the brake is determined from the formula

$$T = \frac{5250 \text{ hp}}{N} \tag{1}$$

where T = torque in pound-feet.
  hp = rated motor horsepower.
  N = full-load motor speed in rpm.

The brake should have a torque rating equal to, or greater than, that obtained from the formula. Where adjustable-speed motors are used, the torque should be calculated at the lowest operating speed.

The time required for a brake alone to stop a moving mass may be calculated from the formula

$$t = t_a + t_d = t_a + \frac{120KE}{2\pi T N_b} \qquad [2]$$

where t = time in seconds, required to stop the moving mass after the
brake is de-energized.

t_a = time in seconds for the brake shoe to apply against the wheel
after the brake is de-energized.

t_d = time in seconds for the moving mass to stop after the brake
shoes apply.

KE = total kinetic energy in the moving system at the instant the
brake applies.

T = retarding torque in pound feet. This torque is the sum of
the brake torque and the friction torque of the moving system. In most calculations the brake torque only is considered, unless the friction torque is high.

N_b = rpm of the brake wheel.

For a rotating body,

$$KE = \tfrac{1}{2}I\omega^2 \qquad [3]$$

where $I = \dfrac{WR^2}{g}$, which is the moment of inertia of the body in lb-ft^2.

$\omega = \dfrac{2\pi N}{60}$, which is the angular velocity in radians per second.

If we substitute for I and ω, the equation reduces to

$$KE = 1.7 \ WR^2 \left(\frac{N}{100}\right)^2 \qquad [4]$$

where W = weight of the rotating mass in pounds.

R = radius of gyration of the mass in feet.

N = rpm of the mass.

For a body with linear motion,

$$KE = \tfrac{1}{2}Mv^2 \qquad [5]$$

or

$$KE = \frac{1}{2}\frac{W}{g}\left(\frac{V}{60}\right)^2 \qquad [6]$$

where v = linear velocity in feet per second.

V = linear velocity in feet per minute.

g = 32.2.

Equation 2 may be rewritten

$$t = i_a + \frac{WR^2 N_b}{308T} \qquad [7]$$

Equation 7 applies to a machine having a single rotating element, or a group of elements rotating at the same speed. If the machine has elements which are rotating at speeds different from that of the brake wheel, the equivalent WR^2 of any such element is

$$\text{Equivalent } WR^2 = W_1 R_1 \left(\frac{N}{N_b}\right)^2$$

where $W_1 R_1 =$ the WR^2 of the element at its actual speed N.

The second factor in a brake rating is the heat-dissipating capacity of the brake wheel and the shoe lining. It is the foot-pounds of kinetic energy which can be absorbed by the wheel and lining and dissipated as heat, without causing the wheel face or the lining to become dangerously hot. The lining is a poor heat conductor, and deteriorates rapidly at temperatures above 400 F. The heat-dissipating capacity of the wheel is determined by its surface area, by the operating cycle, and by the ventilation. Where a brake is used only for holding a load, and not for stopping it, this factor need not be considered. Manufacturers do not ordinarily list figures for the heat-dissipating capacity of their brakes, since there are so many variables in the conditions encountered in service. It is customary to list limiting horsepowers with which specific brakes may be safely used, these being determined by calculation and test, and being satisfactory for most applications. Where the frequency of operation is very high, or the energy of motion is very great, the brake manufacturer should be consulted before the brake is selected.

The third factor is the duty of the operating coil or mechanism, which must be strong enough to release the brake shoes against the pressure of the brake springs, and must hold the shoes released for a period of time which depends on the duty cycle of the brake. Shunt coils are rated in voltage, for intermittent or for continuous duty. Continuous duty means that the coil will hold the brake released continuously without overheating of the coil. Series coils are rated in amperes for ½-hour or 1-hour duty, to correspond to the ratings of series motors. The ½-hour rating means that the brake coil will carry full-rated motor current for ½ hour without overheating. This is equivalent to a duty cycle of 1 minute on and 2 minutes off (⅓ time

TABLE 42

DIRECT-CURRENT BRAKE DATA

Size of Brake in inches	Maximum Torque in pound-feet				Power Required in Watts				WR² of Wheel	Safe Maximum rpm	Weight of Brake in pounds	Brake Wheel Face in inches
	Shunt-wound		Series-wound		Shunt-wound		Series-wound					
	1-hour Inter-mittent	Contin-uous	½ hr	1 hr	Inter-mittent	Contin-uous	½ hr	1 hr				
8	90	70	90	60	200	100	225	90	1.06	5000	123	3.25
10	200	150	200	135	230	100	420	160	2.25	4000	180	3.25
14	525	400	525	350	660	140	580	225	11	2860	365	4.75
18	900	675	900	600	945	375	780	300	36	2240	575	6.25
21	1800	1350	1800	1200	930	685	880	340	74	1960	900	7.5
30	3600	2700	3600	2400	1255	675	1100	435	313	1340	1700	8.5

duty), repeated continuously. Similarly, the 1-hour rating is equivalent to a duty cycle of 1 minute on and 1 minute off (½ time duty), repeated continuously.

Other considerations which enter into the selection of a brake are safety, ambient temperature, and maintenance. The safety consideration enters into such applications as balanced hoists, where the brake should be large enough to hold a loaded car or bucket in case a broken cable removes the counterbalance. A high ambient temperature will reduce the heat-dissipating capacity of the brake and may necessitate the selection of a larger size. Maintenance should be considered, as the severity of the service has a direct bearing on the life of the brake lining and wheel. Most brakes are designed to make adjustment simple and replacement of linings easy. Brakes which are in hard service should be inspected frequently, with particular attention to the following points:

1. Proper adjustment of the air gap between the wheel and the linings.
2. Equal clearance on the two shoes.
3. Tightening of bolts in the motor and brake bosses.
4. Grounds in the coil or leads.

Typical Brake Data. Table 42 gives data applying to a typical line of direct-current direct-operated shoe brakes.

Table 43 gives data applying to a typical line of alternating-current torque-motor-operated shoe brakes.

TABLE 43

ALTERNATING-CURRENT BRAKE DATA

Size of Brake in inches	Maximum Torque in pound-feet		3-phase, 60-cycle, volt-amperes		WR^2 of Wheel	Safe Maximum rpm	Weight of Brake in pounds	Brake Wheel Face in inches
	Inter- mittent Duty	Contin- uous Duty	Inter- mittent	Contin- uous				
10	160	125	160	110	3.1	4000	150	4.25
13	400	325	210	135	12	3100	240	5.25
16	800	600	300	235	25	2520	370	6.75
20	1600	1200	1080	460	75	2025	750	8.25
25	3200	2400	1520	530	220	1600	1210	10.25

Standard ratings for the smaller brakes are given below. There are no standard ratings for direct-current series brakes smaller than those listed above.

| D-c | | A-c | |
| Torque in pound-feet | | Torque in pound-feet | |
Continuous	1 hour	Continuous	Intermittent
3	..	1.5	..
10	15	3	..
25	35	10	15
50	75	25	35
70	90	50	75
		125	160

Alternating-current brakes will release at 85 per cent of full line voltage and will operate satisfactorily at 110 per cent of full line voltage.

Shunt brakes will release at 85 per cent of full line voltage and will operate satisfactorily at 110 per cent of full line voltage.

Series brakes will release at 40 per cent of full-load motor current and will remain released down to 10 per cent of full-load motor current.

Standardization of Brakes. A number of attempts have been made to reach a standardization of brakes, not only so far as torque is concerned, but also in wheel sizes and mounting dimensions. There has been little progress along these lines except in the direct-current brakes for mill motors. In 1947 the Association of Iron & Steel Engineers, working with motor manufacturers, developed a new line of mill motors known as the 600 series of motors. Motor ratings and essential dimensions were standardized. Then, in 1948, the AISE, working with NEMA, began a program to standardize brakes for the new motors. Since all brake manufacturers were faced with the problem of redesigning their brakes to suit the new motors, whether or not there was a standardization, the value of standardization at that time was evident. The proposed standards are included here, although at the time of this writing (late 1952) most manufacturers had these brakes only in the development stage.

References

A. E. Lillquist, "Selection and Maintenance of Magnetic Brakes," *Iron and Steel Engineer,* February, 1945.

R. T. Halstead, "Fundamentals of Asbestos Friction Materials," *Paper Trade Journal,* March 2, 1944.

Problems

1. Calculate the torque of a 25-horsepower 600-rpm motor when it is operating at its rating.

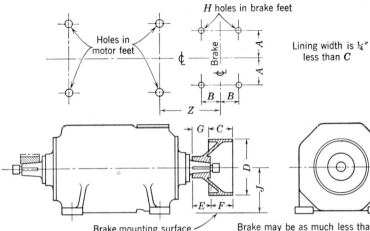

H holes in brake feet
Holes in motor feet
Brake
A
A
B
B
Z
Lining width is ¼″ less than C
G
C
D
J
E
F
Brake mounting surface
Brake may be as much less than J as maker's design permits

Motor	Series Motor, lb-ft		Brake Rating, lb-ft			Mounting Dimensions					Wheel				
	0.5 hr	1 hr	0.5-hr Series, 1-hr Shunt	1-hr Series	8-hr Shunt	*A*	*B*	*H*	*Z*	Max *J*	*D*	*C*	*E*	*F*	*G*
2	46	29	100	65	75	3¼	2⅞	1 1/16	8¼	7	8	3¼	3	2⅝	2⅜
602	78	49													
603	116	72	200	130	150	4	3⅛	1 1/16	9¼	8⅜	10	3¾	3½	2⅝	2⅜
604	166	121							9¾						
606	337	228	550	365	400	5¾	4½	13/16	10½	9⅞	13	5¾	4	3⅞	2⅛
608	502	350							11				4½	3¾	2½
610	765	525	1000	650	750	7½	5⅜	1 1/16	12¾	12⅛	16	6¾	4½	5⅜	3⅛
612	1220	830	2000	1300	1500	9¼	6½	1 1/16	14¼	13¼	19	8¾	5	6⅞	3⅛
614	1780	1140							15¼						
616	2625	1750	4000	2600	3000	11¾	8	1 5/16	17¼	15⅞	23	11¼	5½	8⅜	2⅝
618	3615	2560											6		3⅛

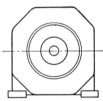

2. If a 25-horsepower 600-rpm motor is used to hoist a load which requires full-rated torque when the efficiency of the hoisting mechanism is 60 per cent, what torque must a brake supply to hold the load stationary after it is hoisted?

3. The trolley of a crane weighs 2000 pounds and travels at 90 feet per minute. The WR^2 of the driving motor, plus that of all rotating parts of the trolley, is 15 lb-ft². Calculate the torque required of a brake which will stop the motor in 10 revolutions.

4. The WR^2 of a 200-horsepower 450-rpm motor is 800 lb-ft². How long will it take to stop the motor with a brake which delivers a torque equal to 50 per cent more than the rated torque of the motor?

5. If the motor of problem 4 is driving a direct-connected load having a WR^2 of 2000 lb-ft², how long will it take to stop the motor with a brake which delivers a torque equal to 50 per cent more than the motor torque?

6. How much torque would be required of a brake which would stop the motor and load of problem 5 in the same time that the brake of problem 4 stopped the motor alone?

7. A 150-horsepower 460-rpm shunt motor having a WR^2 of 415 lb-ft² is driving a direct-connected load having a WR^2 of 500 lb-ft². If the motor is fitted with a brake which delivers a torque equal to the motor torque, and in addition the controller is arranged for dynamic braking which varies from three times the motor torque at the start to zero at standstill, how long will it take to stop the motor?

8. A 75-horsepower 1750-rpm motor having a WR^2 of 118 lb-ft² is driving a flywheel which is a solid cylinder having a diameter of 3 feet and a weight of 2000 pounds. The gearing between the motor and the flywheel is 5 to 1. Calculate the equivalent WR^2 of the system.

9. How long will it take to stop the motor and flywheel using a brake which delivers a torque of twice the motor torque.

10. Calculate the kinetic energy in an armature having a WR^2 of 1300 pound-feet² and a speed of 1750 rpm.

11. If the rating of the motor of problem 10 is 700 horsepower, how many revolutions will be required to stop the motor after the brake sets if the brake torque is equal to the motor rated torque?

12. How many seconds will it take to stop the motor?

13. If the 700-horsepower 1750-rpm motor of problem 10 is driving a load having an equivalent WR^2 of 1500 including the brake wheel, calculate the torque required to reach zero speed in 15 seconds, allowing 0.40 seconds for the brake to set.

14. A brake which operates very infrequently can dissipate 1500 foot-pounds per square inch of wheel face, per minute, without reaching a temperature which will destroy the lining material. If the width of the wheel is 0.40 times the wheel diameter, what is the wheel diameter that is required?

15. The bucket of an ore-bridge hoist is operated by two 325-horsepower 390-rpm motors. One called the hoist motor is geared to cables which connect to the top of the bucket. The other called the shell-line motor is geared to cables which connect to the hinged lips of the bucket, and this motor is used to open and close the bucket. In hoisting a full bucket, the motors divide the load equally. When opening the bucket, the brake on the hoist motor must hold the entire load, since the shell-line motor is paying out cable to permit the bucket to open. Calculate the torque required of the two motors in hoisting when

The bucket weighs 45,000 pounds.

The ore weighs 45,000 pounds.

The transmission efficiency is 0.70.

The hoisting speed is 172 feet per minute.

16. What torque is required of the brake which must hold the load while the bucket is opening?

17. When the empty bucket is lowered to pick up another load, the two motors must decelerate at the same rate. Calculate the number of revolutions of the hoist motor after the brake applies if

The lowering speed is twice the hoisting speed.

The WR^2 of the brake wheel and rotating parts is 500 lb-ft^2.

The WR^2 of the motor is 1000 lb-ft^2.

Note. The full weight of the bucket is on the hoisting line cables.

18. What torque is needed on the shell-line brake to stop the unloaded shell-line motor in the same number of revolutions?

19. A 280-horsepower 420-rpm motor having a WR^2 of 1000 lb-ft^2 is driving a direct-connected load having a WR^2 of 300 lb-ft^2. Calculate the motor torque, and select a suitable shunt-wound 1-hour intermittent-duty brake from Table 42.

20. Add the WR^2 of the wheel of the selected brake, and calculate the time to stop motor, brake, and load.

21. In order to secure faster stopping the 280-horsepower motor is replaced by two 140-horsepower motors, each having a WR^2 of 350 lb-ft^2. Calculate the torque of each motor, and select suitable shunt-wound 1-hour intermittent-duty brakes from Table 42.

22. Add the WR^2 of the wheels of the selected brakes, and calculate the time to stop motor, brake, and load. How much has the stopping time been shortened by the use of two motors?

23. A factory has a flywheel which is of irregular shape and which weighs 1000 pounds. It is necessary to determine the radius of gyration. The flywheel is clutched to a motor, accelerated to 1200 rpm, and then declutched. At the instant of declutching, a 14-inch continuous-duty brake (Table 42) is applied. The flywheel stops in 20 seconds. What is the radius of gyration?

24. A motor-driven car in a factory weighs 10,000 pounds and travels at 200 feet per minute. The WR^2 of the motor brake wheel, and of all rotating parts of the car, is 150 lb-ft^2. There is a safety limit switch which cuts off power and sets the brake if the car is driven too near to the end of the track. How far from the end of the track should the limit switch be placed to insure safe stopping from full speed?

25. A machine consists of three rolls, each weighing 2000 pounds. The radius of one roll is 18 inches, and it is geared to the motor through a 5-to-1 gear train. The radius of the second roll is 2 feet, and it is geared through a 20-to-1 gear train. The third roll has a radius of 12 inches and is geared through a 2-to-1 gear train. The 150-horsepower 480-rpm motor has a WR^2 of 415 lb-ft^2. The WR^2 of the brake wheel is 313 lb-ft^2. What is the equivalent WR^2 of the whole system?

26. If the motor of problem 25 is equipped with an electronic controller which will hold the accelerating torque essentially constant at twice the full-load torque of the motor, how long will it take the motor to accelerate the system?

27. If the brake torque is 3600 pound-feet, how long will it take to stop the system?

28. If the controller is changed to a magnetic controller which permits an average accelerating torque of 50 per cent of full-load torque, what will be the accelerating time?

29. If dynamic braking is provided to give an average decelerating torque equal to the motor full-load torque, in addition to the torque of the brake, what will be the time required to stop?

30. A motor on a crane is hoisting a load of 10 tons at a speed of 100 feet per minute. The gear ratio between motor and load is 20 to 1. The efficiency of the hoist is 80 per cent. How much torque must a brake provide to hold the load if power fails while hoisting?

21

RESISTOR DESIGN

Design Operations. The design of a resistor may be divided into three operations:

Calculation of the ohmic values.
Calculation of the current-carrying capacity required.
Selection of the actual materials to be used.

The calculation of the ohmic values is generally not difficult. The ohms required depend upon the function of the resistor, that is, whether it is for accelerating purposes or for speed regulating or for dynamic braking. Where a number of similar resistors have to be designed, as, for instance, the accelerating resistors for a line of similar automatic starters, covering a range of horsepower, tables may be prepared which make the calculation a very simple matter. Similar tables may be prepared for the calculation of the current capacity, although the preparation of such tables is more difficult. The capacity depends upon the amount of current to be carried by the resistor and the percentage of time on in each cycle. If the current is constant, the calculation is simple, but, if the current varies, the calculation becomes more involved.

The selection of the actual materials to be used is a matter for which no general rules can be set down, as it depends upon the materials available. Each manufacturer of controllers has his own line of cast grids, ribbon resistors, and wire-wound units, the characteristics of which are known to his engineers. After the ohms and the current capacity required have been calculated, the material is selected on the basis of minimum cost, minimum space requirement, or service requirements.

The calculation of ohmic values for various purposes is described in the chapters which cover the different types of motors and their control.

Resistor Materials. Since resistors serve so many purposes, they must be available in a wide range of ohmic values and current-carrying capacities. For low ohms and high capacity, cast-iron grids are generally used. For high ohms and low capacity, wire-wound units of various types are available. Resistors having a ribbon of steel or other material form an intermediate class.

Cast-iron Grids. Cast-iron grids, as the name implies, are resistors made of cast iron, in the form of grids, and with an eye at each end for mounting. The eyes are usually ground and copper-plated to

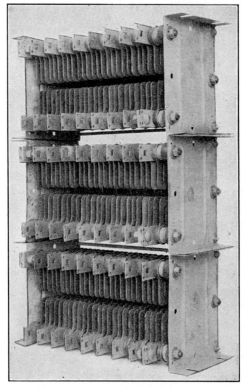

FIG. 233. Bank of Cast-iron Grids.

insure a good connection between grids. The grids are stacked in bunches on steel mounting rods. The rods are first insulated by being covered with a mica tube or wound with an insulating material. Mica washers are inserted between the grids for insulation. Grids are made in many sizes and forms. The resistance obtainable with a single grid is about 0.125 ohm for the grid of minimum cross-section, and may go to 0.005 ohm or less for the larger cross-sections.

Cast-iron grids are cheap and strong, and, contrary to what might be expected, they are not easily damaged by corrosion. They will rust, of course, but the surface hardness produced in casting prevents rapid corrosion beyond the first layer of rust. Where protection against corrosion is important, as in marine service, the grids may be plated with zinc or cadmium or painted with aluminum paint.

If grids are to be mounted as a part of a controller, the mounting rods are made of the proper length to extend across the frame at the rear of the slate panel, or they may be fastened to brackets or cross-angles in an enclosing frame. If the grids are mounted separately from the controller, as is standard practice in steel-mill and other large installations, the rods are mounted between steel end frames. The size of the box thus formed and the number of grids in it are usually standardized by the control manufacturer, so that any box purchased will fit the mounting of any other box. Figure 233 shows three grid boxes of this type.

Punched Grids. Instead of grids being made of cast iron, they may be punched out of sheet steel, some corrosion-resistant alloy being

Fig. 234.   E. C. & M. Tab Weld Resistor.

preferable. Such an alloy may also have a negligible temperature-resistance coefficient. The grids are, of course, much stronger than cast-iron grids. Figure 234 shows a resistor of this type made by the Electric Controller and Manufacturing Company. In this design the ends of the grids are welded together to obtain a good electric contact, and the resistor becomes, in effect, a continuous strip.

Ribbon Resistors. Some resistor installations are subject to severe shocks, as, for example, installations on open-hearth charging machines or on battleships. Grids cast of a special alloy are sometimes used on such installations, but ribbon resistor is more common. The ribbon may be a copper-nickel alloy or stainless iron or Nichrome. The ribbon is wound edgewise, either in a spiral form on tubular porcelain

FIG. 235. Ribbon-type Resistor.

insulators or between insulated mounting supports (see Figs. 235 and 236). An assembly of either type may be mounted as a part of the controller or made up in the form of the mill-type box. The principal advantage of the ribbon resistors is that they are shock-proof. In addition they are rust-proof, light in weight, and compact. They are more costly than cast-iron resistors.

Wire-wound Units. Wire-wound units take many forms, some of which are shown in Fig. 237. The flat units have a base of clay or of some other insulating material. The wire, usually a copper-nickel

alloy, is wound on the base, and the unit is covered with a cement
and baked. Another method is to cover the unit with a highly heat-
resistant enamel. These units are assembled on rods for mounting
in a controller, or they may be mounted directly on the rear of the
slate panel. In resistance they may be wound for anything from a
fraction of an ohm up to several thousand ohms per unit.

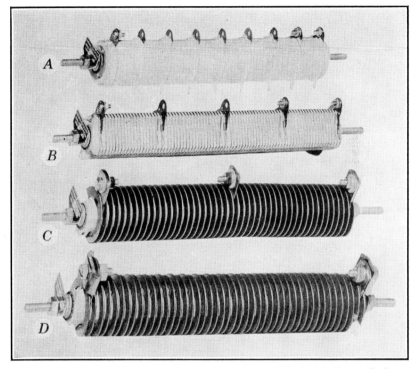

Fig. 236. General Electric Resistor Units, *A*. Smooth-wound with Taps. *B*. Open-
wound with 3 Taps. *C*. Edgewise-wound, with Midtap. *D*. Multiple Edgewise-
wound.

The tubular units are wound on porcelain bases, and cemented or
enameled after winding. The type-*R* (Fig. 237) unit has a metal
sheath over the cement for protective purposes.

Figure 238 shows a mill-type box made up of heavy units. A base
of lava has been used, cut with a spiral groove to take the wire winding.
The wire itself is first wound into a spiral, which is then wound on
the base. Clamps at each end of the unit serve to hold the winding
in place and to provide for a connecting terminal.

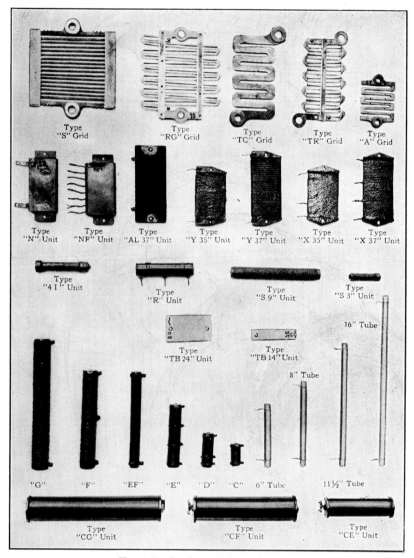

Fig. 237. Resistor Units and Grids.

A column of thin graphite disks may also serve as a resistor. When these disks are loosely stacked, the resistance of the column is high. To reduce the resistance, the disks are put under pressure. A cam provides the variation of pressure, giving equal resistance changes for equal movements of the control lever. When used for accelerating purposes, the column is finally short-circuited by a copper-to-copper contact or by a magnetic contactor.

Fig. 238. Bank of Wire-wound Resistor Units.

Current Capacity. The capacity of a resistor and the amount of material required for a given application are determined by the wattage to be dissipated, the length of time on, and the cooling time, or time off. On a single start, the resistor will absorb a certain amount of heat, depending upon its mass; and if the duty is infrequent, this may be the determining factor. With repeated starts, the resistor does not have time to cool fully, and the criterion is then the ability of the resistor to radiate heat to the surrounding atmosphere. In the first case the mass of material is the important factor and ventilation is not so important; but in the second case the ventilation available becomes of considerable importance. If the grids are stacked closely together on the rods, the ventilation will be reduced, and more grids will be required to dissipate the same energy. Also, if several banks of grids are stacked one above the other, the heat of each one will affect the others, and the dissipating capacity of the whole bank will be reduced (see Fig. 239).

In order to arrive at a rating for his resistor materials, the manufacturer must test each size of grid or unit, not only for continuous carrying capacity but also on a number of intermittent cycles. He must also determine the effects of close and wide stacking, and of mounting different numbers of stacks one above the other. To enable manufacturers to make these tests under the same conditions, and so have a common basis for rating resistors, NEMA has set up the following definitions and resistor classes.

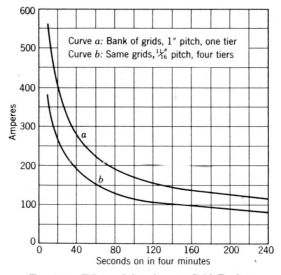

FIG. 239.   Effect of Spacing on Grid Rating.

Definition—Periodic Rating. The periodic rating defines the load which can be carried for the periods of load and rest specified in the rating, the apparatus starting cold, and for the total time specified in the rating, without causing any of the limitations established herein to be exceeded.

Service Classification.   (a) Standard resistors to meet various classes of service shall be designated by class numbers in accordance with the table of classification of resistors (Tables 44, 45, and 46).

(b) Starting and intermittent-duty resistors are primarily designed for use with motors requiring an initial torque corresponding to the stated percentage of full-load current on the first point, and requiring an average (root-mean-square) accelerating current of 125 per cent of full-load current.

(c) Starting and intermittent-duty primary resistors for squirrel-cage motors, requiring greater accelerating current, are included in the standard classification subject to test specifications (see below).

(d) Continuous-duty resistors shall be capable of carrying continuously the current for which they are designed.

TABLE 44

CLASSIFICATION OF RESISTORS FOR NON-REVERSING SERVICE AND REVERSING NON-PLUGGING SERVICE

Approx. % of Full-load Current on First Point	30 sec of Each 15 min	5 sec of Each 80 sec	10 sec of Each 80 sec	15 sec of Each 90 sec	15 sec of Each 60 sec	15 sec of Each 45 sec	15 sec of Each 30 sec	Continuous Duty *
				Class Numbers Applying to Duty Cycles, Time on				
25	101	111	131	141	151	161	171	91
50	102	112	132	142	152	162	172	92
70	103	113	133	143	153	163	173	93
100	104	114	134	144	154	164	174	94
150	105	115	135	145	155	165	175	95
200 or over	106	116	136	146	156	166	176	96

When an armature shunt resistor is added to any one of the above classes, the class number will include the suffix AS.

Example. Class 155AS is a resistor which includes an armature shunt and which will allow an initial inrush of 150 per cent with the armature shunt open.

When a dynamic-braking resistor is added to any one of the above classes, the class number will include the suffix DB.

Example. Class 155DB.

* For speed-regulating duty see Table 47.

TABLE 45

CLASSIFICATION OF RESISTORS FOR REVERSING PLUGGING SERVICE—WITHOUT ARMATURE SHUNT OR DYNAMIC BRAKING

Approx. % of Full-load Current on First Point Starting from Rest with All Resistance in Circuit	15 sec of Each 60 sec	15 sec of Each 45 sec	15 sec of Each 30 sec	Continuous Duty
		Class Numbers Applying to Duty Cycles, Time on		
25	151P	161P	171P	91P
50	152P	162P	172P	92P
70	153P	163P	173P	93P
100	154P	164P	174P	94P

Note. The class numbers apply to the complete resistor, but the duty cycles are those of the accelerating resistor only.

When an armature shunt resistor is added to any one of the above classes, the class number will include the suffix AS.

Example. Class 153P-AS is a plugging resistor which includes an armature shunt and which will allow an initial inrush of 70 per cent with the armature shunt open.

When a dynamic-braking resistor is added to any one of the above classes, the class number will include the suffix DB.

Example. Class 153P-DB.

TABLE 46

CLASSIFICATION OF RESISTORS FOR DYNAMIC LOWERING CRANE
AND HOIST CONTROLLERS

Approx. % of Full-load Current on First Point Hoisting Starting from Rest without Armature Shunt	Class Numbers App'ying to Duty Cycles, Time on			
	15 sec of Each 60 sec	15 sec of Each 45 sec	15 sec of Each 30 sec	Continuous Duty
50	152DL	162DL	172DL	92DL
70	153DL	163DL	173DL	93DL

TABLE 47

CLASSIFICATION OF RESISTORS FOR CONTINUOUS-DUTY, SPEED-REGULATING
SERVICE, WITH D-C SHUNT MOTORS AND A-C WOUND-ROTOR MOTORS

% of Speed Reduction	Class Numbers % of Rated Motor Torque at Reduced Speed						
	40	50	60	70	80	90	100
5	405	505	605	705	805	905	1005
10	410	510	610	710	810	910	1010
15	415	515	615	715	815	915	1015
20	420	520	620	720	820	920	1020
25	425	525	625	725	825	925	1025
30	430	530	630	730	830	930	1030
35	435	535	635	735	835	935	1035
40	440	540	640	740	840	940	1040
45	445	545	645	745	845	945	1045
50	450	550	650	750	850	950	1050

Note 1. The base speed of an adjustable-speed motor is the lowest speed obtained at rated load and rated voltage at the temperature rise specified in the rating.

Note 2. The stability of the motor speed obtained by simple rheostatic control is dependent upon the stability of the load on the motor. The degree of instability is directly proportional to the amount of speed reduction. Variations in load have a greater proportional effect on the speed when the load is light. For these reasons the Standard has not been carried beyond a speed reduction of 50 per cent and a load torque of 40 per cent.

Note 3. With a direct-current shunt motor the per cent of rated motor current which is obtained at the reduced speed is assumed to be the same as the per cent of rated torque.

With a wound-rotor motor and resistor in the rotor circuit the per cent of rated rotor (secondary) current which is obtained at the reduced speed is assumed to be the same as the per cent of rated torque.

Note 4. A speed-regulating resistor is so designed that it may be operated continuously at any point in the speed-regulating range when the load follows its normal speed-torque curve. When additional resistor is required to obtain the starting current specified, that portion of the resistor is designed for a duty cycle selected from Table 44. Such a resistor may be completely specified by a compound number.

For example: 154/950 designates a resistor which is designed for starting and speed-regulating duty. The starting section is designed to allow 100 per cent of full-load current on the first point starting from rest, and a duty cycle of 15 seconds on and 45 seconds off. The regulating section is designed to give 50 per cent speed reduction at 80 per cent of rated torque, and for continuous duty when the load follows its normal speed-torque curve.

Note 5. The approximate per cent of rated current which will be obtained on the first point of the controller when starting from rest if the speed-regulating resistor alone is used may be determined from the equation

$$\text{Per cent current} = \frac{\text{Per cent torque at reduced speed}}{\text{Per cent of speed reduction}} \times 100$$

The following rules for determining the rating of a resistor under the above classifications are also taken from the NEMA Standards.

Temperature Test. (*a*) When a temperature test is made on a starting or intermittent-duty resistor without its motor, the resistor shall be connected to a voltage that will give the initial inrush current specified, and the current shall be maintained at 125 per cent of the full-load current for those steps through which 125 per cent of full-load current can flow. The specified cycle shall be repeated for 1 hour.

(*b*) When a temperature test is made on a continuous-duty resistor without its motor, any tested step shall be subjected to 100 per cent of the current for which it is designed, and this value of current shall be maintained until the maximum temperatures are reached.

(*c*) When a test is made on a primary-resistor starter for a squirrel-cage motor, without its motor, 300 per cent of normal full-load current of the motor with which the starter is to be used shall be maintained for a time-on period of 5 seconds out of each 80 seconds, this cycle to be repeated for 1 hour.

Temperature of Resistors. When a temperature test is made upon a resistor at the current values, duty cycle, and elapsed time specified, the limiting temperature rise above the cooling air and the methods of temperature measurement shall be as follows:

1. For bare resistive conductors the temperature rise shall not exceed 375 C as measured by thermocouple in contact with the resistive conductor.

2. For imbedded resistive conductors temperature rise shall not exceed 300 C as measured by a thermocouple in contact with the surface of the imbedding material.

3. The temperature rise of the issuing air shall not exceed 175 C as measured by mercury thermometer at a distance of 1 inch from the enclosure.

Before ribbon resistors were extensively used, the classification table was based on a 4-minute cycle as practically all resistors had enough heat-absorbing capacity so that they did not reach their ultimate temperature in that time. When ribbon resistors came into general acceptance, this table no longer served, because the heat-absorbing capacity of the ribbon is relatively low. A resistor of ribbon designed for half time on the basis of 2 minutes out of 4 requires practically the same amount of material as one designed for continuous duty. Since the actual operating cycle of most intermittent-duty motor-driven machines is much less than 4 minutes, it is practical to base the resistor on a shorter cycle. Resistors of thin ribbon, based on the short cycle, will require only about half as much material as for the same duty based on the long cycle.

Very Short Cycles. For very short cycles, in which the resistor is in circuit for only a second or two, the capacity can be calculated on the basis of heat-absorbing ability only, ventilation being neglected. As an example, suppose that it is desired to calculate the temperature rise of a ribbon resistor for dynamic braking, the peak current being 700 amperes and the time 1 second. The specific heat of the material is 0.09. The weight of the ribbon is calculated and found to be 4.8 pounds, and the resistance is 0.5 ohm.

$$\text{Watts} = 700^2 \times 0.5 = 245,000$$

$$\text{Btu per hour} = 245,000 \times 3.412 = 835,000$$

$$\text{Btu per pound for 1 second} = \frac{835,000}{4.8 \times 60 \times 60} = 48.3$$

Since 1 Btu will raise 1 pound of water 1 F, the temperature rise of the ribbon will be

$$T = \frac{48.3}{0.09} = 537 \text{ F or } 298 \text{ C}$$

Intermittent-duty Rating. The following example will illustrate a method of calculating the amount of resistor required for an intermittent-duty controller. Assume that it is desired to design a three-step class 153P resistor for a 100-horsepower 230-volt motor whose full-load current is 375 amperes. Class 153P indicates that this is a plugging controller, and that the resistor will be in circuit for 15 seconds in each 60 seconds.

The ohmic values are:

$$\text{Total resistance} = \frac{230 \times 1.8}{375 \times 1.5} = 0.736 \text{ ohm}$$

$$\text{Accelerating resistance} = \frac{230}{375 \times 1.6} = 0.383 \text{ ohm}$$

The steps are tapered as follows:

Step	Percentage of Total	Ohms
1	48	0.353
2	34.4	0.253
3	17.6	0.130
Total	100	0.736

The time required on each point of the controller may be assumed to be in the same ratio as that of the resistance of the steps, so that the time on in each cycle will be

Step	Percentage of Total	Seconds
1	48	7.2
2	82.4	12.4
3	100	15

On the plugging step the inrush is 150 per cent and the base current 100 per cent. The heating of the resistor is determined by the root-mean-square current, which is

$$\text{Rms current} = \sqrt{\frac{150^2 + 150 \times 100 + 100^2}{3}}$$

$$= 126 \text{ per cent or } 460 \text{ amperes}$$

On the other steps the inrush is 160 per cent, and the rms current is

$$\sqrt{\frac{160^2 + 160 \times 100 + 100^2}{3}} = 131 \text{ per cent or } 492 \text{ amperes}$$

The watts to be dissipated by each step are determined by multiplying the resistance by the square of the rms current. The wattage value is then multiplied by the time on to obtain the watt-seconds on each step. The last two steps are on part of the time at the lower current and part at the higher current.

Step	Resist- ance	Seconds On	Rms amperes	Rms watts	Watt- seconds
1	0.353	7.2	460	74,600	537,000
2	0.253	7.2 + 5.2	460–492	53,500 and 61,200	703,000
3	0.130	7.2 + 7.8	460–492	27,500 and 31,400	443,000

It is now necessary to refer to a table giving the wattage rating of the particular type of resistor material. Assuming that cast-iron grids are used, and that the rating of each is 600 watts, on a duty of 15 seconds in 60 seconds, the watt-second rating is then 9000 per grid. The number of grids required for each step is determined by dividing the watt-seconds required by the step, by the grid rating.

$$\text{First step} \qquad \frac{537,000}{9,000} = 60 \text{ grids}$$

$$\text{Second step} \qquad \frac{703,000}{9,000} = 78 \text{ grids}$$

$$\text{Third step} \qquad \frac{443,000}{9,000} = 49 \text{ grids}$$

$$\text{Total} \qquad\qquad = 187 \text{ grids}$$

Since the number of grids required varies directly with the horse-power of the motor, it is possible to reduce the above calculations to a simple general form from which a similar resistor can be calculated for any size of motor.

A convenient method of expressing the ohmic value is as percentage of E/I, where E is the line voltage and I the rated current of the motor.

The first step is 0.353 ohm.

$$0.353 = \frac{KE}{I}$$

$$K = \frac{0.353 \times 375}{230}$$

$$K = 0.575, \text{ or } 57.5 \text{ per cent of } E/I$$

The second step is $\dfrac{0.253 \times 375}{230} = 0.41$, or 41 per cent of E/I.

The third step is $\dfrac{0.130 \times 375}{230} = 0.21$, or 21 per cent of E/I.

Grid tables are generally arranged to give the current-carrying capacity of the grid, for any duty cycle. The most convenient way to express the capacity required for a step is, therefore, in terms of the full rated current of the motor. It is convenient to reduce the rating to a continuous-duty basis, so that any resistor can be calculated from the continuous-duty grid table.

Assume that the type of grid to be used has a continuous rating of 125 watts. The 60 grids of the first step will have a continuous rating of 60×125, or 7500 watts. The continuous current capacity of this step will be

$$\sqrt{\frac{\text{Watts}}{\text{Resistance}}} = \sqrt{\frac{7500}{0.353}} = 143 \text{ amperes}$$

Expressed in terms of rated motor current, this is

$$\frac{143}{375} = 0.39I$$

Similarly, the capacity required in the second step is

$$\sqrt{\frac{125 \times 78}{0.253}} = 196 \text{ amperes} = 0.52I$$

And the capacity required in the third step is

$$\sqrt{\frac{125 \times 49}{0.130}} = 217 \text{ amperes} = 0.58I$$

The complete formula for the resistance is as follows:

Step	Ohms in Percentage of E/I	Current Capacity in Percentage of I
1	57.5	39
2	41	52
3	21	58
Total	119.5	

This formula is applicable to any motor requiring a three-step class-153P resistor and using the particular type of grid on which the calculations are based.

Parallel Resistance. When the resistor steps are connected in parallel instead of in series, the distribution of the resistor material is quite different. The resistance of the first step is 119.5 per cent of

E/I. When the second step is parallel with the first step, the resultant resistance must be the same as that obtained with a series resistance when the first step is cut out, or 62 per cent of E/I. When the third step is parallel with the first two steps, the resultant resistance must be 21 per cent of E/I. The final contactor short-circuits all the steps. To obtain these results,

$$\text{Step 1} = 1.19E/I = 0.73 \quad \text{ohm}$$

$$\text{Step 2} = 1.29E/I = 0.79 \quad \text{ohm}$$

$$\text{Step 3} = 0.32E/I = 0.196 \text{ ohm}$$

When the first step above is in circuit, the rms current is 126 per cent, or 460 amperes. With the second step connected in, the total rms current is 131 per cent, or 492 amperes. This current divides through the two steps in inverse ratio to their resistance. With three steps in circuit the current divides through the three resistors. The first step is in circuit for the total time period, but with varying currents as the other steps are cut in. The currents and times are as follows:

	Ohms	Rms amperes	Seconds	Watt-seconds
Step 1				
On the first point	0.73	460	7.2	1,110,000
On the second point	0.73	256	5.1	244,000
On the third point	0.73	87	2.7	15,000
Total watt-seconds				1,369,000
Grids required at 9000 watt-seconds per grid				153
Step 2				
On the second point	0.79	236	5.1	224,000
On the third point	0.79	81	2.7	14,000
Total watt-seconds				238,000
Grids required				27
Step 3				
On the third point	0.196	324	2.7	55,600
Total watt-seconds				55,600
Grids required				7

From these calculations it is evident that the parallel resistor requires the same number of grids as the series resistor, but that the greater part of the parallel resistor is required in the first step. This is true only in intermittent duty. On continuous regulating duty the parallel resistor will require a greater number of grids.

The current capacity required may be reduced to terms of full rated current in the same manner as with the series resistor.

The capacity of the first step is

$$\sqrt{\frac{125 \times 153}{0.73}} = 161 \text{ amperes} = 0.43I$$

That of the second step is

$$\sqrt{\frac{125 \times 27}{0.79}} = 65 \text{ amperes} = 0.17I$$

And that of the third step is

$$\sqrt{\frac{125 \times 7}{0.196}} = 67 \text{ amperes} = 0.18I$$

The complete formula for the parallel resistor is as follows:

Step	Ohms in per cent of E/I	Current Capacity in per cent of I
1	119	43
2	129	17
3	32	18

Regulating Duty. When the resistor is to be used for regulating duty, it must carry continuously the current required by the load. If the load is definitely known, that value should be used. Ordinarily the load will be known only to the extent of whether it is fan or machine duty. The current required may be read from the load curves of Figs. 67 and 68. The following demonstration is given to determine the relation between the material required for a series resistor and that of a parallel resistor. Assume that 80 per cent of full-load current is required on each point of the controller and that the grids have a capacity of 125 watts per grid. With the series resistor the number of grids required is as follows:

$$\text{First step} \quad \frac{0.353 \times 300^2}{125} = 254 \text{ grids}$$

$$\text{Second step} \quad \frac{0.253 \times 300^2}{125} = 180 \text{ grids}$$

$$\text{Third step} \quad \frac{0.130 \times 300^2}{125} = 94 \text{ grids}$$

$$\text{Total} \qquad\qquad\qquad = \overline{528} \text{ grids}$$

With the parallel resistance, the first step requires

$$\frac{0.73 \times 300^2}{125} = 528 \text{ grids}$$

The second step has to carry only the current through it, or 142 amperes.

$$\frac{0.79 \times 142^2}{125} = 128 \text{ grids}$$

The third step has to carry 198 amperes.

$$\frac{0.196 \times 198^2}{125} = 62 \text{ grids}$$

$$\text{Total} \quad = 718 \text{ grids}$$

The parallel regulating resistor, therefore, requires 36 per cent more grids than the series regulating resistor.

Any resistor may be reduced to terms of E/I and percentage of I, but it must be borne in mind that the resultant table is applicable only to the particular type of grid upon whose characteristics it is based. Such a table, worked out for cast grids, will give entirely erroneous results if used to calculate a resistor of ribbon material or of wire-wound units.

TABLE 48
TYPICAL RATING TABLE FOR CAST-IRON GRIDS

Grid Number	1	2	3	4	5	6	7	8	9
Grid Ohms	0.007	0.010	0.015	0.020	0.030	0.040	0.060	0.080	0.110
Per cent of Time On				Capacity in Amperes					
6.25	515	430	365	305	255	215	180	150	128
12.50	365	305	260	215	180	153	127	107	90
16.67	315	265	225	187	157	132	110	93	79
25.00	255	215	182	152	128	108	90	76	64
33.33	215	185	156	130	110	92	76	65	55
50.00	180	153	130	108	90	76	62	54	45
75.00	150	125	105	88	75	62	51	44	37
100.00	130	108	89	76	63	54	44	38	32

This table is fictitious and does not apply to the grids of any manufacturer.

NEMA Resistor Application Table. Table 49 is intended as a guide in specifying or designing resistors. The classifications are those which experience has shown to be correct for the average installation. It is recognized that there will be exceptions. The table applies to resistors composed of wire-wound units or cast grids, and unbreakable ribbon resistors, provided that the time-on period does not exceed the values given in Table 44.

TABLE 49

	NEMA Resistance Class		NEMA Resistance Class
Blowers		*Coal Mines (Cont.)*	
Constant pressure	135–195	Picking tables	135
Centrifugal	133–193	Rotary car dumpers	153
		Shaker screens	135
Brick Plants			
Augers	135	*Compressors*	
Conveyors	135	Constant speed	135
Dry pans	135	Varying speed, plunger type	135–195
Pug mills	135	Centrifugal	93
By-products Coke Plants		*Concrete Mixers*	135
Reversing machines	153		
Leveler ram	153	*Cranes—General Purpose*	
Pusher bar	153	Hoist	153
Door machine	153	Bridge, sleeve-bearing	153
		Trolley, sleeve-bearing	153
Cement Mills		Bridge or trolley, roller-bearing	152
Conveyors	135		
Crushers	145	*Flour Mills*	135
Rotary dryers	145–195	Line shafting	135
Elevators	135		
Grinders, pulverizers	135	*Food Plants*	
Kilns	135–195	Dough mixers	135
		Butter churns	135
Coal and Ore Bridges			
Holding line	162	*Hoists*	
Closing line	162	Winch	153
Trolley	163	Mine slope	172
Bridge	153	Mine vertical	162
		Contractors' hoists	152
Coal Mines			
Car hauls	162	*Larry Cars*	153
Conveyors	135–155		
Cutters	135	*Lift Bridges*	152
Crushers	145		
Fans	134–193	*Machine Tools*	
Hoists, slope	172	Bending rolls, rev.	163–164
Vertical	162	Non-rev.	115
Jigs	135	Boring mills	135

Machine Tools (Cont.)	NEMA Resistance Class	Steel Mills	NEMA Resistance Class
Bulldozers	135	Accumulators	153
Drills	115	Casting machines, pig	153
Gear cutters	115	Charging machines, bridge	153–163
Grinders	135	Peel	153–163
Hobbing machines	115	Trolley	153–163
Lathes	115	Coiling machines	135
Milling machines	115	Conveyors	135–155
Presses	135	Converters, metal	154
Punches	135	Cranes, ladle, bridge, trolleys, sleeve-bearings	153–163
Saws	115	Roller-bearing	152–162
Shapers	115	Hoist	153–163
Metal Mining		Crushers	145
Ball, rod, tube mills	135	Furnace doors	155
Car dumpers, rotary	153	Gas valves	155
Converters, copper	154	Gas washers	155
Conveyors	135	Hot metal mixers	163
Crushers	145	Ingot buggy	153
Tilting furnace	153	Kickoff	153
Paper Mills		Levelers	153
Heaters	135	Manipulator fingers	153–163
Calenders	154–192	Side guards	153–163
Pipe Working		Pickling machine	153
Cutting and threading	135	Pilers, slab	153
Expanding and flanging	135–195	Racks	153
Power Plants		Reelers	135
Clinker grinders	135	Saws, hot or cold	155
Coal crushers	135	Screwdowns	153–163
Conveyors, belt	135	Shears	155
Screw	135	Shuffle bars	155
Pulverized fuel feeders	135	Sizing rolls	155
Pulverizers, ball type	135	Slab buggy	155
Centrifugal	134	Soaking pit covers	155
Stokers	135–193	Straighteners	153
Pumps		Tables, main roll	153–163
Centrifugal	134–193	Shear approach	153–163
Plunger	135–195	Lift	153–163
Rubber Mills		Roll	153
Calenders	155	Transfer	153
Crackers	135	Approach	153
Mixing mills	135	Tilting furnace	153
Washers	135	Wire stranding machine	153
		Woodworking Plants	
		Boring machines	115
		Lathe	115

Woodworking Plants (Cont.)	*NEMA Resistance Class*	*Woodworking Plants (Cont.)*	*NEMA Resistance Class*
Mortiser	115	Sanders	115
Molder	115	Saws	115
Planers	115	Shapers	115
Power trimmer and miter	115	Shingle machine	115

References

J. Ragazinni, "Calculation of Resistance Steps in Starting Rheostats," *Electrical Engineering,* July, 1939, Vol. 58, p. 318.

H. F. Wilson, "Water-cooled Resistors," *General Electric Review,* 1923, p. 258.

R. F. Emerson, "Motor Starting Resistors," *Factory Management and Maintenance,* November, 1936.

J. Cotterell, "D-c Motor Starters," *Electrical Review,* 1945, Vol. 137, p. 533.

G. C. Armstrong, "Theory and Design of NEMA Resistors for Motor Starting and Speed Control," *Electrical Engineering,* May, 1940.

Problems

1. A 2.0-ohm grounding resistor for a transmission line must carry 2000 amperes for 12 seconds without exceeding a temperature rise of 900 F. The specific heat of the resistor material is 0.09. How many pounds of resistor material are required?

2. A certain cast-iron grid has a resistance of 0.01 ohm, and its heating curve shows that if it carries 290 amperes for 2 minutes it will have a temperature rise of 500 C. At this temperature rise, how many grids will be required for a 4-ohm resistor which will carry 1600 amperes for 1 minute?

3. What would be the total ohmic value of a class-163P resistor for a 50-horsepower 230-volt 180-ampere series motor, neglecting motor resistance?

4. What would be the total ohmic value of a class-750 resistor for this motor, neglecting motor resistance?

5. If the resistor of problem 4 is tapered as follows, what will be the approximate rms amperes which each step must carry for the specified time cycle?

Step	Per cent of Total ohms
1	48
2	34.4
3	17.6

6. A dynamic-braking resistor is used to stop a certain motor once a day. The voltage is 250, the initial braking current 500 amperes, duration of braking 8 seconds, and the braking current decreases in direct proportion to the time. How many resistor grids will be required if the grids weigh 1.5 pounds each, the specific heat of the material is 0.09, and the temperature rise is limited to 500 F?

7. A resistor which must dissipate 12,000 watts is made up of units having an overall end dimension of 2×2 inches. These units are to be mounted in an enclosure, and may be mounted in one horizontal row, or in two, three, or four rows. Determine the most economical arrangement, and calculate the cost, using the following data.

When mounted in one row each unit will dissipate 600 watts, in two rows 500 watts, in three rows 400 watts, and in four rows 300 watts. The units cost $1.50 each. The cost of the enclosing cabinet is $0.50 per inch of width, for any height.

8. Using Table 48, determine the size of grid and number of grids in each step of a starting resistor for a 100-horsepower 230-volt 350-ampere shunt motor, assuming the following:

> Resistor class 155.
> 4 steps of resistance.
> Ohmic taper 40–30–20–10 per cent of total.
> Time taper same as step taper.
> Inrush current on each step 150 per cent of rated current.
> Contactors close at 100 per cent of rated current.
> Disregard motor resistance.

9. Using Table 48, determine the size of grid and the number of grids in each step of a starting resistor for a 50-horsepower 230-volt 175-ampere shunt motor, assuming the following:

> Resistor class 175.
> 3 steps of resistance.
> Ohmic taper 48–35–17 per cent of total.
> Time taper same as step taper.
> Inrush on first step 150 per cent of rated current.
> Inrush on other steps 160 per cent of rated current.
> Contactors close at 100 per cent of rated current.
> Disregard motor resistance.

10. Using the data of problem 8, calculate the ohmic values of the resistor steps, using a parallel arrangement instead of a series arrangement of the steps.

11. Calculate the size of grid and the number of grids in each step of the parallel arrangement.

12. A series speed-regulating resistor is designed to carry 200 amperes continuously on any step. The ohmic value of the resistance is as follows:

Point of Regulator	Ohms in Circuit
First	3.0
Second	2.5
Third	2.0
Fourth	1.5
Fifth	1.0
Sixth	0.5
Seventh	0.0

Determine the size of grid, and the number required in each step.

13. Calculate the ohms, current-carrying capacity, size of grid, and number of grids in each step of this regulator, if the resistor is connected in a parallel arrangement.

14. A 250-horsepower 440-volt three-phase 60-cycle slip-ring motor has rotor characteristics as follows:

Volts across slip rings at standstill   625
Rotor amperes per ring at full rated load   180

Calculate the ohmic values of a six-step class-165 resistor for this motor, using the data of Table 33. Motor resistance may be disregarded.

15. Calculate the size of grid, and the number of grids, in each step of the resistor, using the data of Table 48.

16. If the grids are available only in boxes of 50 grids all of one size, determine the grid sizes and the number of grids which would result in the most economical design. The grids in a box may be all in series or may be in parallel of two.

17. A 400-horsepower 440-volt three-phase 60-cycle slip-ring motor has rotor characteristics as follows:

Volts across slip rings at standstill   800
Rotor amperes per ring at full rated load   220

Calculate the ohmic values, grid sizes, and number of grids for a five-step class-135 resistor for this motor, using Tables 33 and 48. Motor resistance may be disregarded.

18. Calculate a six-step resistor for the motor of problem **17,** under the following conditions:

Motor may run continuously with the last two steps of resistance in circuit.

Motor may run half time with the last three steps of resistance in circuit.

The rest of the resistor to be starting duty only, class 145.

19. A shunt motor having an armature resistance of $0.07E/I$ has a four-step starting resistor which permits a current peak of 150 per cent of rated current at the start, and which is tapered in the ratio of 40–30–20–10. If the accelerating contactors close when the current reaches 100 per cent of rated current, what is the ohmic value of the resistor steps in per cent of E/I? What inrush current is obtained on each point of the controller?

20. Engineering design data for a certain crane controller resistor is as follows:

Step	Ohms in per cent of E/I	Continuous Current-carrying Capacity in per cent I
R1–R2	100	39
R2–R3	40	46
R3–R4	28	52.5
R4–R5	20	57.5
	188	

Calculate a resistor of this type for a 150-horsepower 230-volt series motor, and determine the sizes and number of grids from Table 48.

Ampere Ratings of Single-phase A-C Motors

60 cycles

Average values, in amperes

½-40 hp

Hp	Syn. Speed rpm	Current in Amperes					Hp	Syn. Speed rpm	Current in Amperes				
		115 volts	230 volts	440 volts	550 volts	2200 volts			115 volts	230 volts	440 volts	550 volts	2200 volts
½	1200	7.16	3.58	1.80	1.44		10	3600	84.8	42.4	21.2	17.0	
	900	10.0	5.02	2.50	2.00			1800	87.2	43.6	21.8	17.5	
								1200	92.0	46.0	23.0	18.3	
	1800	8.06	4.04	2.02	1.62			900	100	50.0	25.0	20.0	
¾	1200	9.86	4.94	2.48	1.98			600	117	58.4	29.2	23.4	
	900	11.9	5.96	2.98	2.38								
							15	3600	127	63.4	31.8	25.4	
	3600	9.5	4.76	2.38	1.90			1800	132	66.0	33.0	26.4	
1	1800	10.6	5.28	2.64	2.12			1200	138	69.0	34.6	27.6	
	1200	12.3	6.12	3.06	2.46			900	145	72.6	36.4	29.0	
	900	12.9	6.48	3.24	2.60			600	167	83.6	41.8	33.4	
	3600	14.4	7.22	3.62	2.90		20	3600	170	84.8	42.4	34.0	9.0
1½	1800	14.8	7.40	3.70	2.96			1800	175	87.4	43.8	35.0	9.2
	1200	16.8	8.40	4.20	3.36			1200	178	89.4	44.8	35.6	9.4
	900	20.0	10.10	5.04	4.02			900	189	94.6	47.2	37.8	10.0
								600	212	106	53.4	42.6	11.0
	3600	19.2	9.6	4.82	3.84								
2	1800	20.0	10.0	4.98	3.98		25	3600	204	102	51.2	40.8	10.8
	1200	22.0	11.0	5.50	4.40			1800	216	108	54.3	43.2	11.2
	900	25.0	12.5	6.24	4.98			1200	224	112	56.0	44.6	11.6
								900	234	117	58.3	46.8	12.0
	3600	27.2	13.6	6.82	5.44			600	250	125	62.4	49.8	14.0
3	1800	28.8	14.3	7.18	5.74								
	1200	30.8	15.4	7.72	6.16			1800	252	126	63.0	50.6	13.6
	900	35.4	17.6	8.80	7.08		30	1200	266	133	66.7	53.4	13.8
								900	276	138	68.7	55.0	14.2
	3600	44.0	22.0	11.0	8.80			600	304	152	76.1	61.0	16.0
5	1800	45.6	22.8	11.4	9.14								
	1200	48.8	24.4	12.2	9.76			1800	340	170	85.0	67.8	17.4
	900	54.0	27.0	13.5	10.8		40	1200	344	172	86.0	68.6	17.8
								900	360	180	90.0	72.0	18.4
	3600	66.4	33.2	16.6	13.3			600	392	196	98.0	78.2	20.0
7½	1800	67.0	33.4	16.8	13.4								
	1200	70.2	35.2	17.6	14.0								
	900	82.4	41.2	20.6	16.5								

Ampere Ratings of Two-phase Induction Motors

For normal torque, normal starting current, squirrel-cage or wound-rotor motors.
Average values, in amperes per phase.

½–40 hp (60 cycles)

Hp	Syn. Speed rpm	Current in Amperes					Hp	Syn. Speed rpm	Current in Amperes				
		110 volts	220 volts	440 volts	550 volts	2200 volts			110 volts	220 volts	440 volts	550 volts	2200 volts
½	1200	3.58	1.79	.90	.72			3600	42.4	21.2	10.6	8.48	
	900	5.02	2.51	1.25	1.00			1800	43.6	21.8	10.9	8.75	
							10	1200	46.0	23.0	11.5	9.17	
¾	1800	4.03	2.02	1.01	.81			900	50.0	25.0	12.5	10.0	
	1200	4.93	2.47	1.24	.99			600	58.5	29.2	14.6	11.7	
	900	5.97	2.98	1.50	1.19								
								3600	63.5	31.7	15.9	12.7	
	3600	4.76	2.38	1.19	.95			1800	66.0	33.0	16.5	13.2	
	1800	5.28	2.64	1.32	1.06		15	1200	69.0	34.5	17.3	13.8	
1	1200	6.13	3.06	1.53	1.23			900	72.5	36.3	18.2	14.5	
	900	6.47	3.24	1.62	1.30			600	83.6	41.8	20.9	16.7	
	3600	7.22	3.61	1.81	1.45			3600	84.8	42.4	21.2	17.0	4.5
	1800	7.41	3.70	1.85	1.48			1800	87.5	43.7	21.9	17.5	4.6
1½	1200	8.40	4.20	2.10	1.68		20	1200	89.2	44.7	22.4	17.8	4.7
	900	10.0	5.03	2.52	2.01			900	94.4	47.3	23.6	18.9	5.0
								600	106	53.0	26.7	21.3	5.5
	3600	9.6	4.81	2.41	1.92								
	1800	10.0	4.98	2.49	1.99			3600	102	51.2	25.6	20.4	5.4
2	1200	11.0	5.50	2.75	2.20			1800	108	54.3	27.1	21.6	5.6
	900	12.5	6.23	3.12	2.49		25	1200	112	56.0	28.0	22.3	5.8
								900	117	58.3	29.2	23.4	6.0
	3600	13.6	6.81	3.41	2.72			600	125	62.4	31.2	24.9	7.0
	1800	14.4	7.17	3.59	2.87								
3	1200	15.4	7.72	3.86	3.08			1800	126	63.0	31.5	25.3	6.8
	900	17.7	8.80	4.40	3.54			1200	133	66.7	33.4	26.7	6.9
							30	900	138	68.7	34.3	27.5	7.1
	3600	22.0	11.0	5.50	4.40			600	152	76.1	38.0	30.5	8.0
	1800	22.8	11.4	5.71	4.57								
5	1200	24.4	12.2	6.10	4.88			1800	170	85.0	42.5	33.9	8.7
	900	27.0	13.5	6.75	5.40			1200	172	86.0	43.0	34.3	8.9
							40	900	180	90.0	45.0	36.0	9.2
	3600	33.2	16.6	8.31	6.65			600	196	98.0	49.0	39.1	10.0
	1800	33.5	16.7	8.40	6.68								
7½	1200	35.1	17.6	8.80	7.02								
	900	41.2	20.6	10.3	8.23								

NOTE: For high-torque squirrel-cage motors the ampere ratings will be at least 10 per cent greater than those given above. The current in the common line of a two-phase, three-wire system is 1.4 times the phase current.

AMPERE RATINGS OF TWO-PHASE INDUCTION MOTORS

For normal torque, normal starting current, squirrel-cage or wound-rotor motors. Average values, in amperes per phase.

50–500 hp   (60 cycles)

Hp	Syn. Speed rpm	Current in Amperes					Hp	Syn. Speed rpm	Current in Amperes				
		110 volts	220 volts	440 volts	550 volts	2200 volts			110 volts	220 volts	440 volts	550 volts	2200 volts
50	1800	209	105	52.4	41.9	10.6	200	1800	796	398	199	159	40.4
	1200	211	106	52.8	42.3	10.7		1200	807	404	202	161	40.7
	900	220	110	55.0	44.0	11.3		900	848	424	212	169	42.8
	600	239	120	60.0	47.7	12.3		720	855	428	214	171	42.4
								600	862	431	215	172	44.1
60	1800	248	124	62.0	49.5	12.6		450	915	457	228	183	46.5
	1200	256	128	64.0	51.2	12.9							
	900	261	131	65.4	52.3	13.3	250	1800	990	495	248	198	49.8
	600	280	140	70.0	56.0	14.5		1200	1000	500	250	201	50.6
								900	1050	524	262	209	53.2
75	1800	308	154	77.0	61.6	15.6		720	1080	540	270	216	53.2
	1200	313	157	78.4	62.6	15.8		600	1088	544	272	218	52.8
	900	324	162	81.0	64.8	16.4		450	1092	546	273	219	56.5
	600	344	172	86.0	68.8	18.2		360	1170	585	292	234	60.6
100	1800	403	202	100	80.6	20.4	300	1800	1190	594	297	237	59.7
	1200	413	207	104	82.7	20.9		1200	1210	604	302	241	60.6
	900	424	212	106	84.8	21.5		900	1250	625	312	250	63.6
	600	445	223	111	89.2	22.8		600	1250	625	312	250	62.6
	450	502	251	126	101	25.8		450	1320	660	329	263	65.8
								360	1440	720	360	287	71.7
125	1800	500	250	125	100	25.3							
	1200	516	258	129	103	25.9	400	1800	1570	786	394	315	79.4
	900	528	264	132	106	26.8		1200	1610	806	403	323	81.0
	720	543	272	136	109	27.1		600	1650	826	413	330	83.0
	600	554	277	139	111	28.4		450	1730	866	433	346	86.5
	450	607	304	152	121	31.2		360	1810	905	452	362	91.0
150	1800	599	300	150	119	30.1	500	1800	2000	1000	500	400	100
	1200	606	303	152	121	30.7		1200	1940	970	485	388	98
	900	628	314	157	126	32.0		600	2040	1020	510	408	102
	720	650	325	163	130	32.0		450	2090	1040	522	417	107
	600	655	327	164	131	33.6		360	2280	1140	570	455	114
	450	723	362	181	144	36.3							

NOTE: For high-torque squirrel-cage motors the ampere ratings will be at least 10 per cent greater than those given above.

The current in the common line of a two-phase, three-wire system is 1.4 times the phase current.

AMPERE RATINGS OF THREE-PHASE INDUCTION MOTORS

For normal torque, normal starting current, squirrel-cage or wound-rotor motors. Average values, in amperes per phase.

½–40 hp   (60 cycles)

Hp	Syn. Speed rpm	Current in Amperes 110 volts	220 volts	440 volts	550 volts	2200 volts
½	1200	4.14	2.07	1.04	.83	
	900	5.80	2.90	1.45	1.16	
¾	1800	4.66	2.33	1.17	.93	
	1200	5.70	2.85	1.43	1.14	
	900	6.90	3.45	1.73	1.38	
1	3600	5.50	2.75	1.38	1.10	
	1800	6.10	3.05	1.53	1.22	
	1200	7.08	3.54	1.77	1.42	
	900	7.48	3.74	1.87	1.50	
1½	3600	8.34	4.17	2.09	1.67	
	1800	8.56	4.28	2.14	1.71	
	1200	9.70	4.85	2.43	1.94	
	900	11.60	5.81	2.91	2.32	
2	3600	11.1	5.56	2.78	2.22	
	1800	11.5	5.76	2.88	2.30	
	1200	12.7	6.35	3.18	2.54	
	900	14.4	7.21	3.61	2.88	
3	3600	15.7	7.87	3.94	3.14	
	1800	16.6	8.29	4.14	3.32	
	1200	17.8	8.92	4.46	3.56	
	900	20.4	10.20	5.09	4.08	
5	3600	25.4	12.7	6.34	5.08	
	1800	26.4	13.2	6.60	5.28	
	1200	28.2	14.1	7.05	5.64	
	900	31.2	15.6	7.80	6.24	
7½	3600	38.4	19.2	9.6	7.68	
	1800	38.6	19.3	9.7	7.72	
	1200	40.6	20.3	10.2	8.12	
	900	47.6	23.8	11.9	9.51	

Hp	Syn. Speed rpm	Current in Amperes 110 volts	220 volts	440 volts	550 volts	2200 volts
10	3600	49.0	24.5	12.3	9.8	
	1800	50.4	25.2	12.6	10.1	
	1200	53.2	26.6	13.3	10.6	
	900	57.8	28.9	14.5	11.6	
	600	67.6	33.8	16.9	13.5	
15	3600	73.4	36.7	18.4	14.7	
	1800	76.2	38.1	19.1	15.2	
	1200	79.8	39.9	20.0	16.0	
	900	83.8	41.9	21.0	16.8	
	600	96.6	48.3	24.2	19.3	
20	3600	98	49.0	24.5	19.6	5.2
	1800	101	50.5	25.3	20.2	5.3
	1200	103	51.7	25.9	20.6	5.4
	900	109	54.6	27.3	21.8	5.8
	600	123	61.5	30.8	24.6	6.4
25	3600	118	59.2	29.6	23.6	6.3
	1800	125	62.7	31.3	25.0	6.5
	1200	129	64.7	32.3	25.8	6.7
	900	135	67.4	33.7	27.0	6.9
	600	144	71.9	35.9	28.8	8.1
30	1800	146	72.8	36.4	29.2	7.8
	1200	154	77.1	38.6	30.8	8.0
	900	159	79.4	39.7	31.8	8.2
	600	176	87.9	43.9	35.2	9.3
40	1800	196	98	49.0	39.2	10.0
	1200	198	99	49.4	39.6	10.3
	900	208	104	52.0	41.6	10.6
	600	226	113	56.5	45.2	11.5

NOTE: For high-torque squirrel-cage motors the ampere ratings will be at least 10 per cent greater than those given above.

Ampere Ratings of Three-phase Induction Motors

For normal torque, normal starting current, squirrel-cage or wound-rotor motors. Average values, in amperes per phase.

50–500 hp　(60 cycles)

Hp	Syn. Speed rpm	Current in Amperes					Hp	Syn. Speed rpm	Current in Amperes				
		110 volts	220 volts	440 volts	550 volts	2200 volts			110 volts	220 volts	440 volts	550 volts	2200 volts
50	1800	242	121	60.5	48.4	12.3		1800	920	460	230	184	46.7
	1200	244	122	61.0	48.8	12.4		1200	932	466	233	186	47.0
	900	254	127	63.5	50.8	13.1	200	900	980	490	245	196	49.4
	600	276	138	69.0	55.2	14.2		720	988	494	247	197	49.0
								600	996	498	249	199	50.9
								450	1060	528	264	211	53.7
60	1800	286	143	71.5	57.2	14.6							
	1200	296	148	74.0	59.2	14.9							
	900	302	151	75.5	60.4	15.4		1800	1140	572	286	229	57.5
	600	324	162	81.0	64.8	16.7		1200	1160	580	290	232	58.5
								900	1210	604	302	242	61.5
75	1800	356	178	89.0	71.2	18.0	250	720	1250	625	312	250	61.5
	1200	362	181	90.5	72.4	18.2		600	1260	630	315	252	61.0
	900	374	187	93.5	74.8	19.0		450	1260	630	315	252	65.3
	600	398	199	99.5	79.6	21.0		360	1350	676	338	270	70.0
100	1800	466	233	116	93.2	23.6		1800	1370	685	342	274	69.0
	1200	478	239	120	95.6	24.2		1200	1390	696	348	278	70.0
	900	490	245	123	98.0	24.8	300	900	1440	722	361	289	73.5
	600	514	257	128	103	26.4		600	1440	722	361	289	72.3
	450	580	290	145	116	29.8		450	1520	760	380	304	76.0
								360	1660	830	415	332	82.8
125	1800	578	289	144	115	29.2							
	1200	596	298	149	119	29.9		1800	1820	910	455	364	91.8
	900	610	305	153	122	30.9		1200	1870	933	466	373	93.5
	720	628	314	157	126	31.3	400	600	1910	955	477	382	96.0
	600	640	320	160	128	32.8		450	2000	1000	500	400	100
	450	702	351	175	140	36.0		360	2090	1050	523	418	105
150	1800	692	346	173	138	34.8		1800	2310	1160	578	462	116
	1200	700	350	175	140	35.5		1200	2240	1120	560	448	113
	900	726	363	182	145	37.0	500	600	2360	1180	590	472	118
	720	752	376	188	150	37.0		450	2410	1200	602	482	124
	600	756	378	189	151	38.8		360	2630	1320	658	526	132
	450	836	418	209	166	42.0							

Note: For high-torque squirrel-cage motors the ampere ratings will be at least 10 per cent greater than those given above.

AMPERE RATINGS OF DIRECT-CURRENT MOTORS

Hp	Full-load Current			Recommended Fuse Size		
	115 volts	230 volts	550 volts	115 volts	230 volts	550 volts
⅛	1.4	0.7	0.3	3	3	3
⅙	1.8	0.9	0.4	3	3	3
¼	2.3	1.2	0.5	5	3	3
½	4.5	2.3	1.0	7	3	3
¾	6.5	3.3	1.4	10	5	3
1	8.4	4.2	1.7	15	7	3
1½	12.5	6.3	2.6	20	10	5
2	16.1	8.3	3.4	25	12	5
3	24.0	12.3	5.0	30	15	7
4	32	16.1	6.6	40	20	10
5	40	19.8	8.2	50	25	12
7½	58	28.7	12.0	80	40	15
10	75	38	16.0	100	50	20
12½	94	47	19.5	125	60	25
15	112	56	23.0	150	75	30
20	148	74	30	200	100	40
25	185	92	38	250	125	50
30	220	110	45	300	150	60
35	257	128	53	350	175	70
40	294	146	61	400	200	80
45	330	163	68	450	225	90
50	364	180	75	500	250	100
60	436	215	90	550	275	125
75	540	268	111	...	350	150
90	648	322	132	...	450	175
100	720	357	146	...	500	200
125	890	443	184	...	600	250
150	1060	528	220	...	...	300
175	1240	617	257	...	...	350
200	1415	705	295	...	...	400

TABLES

Ampere Table

For Three-phase Synchronous Motors

Hp	Assumed Efficiency	Amperes at 100% Power Factor					Hp
		220 volts	440 volts	550 volts	2200 volts	4000 volts	
5	81.0	12	6	4.8	. . . . .	. . . . .	5
7½	82.0	18	9	7.2	. . . . .	. . . . .	7½
10	83.0	23.5	11.8	9.5	. . . . .	. . . . .	10
15	85.0	34.5	17.3	14.0	. . . . .	. . . . .	15
20	86.0	45.5	23	18.5	. . . . .	. . . . .	20
25	87.0	56	28	22.5	. . . . .	. . . . .	25
30	88.0	67	33.5	27	. . . . .	. . . . .	30
40	89.0	88	44	35	9	. . . . .	40
50	89.5	110	55	44	11	. . . . .	50
60	90.0	131	66	53	13.1	. . . . .	60
75	91.0	162	81	65	16.2	. . . . .	75
100	91.5	214	107	86	21.4	12	100
125	91.5	268	134	107	27	15	125
150	92.0	320	160	128	32	17.5	150
200	92.0	426	213	171	43	24	200
250	92.5	526	263	212	53	29	250
300	92.5	636	318	255	64	35	300
350	93.5	734	372	298	74	41	350
400	93.5	840	420	336	84	46	400
450	93.5	942	471	378	94	52	450
500	94.0	1045	523	418	105	58	500
550	94.0	1148	574	460	115	63	550
600	94.0	1250	625	500	125	69	600
650	94.5	1350	675	540	135	75	650
700	94.5	1450	725	580	145	80	700
750	94.5	1560	780	625	156	86	750
800	95.0	1660	830	665	166	91	800
900	95.0	1860	930	745	186	102	900
1000	95.0	2060	1030	825	206	113	1000

Amperes given above are based on an average efficiency for given horsepower at all speeds. For instance, 25 hp amperes are based on 87 per cent efficiency for all speeds and 1000 hp on 95 per cent efficiency for all speeds.

For 2-phase amperes multiply values in table by 0.866.

For 80 per cent power-factor amperes multiply 100 per cent power-factor values by 1.29.

INDEX

531